FINANCIAL MATHEMATICS & STATISTICS

T.M. Jackson
M.Sc.(O.R.), B.A.(Econ.), Cert.Ed.
Lecturer in Economics & Applied Statistics
Wirral Metropolitan College

R. Parkinson
M.Sc.(O.R.), B.Sc.(Mathematics)
Commercial & Productivity Services Manager,
I.C.I., Plant Protection Division

© T.M. JACKSON & R. PARKINSON 1989

First published in Great Britain 1989 by Checkmate Gold Publications,
P.O. Box 36, Ellesmere Port, South Wirral L66 7PB

British Library Cataloguing in Publication Data
Jackson, T., Parkinson, R.
Financial mathematics and statistics.
1. Business mathematics   2. Mathematical statistics
I. Title   II. Series
519.5'024658   HF5691

ISBN 1 85313 037 0

Design & Typesetting
by Merseyside Graphics Ltd., 130 The Parade, Meols, Wirral L47 5AZ
Printed in Great Britain at the Alden Press, Oxford

Cover design by Merseyside Graphics Ltd.

INTRODUCTION

The structure of this book follows closely the Financial Mathematics and Statistics syllabi of the professional accounting bodies but the range of topics covered will, hopefully, make it useful to students of financial mathematics, statistics, and quantitative methods on a variety of professional and undergraduate courses.

In general, the topics covered and the degree of detail are as appropriate for the examinations of the professional bodies but occasionally, out of general interest or to provide some element of completeness, the text goes a little further than is required at this level; for example, the chapter on Linear Programming includes the Simplex method which is not specifically mentioned in the syllabi of the accounting bodies. Students should, therefore, check the syllabus for the examinations they are taking if they wish to avoid studying superfluous material.

We have assumed little prior knowledge of mathematics, introducing the necessary concepts as they become relevant to the topic under consideration. Although we have tried to deal with each new concept in a fairly rigorous manner, the general approach has been a practical problem solving, rather than theoretical, one which we feel is appropriate to the needs of business studies students.

An important feature of the book is the large number of questions which appear at the end of, and within, each chapter. The majority of these questions are drawn from the examination papers of the professional accounting bodies and worked answers are produced at the end of the book. These answers are, of course, the responsibility of the authors and not the accounting bodies.

A small number of questions are marked with an asterisk and no answer is provided for these questions. Lecturers, adopting the book as a course text, may find these questions particularly useful but students studying on their own should find no particular difficulty because these questions have been carefully chosen as either being very similar to questions to which answers are provided, or covering areas which are dealt with in detail within the text.

ACKNOWLEDGEMENTS

We would like to express our thanks to the Chartered Institute of Management Accountants and the Chartered Association of Certified Accountants for permission to use past examination papers as a source of questions for this book.

We would also like to thank the Central Statistical Office for allowing the reproduction of the Index of Retail Prices table from the Annual Abstract of Statistics.

Finally, thanks to colleagues who have helped in the development of this book.

T.M.J./R.P.

To TINA

SUMMARY OF CONTENTS

CHAPTER CONTENTS

Page

Chapter 1
INTRODUCTION TO STATISTICS

1.1 The Nature of Statistics

Statistics is a branch of mathematics concerned with "the collection, presentation, analysis, and interpretation of numerical data."

(a) Collection of data

The application of even the most sophisticated statistical techniques to a collection of data is a waste of time if the original data are incorrect or unreliable. For example, if one tried to draw conclusions about the outcome of a General Election from a sample of voters obtained by telephoning 100 people the conclusions would probably be wrong; the sample is too small and is biased towards people who own telephones.

(b) Presentation of data

An important aspect of statistics is the summary of large amounts of data in the form of tables, graphs, or summary statistics such as means, deviations, etc. These devices for summarising large masses of data are useful because they enable data to be more easily understood and may provide the basis for further analysis. The presentation of information in a more condensed form is referred to as Descriptive Statistics.

(c) Analysis of data

The analysis of data is carried out in many ways, some of which are considered later. The analytical tools of statistics have been developed in many different areas of study and are applicable in a wide range of situations.

(d) Interpretation of data

Interpretation of the results of analysis may be nothing more than a common-sense reading of tables and explanation of simple descriptive statistics or it may involve complex arguments. While the statistician should not seek to avoid the responsibility of interpreting data he must also be cautious in the inferences he draws and consider alternative explanations for the relationships that are observed.

As an example, there has been some debate about the relationship between cigarette smoking and death rates. The debate revolves around the role of cigarette smoking as a causal factor or as an intermediate variable. In other words, it may well be that people who are prone to lung cancer or heart disease smoke because they are nervous types or are in stressful jobs in which case it is the stress or disposition of the person that causes the disease not smoking. However, the statistician does not claim that smoking **causes** lung cancer or heart disease (although other evidence does suggest this), he merely points out that there is sufficient evidence to say that smoking is **associated** with lung and heart disease.

The increasing use of computers to handle computational work has made it relatively easy to produce large amounts of information and the use of statistical packages has made statistical techniques available to a wide range of people who may not understand the assumptions of the methods they employ. There is a danger of "garbage-in, garbage-out" and a need for users to understand the proper and improper applications of statistical techniques.

1.2 Statistics for Business and Management Studies
The basic requirement for correct decision-taking is good information and the more information that is available the better. The role of the statistician is to provide information and advice to management in situations involving numerical information. Nowadays, most large organisations use some statistical techniques and the study of statistics is included in the training of scientists, engineers, economists, accountants, sociologists, psychologists, etc.

Statistical method has, in fact, developed from many different areas of study such as government, medicine, agriculture, insurance, psychology etc. and methods originally developed in one area have often been used more productively in other areas. So, many management techniques in areas such as O&M, Work Study, Inventory Control, Operations Research, etc. have their basis in statistical method.

It is not fruitful, and probably not possible, to distinguish clearly between the various quantitative techniques which are employed in "management science". There is, however, an indication of the unique nature of Statistics in its description as a "science concerned with decision-making in the face of uncertainty". In many situations, the decision-maker is faced with an overwhelming range of choice of alternative courses of action. Often he will know the consequences of each decision with certainty, but the problem is to decide which particular course of action will lead to a result which is optimal according to some criterion. A simple example of such a situation would be the decision about product mix and the obvious criterion would be the maximisation of total contribution. Various mathematical techniques have been developed to assist the decision-maker in such situations and some are introduced later in this book.

On the other hand, the decision-maker will more often be unsure of the consequences of a course of action and some degree of risk is present in all business decisions. In such cases, the decision-maker is dealing with probability and likelihood and it is necessary to develop models which incorporate statistical approaches to deal with variability and chance associations. A typical example of such a situation would be where, say, a certain production process gives 5% defective items whilst the trial of a new method of production indicates that the number of defectives could be reduced to 4%. But how big a sample is necessary to be sure that the new process is better? What is the probability that the reduction in defective items is due to chance? It is in such situations that statistical theory can aid the decision-maker.

Paradoxically, the growth of information available and the development of sophisticated quantitative techniques make it more important than ever that managers (indeed all of us) are numerate and aware of the assumptions implicit in the techniques involved. The misuse of techniques and misinterpretation of information may, at best, lead to sub-optimal solutions to problems and, at worst, be disastrous (e.g. drug testing). Increasingly, decision-takers must understand the information available and be aware of the strengths and weaknesses of the tools used to assist in the interpretation of information.

From the point of view of those advising decision-takers, it is important to encourage the active participation of management at each stage in the problem solving process not only because this is valuable in its own right but because it will engage their support in implementing the solution.

1.3 Statistical symbols and mathematical notation
The use of symbols in place of words in statistical formulae saves time and space. Students sometimes find such symbols a little frightening but they are, in fact, quite easy to learn and will be easily grasped after a few numerical examples.

VARIABLES	A characteristic that is being measured is called a variable. eg. height, weight, income, sales etc.
SUFFIXES	Suffixes are used to distinguish between individual values of a variable. eg. $x_1, x_2, x_3, \ldots, x_n$. In the above example, there are n measurements of the variable x and x_i is the general term for the variable x. x is the collective symbol for all the individual values of the variable. The letter x is usually used to denote independent variables and the letter y is usually used for dependent variables.

ARITHMETIC MEAN	A bar over a symbol indicates that it represents the arithmetic mean of that variable.
	eg. $\bar{x}$ denotes the arithmetic mean of the variable x and is referred to as "x bar".
ESTIMATES	A hat over a symbol indicates that it represents an estimated value of that variable.
	eg. $\hat{y}$ denotes an estimate of the value of the variable y and is referred to as "y hat".
MULTIPLICATION	The multiplication of two, or more, variables can be represented in three ways, viz: $a \times b = a.b = ab$
INEQUALITIES	$x > y$ means x is greater than y;
	$x \geqslant y$ means x is greater than or equal to y;
	$x < y$ means x is less than y;
	$x \leqslant y$ means x is less than or equal to y.
APPROXIMATIONS	$x \simeq y$ means x is approximately equal to y.
SUMMATIONS	$\sum_{i=1}^{i=n} x_i$ means the sum of all the values of the variable x_i from x_1 to x_n ie. $x_1 + x_2 + x_3 + \ldots + x_n$
	If all the values of x are to be summed we may simply write $\sum x$.
	$\sum$ is the Greek letter sigma and we refer to "sigma x" as the sum of all the values of the variable x.
LIMITS	An arrow is used to indicate that a variable tends towards a certain value.
	eg. $x \rightarrow 5$ means x gets closer and closer to 5 under certain conditions.

1.4 Calculations in Statistics

Complete accuracy in statistical work is difficult to achieve because of difficulties of measurement and incomplete data. It is important to achieve as much accuracy as possible but one should not claim greater accuracy than has been achieved.

(a) Spurious accuracy

Most electronic calculators work to six significant figures and are excellent for statistical work. However, one must be careful not to claim more accuracy than can be achieved and final figures must be rounded to show the true precision of the answer. When a number implies greater accuracy than can be achieved it is called spurious accuracy. For example, if I did a survey and asked people their income in £s and then quoted an average income of say £60.75 I would be claiming more accuracy than is possible with the data at my disposal.

(b) Significant figures
Significant figures are those figures in a number which are free of spurious accuracy.

Example:

Calculated figure	Stated figure if accuracy is known to be:		
	4 sig. fig.	3 sig. fig.	2 sig. fig.
50,000	50,000	50,000	50,000
6,583,922	6,584,000	6,580,000	6,600,000
712.93	712.9	713	710
0.003928	.003928	.00393	.0039

(c) Rounding off
To avoid spurious accuracy it may be necessary to reduce a number to a smaller number of significant figures.

If the number after the last significant figure is less than 5 then the last significant figure stays the same, if it is more than 5 or 5 followed by other figures then the last significant figure is increased by one.

Example:

    423.3 to an accuracy of 3 sig. figs. equals 423
    423.6 424
    423.502 424

There is a problem however if the number after the last significant figure is exactly 5. If you round all fives up or down you will introduce bias. A way out of the problem is to round off fives so that the last significant figure becomes even.

Example:

    497.5 becomes 498
    496.5 becomes 496

This should produce as many roundings up as down and avoid bias.

(d) Calculations with rounded numbers
Whenever we use rounded numbers in a calculation the answer obtained can only be as accurate as the least accurate figure used in the calculation.

For example, if we add 123 and 500 where the 500 has been rounded to the nearest 100 then we should quote the answer as 600 rather than 623. However, the 500 may have been anything from 450 to 549 and the answer might therefore lie anywhere between 573 and 672. The latter is of course more accurately rounded to 700 than 600.

Similarly, if we multiply 500 by 2000 where the numbers have been rounded to the nearest hundred and thousand respectively we can only quote an answer accurate to 3 significant figures, ie. 1,000,000 (3 sig. figs.) But once again, as illustrated below, the answer may lie between 675,000 and 1,375,000.

If one wishes to calculate an error free figure, the safest policy is to perform the calculation twice; once with the maximum values that each number can take and once with the minimum values. Thus, the above calculation would become:—

	MAX.	MIN.	
	550	450	
	× 2500	1500	True answer = 1,025,000 ± 350,000
Answer:	1,375,000	675,000	where 1,025,000 is the mid-point between the maximum and minimum answer.

(e) Relative error
The absolute error is the error expressed in the same units as the data. The relative error is the absolute error as a percentage of the estimated figure and is often more informative. In the above example:

$$\text{Relative error} \ = \ \frac{350,000}{1,025,000} \ \times 100 = 34.1\%$$

(f) Use of brackets
Many statistical formulae involve brackets which indicate parts of the calculation that should be grouped together and solved before the rest of the calculation.

Where complicated formulae are employed the calculations should be carried out in accordance with the following rules:
1. Work out the quantities inside brackets first, and
2. Perform multiplications and divisions before additions and subtractions (this rule applies to calculations within brackets as well as outside brackets).

Example: $[6 + 3(7 - 2)] \times 4 - 8 = [6 + 3 \times 5] \times 4 - 8$
$= [6 + 15] \times 4 - 8$
$= 21 \times 4 - 8$
$= 84 - 8$
$= 76$

N.B. Σx^2 means square each value of x and then add up all the figures obtained.
$(\Sigma x)^2$ means add up all the values of x and then square the result.

QUESTIONS

1.1   Round the following numbers to three significant figures:
(a)   439.7
(b)   2042
(c)   0.006902
(d)   0.006805
(e)   4875
(f)   2705.2
(g)   5999
(h)   6.515

1.2   The data below refer to two variables x and y, the corresponding values are:

x	y
1	12
4	6
5	9
3	10
7	4
9	0
12	-1
15	-6

Calculate   (i) Σx
(ii) Σy
(iii) Σx^2
(iv) $(\Sigma x)^2$
(v) Σxy
(vi) $\Sigma x . \Sigma y$
(vii) $\sqrt{\dfrac{1}{n}\left[\Sigma x^2 - \dfrac{(\Sigma x)^2}{n}\right]}$
(viii) $\sqrt{\dfrac{1}{n-1}\left[\Sigma x^2 - \dfrac{(\Sigma x)^2}{n}\right]}$

where n = the number of paired values of x and y.

1.3   The following table is given:

Sri Lanka
Gross Domestic Product by Origin
(Millions of Rupees at current prices)

	1972	1973	1974
Agriculture	4,119	5,025	8,356
Wholesale and retail trade	1,986	2,455	2,560
Manufacturing	1,728	2,017	2,475
Transport, storage, communications	1,333	1,525	1,683
Construction	711	802	1,011
Public administration and defence	575	654	704
All other	2,355	2,787	3,017
	12,807	15,265	19,806

Source: Central Bank of Ceylon, Extracted from Europa year book, vol.II.

You are required to:
(a)   Approximate the above data to the nearest 1,000 million Rupees.
(b)   Estimate the absolute and percentage relative errors of the total obtained in (a) above.
(c)   Explain why the percentage relative error is a superior measure to the absolute error.
(d)   Define a systematic error. Explain your answer by redrafting one of the columns in your answer to (a) above.
(e)   Comment on:
    (i)   the likelihood that the increase shown from 1972 to 1974 is a real volume increase;
    (ii)   the classification of the items in the table.
(f)   Illustrate and explain what is meant by the term significant digits.

(ICMA)

Chapter 2
COLLECTION OF DATA

A survey is simply a fact-finding exercise and the purpose, subject matter, coverage, and sources of information can be numerous. Before discussing some of the methods of collecting numerical data in a little more detail it is worth enumerating the stages in the survey process.

2.1 Preliminary study
As a preparation one should consult with experts in the subject matter under investigation and with those commissioning the survey. It is also essential to study the available literature to become familiar with the subject matter and to discover if similar work to that contemplated has been, or is going to be, carried out by other organisations. Clearly much unnecessary duplication of effort can be avoided if one can collaborate with other workers in similar fields.

2.2 Purpose of the survey
At the outset it is usually essential to decide with a fair degree of precision what information is to be sought as this will dictate the survey methods employed. Often there will be a limited amount of time and money that can be spent on the survey and this will also affect the amount of information sought and the type of survey method employed.

Occasionally, one is given an 'open brief' in which case one is free to explore whatever lines of enquiry one feels will be most fruitful but, usually, the time available and the resources at one's disposal will be limited.

2.3 Coverage of the survey
It is necessary to define the population to be studied. The word population, in Statistics, means all the possible measurements of the particular characteristic under investigation. It may mean every single person in the UK, every household with a TV set, every machine in a factory, every pupil in a class, every motor car used on British roads, etc.

We must then decide whether the population in question is to be fully covered (census) or partially covered (sample). If only a partial coverage is attempted this may well take the form of a number of case studies and these can be valuable and informative. However, if it is intended to draw inferences about the population from the survey then the sample must be chosen according to the rules of statistical theory. It is worth pointing out that the terms census, sample, and survey are sometimes used to mean slightly different things. The word census is sometimes used to mean a complete enumeration as distinct from a partial enumeration associated with a sample. Sometimes, however, census is used to refer to straightforward counts (eg. Census of population, production, etc) as opposed to a survey which implies a more in-depth enquiry. The word survey is also sometimes rather loosely used to refer to what might more accurately be described as a sample survey. The term sample survey is usually reserved for those studies where the part of the population studied is chosen by accepted statistical rules. These rules will be covered later but we must mention that for practical reasons the target population/sample may not coincide with the survey population/sample, ie. you may not achieve what you set out to achieve due to practical difficulties.

2.4 Collection of data

Whilst sampling techniques, data processing, analytical methods, inter-pretation and presentation of data have all been the subject of extensive research and are well developed and systematized, data collection has always been rather neglected. Possibly such things as interviewing and questionnaire design constitute the art of the statistician and can only be learned through experience but data collection methods probably deserve greater attention than they have been given.

There are several methods by which data may be collected and they may be classified in a variety of ways. One classification is as follows:—

(a) **Documentary sources**

It may be possible to obtain information relating to the enquiry from existing documents. Such documents may give information about the survey population or about the various members of the survey population ('units of enquiry').

(i) Published statistics

There is a wealth of data published by various bodies but one has to be very careful in deciding how suitable such information is for the purpose of the survey. Does it cover the population of interest? How accurate is the information contained in these statistics? Are there special features to the way in which the statistics were collected or to the population to which they refer? (see 2.9 Primary and Secondary data).

(ii) Unpublished statistics

Various agencies maintain records about individual survey units. For example, various government departments keep records about people's employment status, health record, income tax payments etc. Firms keep accounting statements, personnel records and so on. There is no shortage of information but access to that information is often limited or costly.

(b) **Observation**

Observation may consist of simply watching people, institutions, or various phenomena in their natural surroundings. There are certain types of information that can only be obtained in this way, such as the number of motor cars using a certain junction over a specified period.

Observation as a systematic method of collecting data is often used in the wider sense of including conversations, interviews, study of documents, etc., the key feature of observation being that the enquirer obtains his information directly rather than from the reports of others or through some medium such as a questionnaire.

Sometimes, the enquirer may study a group of people or an organisation through participant observation, actually joining the organisation and observing its behaviour from the inside. There is a danger with such methods that one obtains a biased viewpoint and there is the possibility that the organisation's behaviour may be modified due to the presence of an observer if this is known.

(c) **Questionnaires**

Most social surveys employ a questionnaire of some kind even if only as a basis for an in-depth interview.

Questionnaires may be administered in a variety of ways:—
(i)   To a group of respondents
        It is sometimes possible for the researcher to meet with a group of respondents and obtain their co-operation in completing his questionnaire. Such a situation has the advantage that the researcher is able to explain the purpose of the survey, assure respondents of the confidentiality of their replies, and answer any questions that may arise. Response rates will be high with this method but there is the problem of incomplete data sets as respondents can easily omit to answer certain questions, accidentally or deliberately. This method is obviously cheaper than mail questionnaires or interviews but it is not often possible.
(ii) Mail questionnaires
        Sending questionnaires through the post is more expensive but it makes it possible to cover a widely spread sample. Postal questionnaires allow respondents time to give carefully considered and detailed replies, people may also be more willing to answer questions of a personal nature than when they are confronted by an interviewer.
However, the major problem associated with postal surveys is the low response rate which can make them costly when measured by the number of completed questionnaires. Generally, it is not so much the cost of non-response that is of concern as the possibility that non-respondents may differ in some way from respondents thus introducing bias into the sample.
Response rates can be improved by a covering letter which in some way encourages the respondent to reply. Quite what form such a letter should

take is debatable; it should certainly explain why the survey is being undertaken and why the respondent was chosen. It should be explained why the respondent should take the trouble to reply and if there are any potential benefits to the respondent then these should certainly be pointed out. It may help to personalise the letter rather than an impersonal 'Dear Householder' or 'Dear Sir/Madam' and word processors make this a simple operation. An obvious point is that a reply paid envelope should be enclosed and the use of a stamp rather than a franked envelope may help create an obligation to reply. Assurances of confidentiality are vital and the use of follow-up letters may increase the response rate further. There are various ways that non-response can be taken into account when one draws inferences about the population but the safest method is to reduce non-response to a level where it cannot introduce serious bias into the results. One way of doing this is to collect information on non-respondents by some other method such as personal interview.

(iii) Interview

The personal interview is the most common method by which data is collected in social surveys. This is clearly the most costly method of acquiring data because it involves the high cost of wages of a team of interviewers. It does, however, have the advantage of permitting in-depth questioning and will elicit a high response.

Interviewing may take a variety of forms but the most usual is the formal interview where set questions are asked and the answers are recorded in a standardised format. Even in this situation, however, it is possible that the interviewer can introduce bias by the way he/she asks questions and this is a particular problem when the interviewer is probing for answers to questions involving opinions. It follows that careful selection and training of interviewers is necessary.

2.5 Pilot survey

It is usual to carry out a small-scale replica of the main survey before the survey itself. This will enable one to assess the suitability of the proposed data collection method, the expected response rate, instructions to be given to interviewers, likely duration of survey, and so on. Probably, most importantly, where questionnaires are used it will provide a check on the suitability of the questions being asked, ambiguity in questions, categories of answers that have been overlooked, and so on.

2.6 Processing the data

The next stage is to get the data into a form in which it can be easily analysed.

This involves classifying answers into categories which constitute the coding frame. The coding frame will usually have been determined before the data collection stage but it may involve 'post-coding' where one was unsure of all the categories of possible answers.

Most modern surveys, even those conducted by individual researchers, are analysed with the aid of a computer. Thus, the coded data is usually transferred to punched cards or directly on to a data file in the memory of a computer. The way in which the data is to be stored can thus affect the way in which the coding frame is prepared.

The actual coding of answers is a time consuming business and where many coders are employed steps have to be taken to ensure consistency in the way answers are coded.

Eventually the data will be transferred to a computer but even at this stage the researcher must be checking for possible errors. In fact, 'cleaning the data' is often left until the data is entered on to the computer. It is not possible to check all the data, and minor errors will be absorbed by the aggregation of information, but certain obvious errors can be spotted by looking for codes outside the range that has been employed.

2.7 Analysis, Interpretation, and Presentation
The final stages of a survey are difficult to describe in brief. The range of statistical methods that can be employed is very wide, ranging from simple descriptive statistics such as averages, measures of dispersion, percentages, correlation coefficients, to complicated techniques designed to establish and interpret relationships between a number of variables.

The results of the survey will usually be presented in the form of a report and this needs to be tailored to the type of reader for which it is intended.

2.8 Questionnaire Design
Questionnaire design is an art rather than a science; it is a lengthy business and occupies much of the time from the start of a project to the completion of the pilot survey. The exact format of the questionnaire will depend upon whether the respondent is to complete the questionnaire unaided or whether an interviewer will administer it.

There are no hard and fast rules when constructing a questionnaire but the following points should be borne in mind:—

(1) The questionnaire should be kept as short as possible whilst covering the information required.

(2) The first page of the questionnaire should assure the respondent of confidentiality and give a clear set of instructions as to how the respondent (or interviewer) should complete the questionnaire.

(3) There should be a clear explanation on the front page of the questionnaire, or in a covering letter, as to the purpose of the questionnaire.

(4) When constructing the questionnaire and deciding how it should be laid out, you should give priority to the convenience of the respondent (or interviewer) but also try to make the job of the coder, and punchcard operator, as easy as possible.

(5) The questions should follow a logical sequence. It is also an idea to put interesting questions and questions which the respondent can complete with little difficulty at the beginning as this will encourage completion of the questionnaire.

Conversely, sensitive questions should be saved until the end so that if the respondent suddenly decides he will not complete the questionnaire, not too much information is lost. On this basis, some would argue that personal questions should be left until the end.

(6) It is probably better, where possible, to have questions which allow one, or a number of, pre-printed answers to be ticked. One reason for this is that it makes coding a simple matter. If you want the respondent to expand upon his answer you can follow up the pre-printed answers with a question such as "Why do you say that?"

The alternative is to have open-ended or free-response questions where the respondent is free to give the answer of his/her choice. Coding such answers can be very time-consuming but they can be revealing and provide colour to subsequent reports when used as quotations.

(7) The questions should be simple and unambiguous. If a question can be interpreted in different ways then different people may be answering different questions and it will not be possible to compare the answers.

(8) Avoid leading questions. Leading questions suggest a particular answer and obviously introduce bias into the survey.

(9) Indicate clearly if some questions can be skipped over by certain people. In this context it is possible to use filter questions so that people who answer in a certain way are directed to the next question relevant to them.

(10) When "sensitive" questions are asked, the purpose is usually to classify the respondent in some way. If this is explained to people they are usually quite willing to co-operate.

(11) Questions which ask for people's opinions are very difficult to deal with. Does the respondent know what he thinks? Has he had time to give the

question sufficient thought? Does the wording tap-in on some particular aspect of the person's opinion? Does the question enable people to express the intensity of their views? etc., etc.

(12) Finally, do not engage in a "fishing expedition". Ask only those questions necessary to fulfil the purpose of the questionnaire.

2.9 Primary and Secondary data

We mentioned earlier that the first step in conducting a survey is to carry out a preliminary study during which one would consult with experts and study the available literature. At this stage one would endeavour to discover what data on the subject of interest are already available **or** likely to be available from other sources in the future. This is no easy task because the amount of published data (let alone unpublished data) is nowadays enormous. The largest provider of statistical data is the government and the "Guide to Official Statistics" provides a comprehensive coverage of what is available from official sources, but relevant data may also be collected by university research organisations, trade associations, individual firms or researchers, individual survey bodies, etc. Of course, those intimately involved with the subject of the research should be aware of such data and that is why consultation with such people at an early stage is so important.

Clearly then, it is important to check the sources of published data in order to avoid duplication of effort. The problem with using such **secondary data** (data collected for some other purpose), even that published by government departments with comprehensive guides as to the methods of collection and classification, is that such data will hardly ever fit the exact requirements of the researcher. To quote the Government Statistical Service "It (the GSS) simply provides a very large source of information which may help in finding solutions; and it is nearly always worth checking to see what is available before embarking on private research". It may also, of course, provide useful background information and useful comparisons with data collected via your own survey.

As we have said, the major source of secondary data is the government and because government statistics are widely used as bases for further analyses they are accompanied by full explanations as to how they are arrived at. Even if the published data do not conform to what is required the department concerned will often produce special tabulations to meet the researcher's specific requirements (at a cost!).

The range of government statistics available is so vast that a detailed knowledge of what is available, let alone the various idiosyncrasies of the different statistics, is just not practicable. What is important is to be able to find out what is available when you need it. A booklet, "Government Statistics — a brief guide to sources", available free from the Central

Statistical Office, gives information on the most important statistical publications together with a comprehensive list of contacts for each government department. For a copy, you should write to the Information Services Division, Cabinet Office, Great George Street, London SW1P 3AQ enclosing a stamped, addressed envelope. As a bonus, you will also receive a pocket-sized summary of some important statistical series — "United Kingdom in Figures".

It is tempting at this point to say, as many textbooks do, that it is vital for students to study a long list of government publications. In the writer's opinion it is not vital and probably not even desirable; examination questions requiring a knowledge of published statistics are rightly becoming less and less frequent. In any event, the time spent acquiring a superficial knowledge of a limited number of published statistics can be more fruitfully spent studying more frequently examined and relevant matters.

There are, nevertheless, certain publications with which any self-respecting student of statistics should be familiar, viz:

- Monthly Digest of Statistics —
   this is a collection of the main statistical series produced by all the government departments and contains information regarding prices, wages, balance of payments, industrial production, employment, national income, government finance, even the weather.

- Annual Abstract of Statistics —
   again, an all-embracing manual with more series for a longer run of years than the Monthly Digest.

- Social Trends —
   this is an annual publication which contains social and demographic series covering many areas of social concern, eg. housing, education, population, leisure activities, etc.

- UK National Accounts —
   the "Blue Book" as it is called analyses our national income, consumption, and expenditure and is essential reading for many economists concerned with economic growth, income distribution, consumer behaviour, and so on.

- UK Balance of Payments —
   the "Pink Book" provides detailed information on the UK Balance of Payments over a number of years.

- Department of Employment Gazette —
   this monthly publication by the DoE provides up-to-date

information on matters relating to employment, unemployment, wages, prices, industrial relations, etc.

- Financial Statistics —
  a monthly publication by the CSO (in conjunction with the Bank of England and other government departments) containing financial and monetary series.

- Bank of England Quarterly Bulletin —
  a more specialised publication for the banking community and those interested in monetary matters.

If you have a particular interest, the "Guide to Official Statistics" should enable you to identify relevant publications. You should also study reports in the quality press when the latest series are published. Not only will this help you to be able to interpret trends in data but it will also familiarise you with some of the shortcomings of published data.

If the data available from other sources are not suitable then the researcher has to generate his own data by one of the methods previously mentioned. Data collected for the specific purpose of the survey are known as **primary data.** The collection, classification and processing of such raw data is a time-consuming business but it has the advantage that the data collected can be tailored to meet the exact requirements of the survey and can be collected in such a way as to facilitate classification, processing, and analysis. Furthermore, it means that the researcher is intimately involved at each stage in the survey process and is consequently aware of all the defects in the data.

It is possible, but unlikely, that the collection of primary data can cover the whole population of interest. The more typical situation is where one has to conduct a survey based upon a sample of the population. Obviously, if one wishes to draw inferences about the whole population, the sample has to be representative of the population and it is to the problem of selecting a representative sample that we now turn.

2.10 SAMPLING METHODS
The idea of sampling is old and widespread; the food or wine taster, the doctor giving a blood test, the geologist taking a rock sample, the farmer picking one of the potatoes in his field, the bingo caller, etc. are all examples of the technique of sampling. The technique is based upon the view that the thing being sampled is so 'well-mixed', or homogeneous, that the sample truly represents the population under consideration.

2.10.1 Advantages of sampling
1. Sampling is less expensive than a census.
2. Sampling saves on labour in terms of fieldworkers and data processors.
3. Sampling saves time in terms of collecting the data and processing the data.

4. Sampling permits more accuracy in collecting and processing the data because less data is involved.
5. Sampling makes it possible to collect more information about each unit of enquiry.
6. When estimates of the population characteristics (parameters) are made from the sample results (statistics), the precision of these estimates can be gauged from the sample results themselves. This will be explained when we deal with standard errors.
7. A census is seldom possible and is, in any case, unlikely in practice to turn out to be complete. If we do not know which items are missing from the census then we cannot judge the possible inaccuracies.
8. Once a certain sample size is reached, very little extra accuracy is achieved by increasing the sample size.

2.10.2 Choice of sample

The ideal sample is one that is free from bias. Bias can arise from a variety of sources — the wording of questions, rounding of figures, interviewer bias, etc. — but our concern for the moment is bias that arises from the sample itself. Such bias can arise for the following reasons:—

(i) The sampling frame (the list of items in the population of interest) may not be complete or may be inadequate in other respects.
(ii) Non-response may introduce bias if non-respondents differ in some important respect from the rest of the sample.
(iii) The method of choosing the sample may produce bias in the sample. The main problem is that we do not always know what factors might introduce bias into our sample and, where human judgement is involved, selection may be influenced by unconscious bias which will invalidate the conclusions just as much as known bias.

It is this last problem, bias that is introduced as a result of the selection procedure, that is our concern here. The only way of avoiding such bias is to employ some sort of random sampling.

2.10.3 Random sampling

A random sample is one in which each member of the population has a calculable probability of being selected. This is often termed probability sampling and the term implies that the theory underlying sampling is based on the assumption that calculable probabilities can be attached to each member of the population.

(a) **Unrestricted random sampling**

This means that each possible sample of n units from a population of N units has an equal chance of being selected. This implies that each member of the population has an equal chance of being selected. This is sampling with replacement, each unit selected is put back into the population before the next selection is made. Most sampling theory is based upon unrestricted random sampling.

(b) **Simple random sampling**

This is sampling without replacement, the selected item is not restored to the population before the next selection is made. If the population is large compared to the sample size the withdrawal of a few members does not greatly affect the population and again, to all intents and purposes, each possible sample and each member has an equal chance of selection. Simple random sampling produces more precise estimators of population parameters than unrestricted random sampling.

(c) **Systematic sampling**

The usual method of selection in random sampling is through the use of random number tables. The items in the population are numbered in sequential order and the numbers are selected from the random number tables in some systematic manner.

Such a process can be laborious and an alternative is to calculate the sampling fraction, k (for example if we wanted a sample size 10 from a population of 100 our fraction would be $100/10 = 10$), and then take every kth item on the list for our sample.

For this to be a random sample the list must be in random order which is not usually the case. Another problem is that once the starting point is determined the whole sample is determined and selection of each item in the sample is determined by the first one selected. With simple random sampling from a large population each selection is independent of every other selection.

(d) **Quasi-random sampling**

When the items in a list from which a systematic sample is chosen are in random order, or where the order is not relevant to the investigation, the method of selection is quasi-random, ie. the method is virtually random. When one employs this method care has to be taken that there is no regular pattern in the list. If such a pattern exists and coincides with the sampling interval then the sample will be biased. Usually such patterns are easily detected and can be overcome by the use of different starting points and/or different sampling intervals.

(e) **Stratified samples**

It must be stressed that a random sample need not turn out to be an ideal, or even a very good, sample. Chance may introduce bias into the sample. All we can say with a random sample is that the method of selection is free of bias.

To reduce the possibility of bias we may introduce stratification into our selection procedure. This involves using our knowledge of the population to obtain a more representative sample.

Before any selection takes place, the population is divided into a number of strata. A random sample is then selected from each stratum. The strata must, of course, be closely related to the subject of study if the stratification is to improve our results in any way.

The most usual form of stratified sample is the proportionate stratified sample where the sample size in each stratum is proportional to the population size of that stratum.

EG.	Population	Sample size (10%)
men	80	8
women	20	2

The effect of stratification is to reduce a source of variability arising from the way in which the sample is selected. Variation between the groups is exactly reflected in the sample and we are left with that component of variation that arises within the groups. Thus, stratified sampling will give more accurate results than simple random sampling.

(f) **Multi-stage sampling**
If the population of interest is widely dispersed then a simple random sample might be very expensive to implement. For example, a random sample of 1,000 electors covering the registered voters of the country could be extremely expensive if it involved interviewers travelling to various corners of the country.

To save time, effort, and money we may use multi-stage sampling. The population is considered to consist of a number of primary-stage units each composed of a number of secondary-stage units and so on. Random samples are taken at each stage (stratification may be used at each stage if desirable). Thus, a multi-stage sample of 1,000 electors could be reduced to a sample of, say, 10 constituencies with 100 interviews in each constituency.

(g) **Cluster sampling**
Again if the population is widely dispersed and costs have to be kept down, but more particularly if there is no satisfactory sampling frame for the population of interest then cluster sampling may have to be employed.

Cluster sampling is simply a special form of multi-stage sampling with a 100% sample being taken at the second stage. The population is divided into a number of small areas, or clusters, and a sample of these clusters is taken at random.

The main advantage is that instead of a sampling frame consisting of all the items in the population one only needs a sampling frame consisting of the clusters.

2.10.4 Non-random methods
The methods already described employ random selection at some stage in the sampling method. The following methods do not select by random methods and it is not possible to estimate the accuracy of the results obtained from the sample. Such non-random methods are sometimes referred to as judgement methods.

(ii) Quota sampling
The method here is to stratify the population according to a number of factors so that the sample is a small scale replica of the population itself.

For example, a social survey might stratify the population by age, sex, and social class; each interviewer would then be given a quota of, say, 20 people to interview.

Sex		Age		Social class	
Male	12	Under 18	4	Lower	5
Female	8	18–25	6	Middle	10
		25+	10	Higher	5
Total	20		20		20

To ensure representativeness the interviewer would be asked to interview 12 males and 8 females, 4 people under 18, 6 people in the age range 18–25, and so on. The stratification could be independent or the various strata could be interrelated. In the latter case the interviewer would be told to interview so many males under 18 in the lower social class, and so on.

The method is cheap and administratively convenient but it has been criticised by statisticians. The main criticism is that selection within each strata is non-random because it is left to the interviewer.

(ii) Purposive sampling
This is stratified sampling where the selection is made by human choice. For example, a researcher may decide to take a sample of school children from one grammar school and two secondary modern schools simply because these schools are near to where he lives. This could hardly be a representative sample of school children (except if the study is deliberately confined to the area where the researcher lives). If inferences are to be drawn about the population as a whole one cannot rely upon human judgement in selecting the sample.

2.10.5 Other sampling techniques

Multi-phase sampling refers to a situation where information is collected on the whole sample and, at the same time or later, extra information is collected on a sub-sample of the full sample.

A panel survey is where information is collected on the sample on several occasions.

In practice many of the different methods of sampling mentioned will be used in combination.

2.10.6 Sample size

When random sampling methods are employed one can estimate the errors within the results and estimate the probability that results will lie within a certain range of their true population values. The theory behind this will be developed later. It is worth pointing out immediately that the errors depend upon the sample size and are independent of the size of the population and the sampling fraction.

QUESTIONS

2.1 A survey was made of the proportion of time between 8.00 a.m. and 1.00 p.m. that the average housewife in an area spends working on household duties. (A housewife is defined as a wife who does not have a regular job). The survey was done by 'activity sampling', whereby interviewers called at houses and asked the housewife whether she was actually working or not at the moment when the interviewer arrived. Responses to 419 calls were as follows:

	Hour during which visit took place					
	8–9	9–10	10–11	11–12	12–1	*Total*
Housewife working	21	21	54	36	9	141
Housewife not working	12	15	39	27	9	102
No information (no reply or housewife not at home)	18	24	60	42	32	176
						419

It was concluded from the survey that between 8.00 a.m. and 1.00 p.m., housewives are busy in the house for around 58% $\left(\dfrac{141}{243}\right)$ of the time.

Required:
(1) Give the main reasons why the conclusions are likely to be biased.
(2) During which hour do the figures suggest that housewives are busiest?

(3) Ignoring the effect of bias in the sample (that is, assuming a random sample) calculate 95% confidence limits for the estimated proportion of 0.58. Explain briefly the meaning of your calculated values. *(20 marks)*

(ACA)

Ignore part (3) at this stage.

2.2 (a) The following table shows the breakdown of a population into categories of sex, age and whether a smoker or non-smoker. (Frequencies are in thousands).

		Age 21–40	Age 41 and over	Total
Male	Smoker	61	45	106
	Non-smoker	41	27	68
Female	Smoker	68	56	124
	Non-smoker	59	43	102

Required:
(1) It is proposed to construct a quota sample of 100 individuals which fully reflects the distribution of these three characteristics in the population. Calculate the numbers in each category of the quota sample.
(2) Suppose that it is decided after all that age is no longer of importance in the survey. How would your quota sample of 100 be affected?
(3) What is the major criticism of a quota sample? *(12 marks)*

(b) Eighty companies are listed in order of profitability and you wish to take a random sample of twenty of these companies. You are provided with a list of randomly generated digits, a section of which is given below:

46819037154583502

Required:
Explain how you could use these random digits to select twenty companies from the complete list and show how the first three companies would be selected using your procedure. *(8 marks)*

(ACA)

*2.3 Statistical sampling techniques are widely used for the collection of data in industry and business. Explain **four** of the following, illustrating your answer with examples:

(a) sampling frame;

(b) simple random sampling;

(c) multi-stage sampling;

(d) stratification;

(e) quota sampling;

(f) sampling with probability proportional to size.

(5 marks for each section)
(Total: 20 marks)
(ICMA)

Chapter 3
PRESENTATION OF DATA

3.1   When one is confronted with a large amount of data, it is necessary to reduce the data into some form that enables one to appreciate the implications of the data. The first step is usually to present the information in the form of a table and this will often provide the basis for some other form of presentation or further analysis.

However, before tables or other forms of presentation can be prepared it may be necessary to arrange a large unordered mass of raw data into an orderly and reduced form.

3.2   Classification of data

Data may be classified according to some numerical criteria which may involve counting or measurement. It may also be classified according to some qualitative feature (attribute) which involves counting how many items possess a particular attribute and how many do not.

This distinction between variables which can take numerical values and attributes is, in fact, not as important as is sometimes made out. A variable can be transformed into an attribute by grouping into two categories above and below a certain numerical value and, similarly, an attribute can be transformed into a variable by assigning the number 1 to those items that possess a certain attribute and the number 0 to those that do not.

Variables may be either (i) discrete variables, or
                         (ii) continuous variables.

A discrete variable is one that is limited to certain specific values and involves counting eg. examination marks, number of children in a family, etc. A continuous variable can take any value on a continuous scale and involves measurement, eg. temperature, height, weight, etc.

Since all measurements can only be made to a certain degree of accuracy, all data are in a sense, discrete.

3.2.1   An array

A useful first step in dealing with raw data may be to arrange it in ascending or descending order. Such an arrangement of data is called an array.

3.2.2   Ungrouped frequency distribution

In any array it is likely that a variable will take the same value a number of times. The number of times that a variable takes a given value is called the frequency (f).

A list of the values that a variable takes, with the corresponding frequency of occurrence, is called an ungrouped frequency distribution.

3.2.3 Grouped frequency distribution

If the variable under consideration takes a great many different values, it will simplify matters, and possibly reveal some pattern, if the data is grouped in some way. Constructing a grouped frequency distribution means that the values that the variable takes are grouped together into classes and the number of times the variable takes a value within each class is recorded as the frequency for that class.

It should be noted that this operation involves some loss of accuracy because we lose the specific values that the variable takes. The assumption that is made in subsequent calculations is that the average value of a variable within each class coincides with the mid-point of the class but this will not be true and calculations of averages, deviations, etc. will be less accurate when grouped frequency distributions are used as the basis for the calculations. The loss of information has to be weighed against the convenience of the presentation and the increased speed with which calculations can be performed.

3.2.3.1 Choice of class

Deciding on the classes to use in a grouped frequency distribution is largely a matter of common-sense but the following suggestions may help.

(a) Class intervals should be equal if possible.
The class interval is the difference between the upper and lower boundaries (class limits) of the class.

(b) Make sure there is no ambiguity in defining the classes. Every value must be covered and each value should fall into one class only.
For example, if one had classes 0–5 and 5–10 where would one put the value 5? It would be better to define the class limits as 0 – under 5, and 5 – under 10.

(c) Try to use class intervals of 5, 10, 20, 30, etc. as it makes calculations easier.

(d) Try to use classes where the frequency of occurrences is concentrated around the mid-points of the class. This will preserve more accuracy in subsequent calculations. It may be necessary to use unequal class intervals to achieve this.

(e) Unequal class intervals may also be necessary where there would otherwise be many classes with few members.

(f) Try to use as few classes as possible without losing too much information. This is not very helpful but circumstances will often dictate. It really hinges on the accuracy one wants in future calculations and whether one wants to compress the information to emphasise some pattern in the data. You therefore decide to use a different number of classes according to your purpose in constructing the distribution.

QUESTION

3.1 A machine in a factory produces the following number of rejects in each of fifty equal time periods:

13	17	7	17	22
3	30	28	23	24
19	23	25	24	15
23	16	18	27	27
11	9	21	24	3
22	33	22	13	23
28	28	19	21	24
22	24	29	26	26
22	23	12	20	26
31	8	20	25	22

(a) Construct an ungrouped frequency distribution from the data.

(b) Construct a grouped frequency distribution from the data using seven class intervals of equal width.

3.2.3.2 Class limits

The true limits to the class may not always be the same as those stated. For example, age is usually quoted as the number of birthdays a person has had but a quoted age of 9 really means anything between exactly 9 and 9 years 364 days.

Example: Age

Quoted limits	True limits
5 — 9	5 — under 10
10 — 19	10 — under 20
20 — 30	20 — under 30

When using secondary data take care to use the true limits rather than the stated limits.

When dealing with discrete data, for example the number of reported accidents, one could not have values greater than, say, 9 but less than 10 and the stated limits are the same as the true limits. It is, however, difficult to perform calculations when there are gaps between the classes and so the class intervals are adjusted as though the data were continuous even though the values could not occur in practice. The example below should clarify the point.

Example: No. of accidents reported
                                          over year

      True limits   Limits for purposes
                                  of calculations

           5 — 9 $4\frac{1}{2}$ — under $9\frac{1}{2}$
         10 — 19 $9\frac{1}{2}$ — under $19\frac{1}{2}$
         20 — 30 $19\frac{1}{2}$ — under $30\frac{1}{2}$

Sometimes you may encounter open-ended classes:—

Age Under 15 15 — under 25 25 — under 55 55 — under 65 65+	Usually the frequency of occurrences in such open-ended classes is small. By convention, and because the low frequencies involved will have only a small effect on any calculations, the class interval of such a class is taken to be the same as the adjacent class. In the example the class interval would be taken as 10 for each of the extreme classes.

3.2.3.3 Histograms

A histogram is a visual display of a grouped frequency distribution. It consists of a number of rectangles on a continuous base. The base of each rectangle is equal to the relevant class interval and the **AREA** of each rectangle is proportional to the frequency in the class. (If the distribution has equal class intervals then the heights of each rectangle will also be proportional to the frequencies.)

We could therefore illustrate the grouped frequency distribution for Question 3.1 as below:

DIAGRAM 3.1

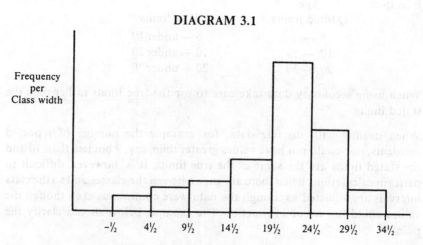

Frequency
per
Class width

       $-\frac{1}{2}$ $4\frac{1}{2}$ $9\frac{1}{2}$ $14\frac{1}{2}$ $19\frac{1}{2}$ $24\frac{1}{2}$ $29\frac{1}{2}$ $34\frac{1}{2}$

Because the data is discrete we have adjusted the class intervals as illustrated. Note that the first class interval is $-\frac{1}{2} - 4\frac{1}{2}$.

When we have to deal with unequal class intervals we must ensure that the **area** of each rectangle is proportional to the frequency. To do this:—

(i) decide on a standard class interval (the most frequently occurring one or the smallest one)

(ii) divide each frequency by the actual class interval and multiply by the standard class interval (this will, of course, leave the frequency unaltered if the actual and standard class intervals are the same)

(iii) the answers obtained are the frequencies per standard class width and denote the height of each rectangle.

(iv) If open-ended class intervals occur, make them larger than the standard class interval. Consider the data and use your judgement as to the class width to employ.

Why do we need the area to be proportional to the frequency?

Consider the frequency distribution:—

Earnings (E)	frequency
1,000 — under 2,000	5
2,000 — under 3,000	5
3,000 — under 4,000	8
4,000 — under 5,000	5
5,000 — under 6,000	5

DIAGRAM 3.2

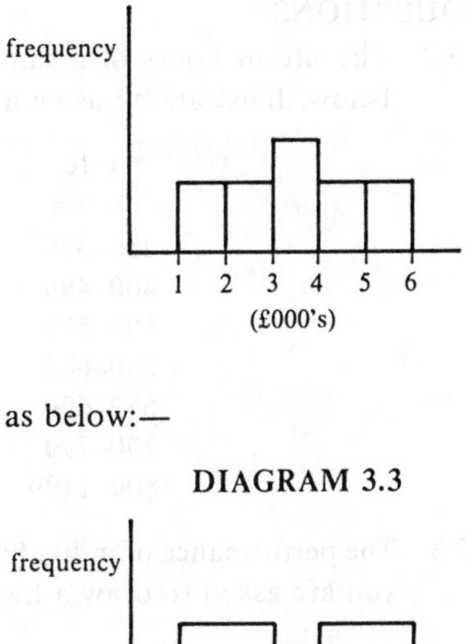

The corresponding histogram is a good visual display of the data, as shown in Diagram 3.2.

But say the same data had been grouped as below:—

DIAGRAM 3.3

£	frequency
1,000 — under 3,000	10
3,000 — under 4,000	8
4,000 — under 6,000	10

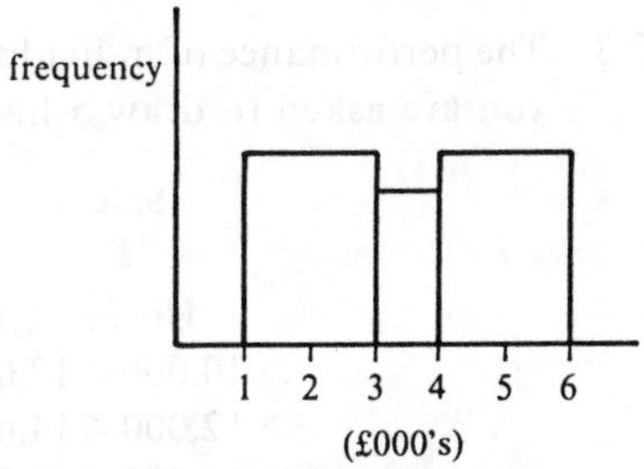

If we draw a diagram with the height of each rectangle proportional to the frequency, this gives a very misleading impression. It looks as though most of the earnings are between £1,000 – £3,000 and £4,000 – £6,000 with a trough between £3,000 and £4,000, as illustrated in Diagram 3.3.

To avoid this we make the **AREA** of each rectangle proportional to the frequency by calculating the FREQUENCY DENSITY or frequency per class width.

DIAGRAM 3.4

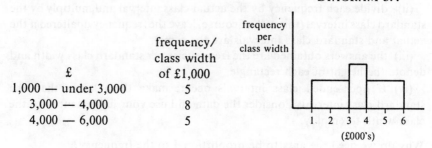

£	frequency/ class width of £1,000
1,000 — under 3,000	5
3,000 — 4,000	8
4,000 — 6,000	5

This gives a clearer impression as in the histogram from the original more detailed distribution. We can now see that the earnings are more concentrated in the £3,000–£4,000 class, as shown in Diagram 3.4.

QUESTIONS

3.2   The life in hours of a sample of 1000 machine components is given below. Illustrate by using a histogram.

Life hours		Frequency	
200–399	2	60	30
400–499	1	80	80
500–599	1	120	120
600–649	0·5	270	
650–699	0·5	250	
700–799	1	140	140
800–1199	4	80	20

*3.3   The performance of individual salesmen has been analysed as below and you are asked to draw a histogram from the data.

Sales £		Number of salesmen	
Up to 10,000	5	1	5
> 10,000 ≤ 12,000	1	10	0·1
> 12,000 ≤ 14,000	1	12	0·12
> 14,000 ≤ 18,000	2	8	
> 18,000 ≤ 22,000	2	4	
> 22,000		1	

3.2.3.4 Frequency Polygon

A frequency polygon is constructed by joining the mid-points of the tops of each rectangle in a histogram with straight lines. The ends are usually extended to join the horizontal axis at a point $\frac{1}{2}$ a class interval beyond the first and last classes so that the area enclosed by the polygon is the same as that of the histogram. It is, of course, possible to draw a frequency polygon without first drawing a histogram.

The solution to Question 3.2 is shown in diagram 3.5 with a frequency polygon superimposed on the histogram.

DIAGRAM 3.5

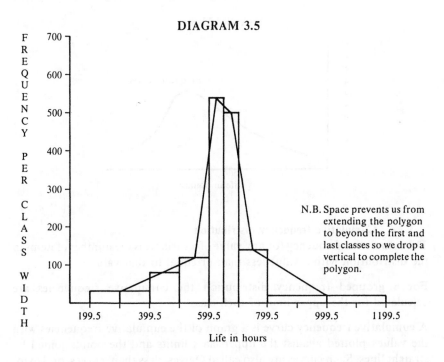

N.B. Space prevents us from extending the polygon to beyond the first and last classes so we drop a vertical to complete the polygon.

Life in hours

Life	Frequency	Class interval	Frequency per class interval of 100
200–399	60	200	60/2 = 30
400–499	80	100	80
500–599	120	100	120
600–649	270	50	540
650–699	250	50	500
700–799	140	100	140
800–1199	80	400	20

3.2.3.5 Frequency curve

An interesting exercise is to combine the classes in the above example so that they all have a class interval of at least 200. The result is a loss of accuracy and some of the variability in the data is disguised.

If on the other hand we were to obtain many more readings with much smaller class intervals the frequency polygon would become less disjointed and eventually become a smooth curve such as below. Such a curve would more accurately represent the distribution within a population as compared to a sample.

DIAGRAM 3.6

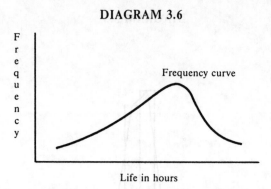

3.2.4 Cumulative frequency distribution

The cumulative frequency for any value of a variable is the number of items in the distribution with a value less than or equal to that value.

For a grouped frequency distribution the cumulative frequencies are calculated for the upper limit of each class.

A cumulative frequency curve is a graph of the cumulative frequencies with the values plotted against the upper class limits and the points joined by straight lines. Such curves are also called Ogives, 'less than' curves, or 'Up to' curves.

Using the data from Question 3.2 we could construct an ogive as follows:—

Life	frequency	Cumulative frequency
200–399	60	60
400–499	80	140
500–599	120	260
600–649	270	530
650–699	250	780
700–799	140	920
800–1199	80	1000

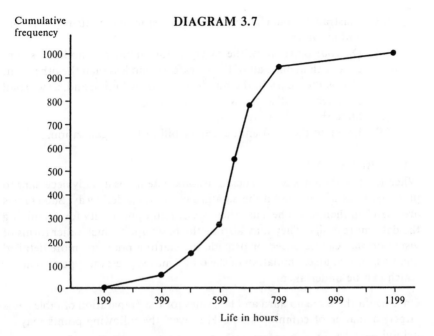

DIAGRAM 3.7

Cumulative
frequency

From our cumulative frequency curve we can read off the frequency of occurrence of less than or equal to a certain value. For example, there are 530 components with a life of less than or equal to 649 hours.

Because estimates from a grouped frequency distribution are never totally accurate it is usually permissible to approximate and say that the 530th component in the distribution has a life of 649 hours.

It is also permissible to smooth ogives if it is felt that a smooth curve will better represent the parent population from which the sample is drawn.

QUESTIONS
3.4   The data below refers to the annual salaries of a group of workers in a certain organisation.

Annual salary £	Number of employees
5000 to < 5500	3
5500 to < 6000	4
6000 to < 7000	7
7000 to < 9000	16
9000 to < 11000	22
11000 to < 12000	31
12000 to < 15000	12
15000 to < 20000	4

(a) Illustrate the data by constructing a histogram, frequency polygon, and an ogive.

(b) On your ogive mark the salary of the employee who has a salary greater than one half of the workforce and less than the other half. This is the salary in the middle of the distribution and, as we shall see later, is called the Median salary.

(c) State the median salary.

(d) Estimate the total annual salary bill of the organisation.

3.3 TABULATION

When the raw data has been ordered to some extent it is usually necessary to prepare tables which present the data in a clear and orderly way. Such tables are useful in themselves because they present an opportunity for examining the data more easily. They may also be the basis upon which other forms of visual display can be based or provide the starting point for more detailed analysis. Indeed an examination of the tables may suggest the type of analysis which can be undertaken.

Once again there are no hard and fast rules for the preparation of tables; it is largely a matter of common sense. However, the following points may be helpful:—

(a) The table should fit its purpose. Some tables are merely a convenient way of presenting a mass of data in an orderly fashion and will inevitably be complex.

Other tables, particularly those employed as part of a report, are produced to emphasise patterns in the data. Usually the reader will be expected to examine and understand the patterns revealed by such tables and they must therefore be kept simple and easy to read. Often two, or more, tables may be preferable to a single large complicated table.

(b) Every table should have a clear and unambiguous title, headings, and sub-headings.

(c) If titles, headings, etc. are too long, use shortened versions with footnotes providing a full explanation.

(d) Headings should be chosen to draw attention to those features of the data that you wish to emphasise. For example, if you want to emphasise sex differences then headings for male and female should be prominent and probably juxtaposed.

(e) The units of measurement must be clearly stated at the top of columns or the start of rows.

(f)   If sub-totals are desirable make sure it is clear that they are sub-totals.

(g)   Similarly, total columns and rows can be useful but make sure it is clear that they refer to totals.

(h)   Often figures can be made more meaningful through the use of percentages or other derived (secondary) statistics. It can therefore be useful to add percentage columns, or rows, to the table. Sometimes it is better to present all the information in the form of percentages or averages but one would normally show the totals upon which the table is based at least as footnotes.

(i)   The source of data upon which the table is based must be stated.

QUESTIONS
3.5   Go to the library and study any government statistical publication to see examples of well-constructed tables.

3.6   In 1964 in Great Britain, 6158 thousand people were in receipt of Retirement pension (including non-contributory retirement pension), 596 thousand women received Widow's benefit and 172 thousand people received Unemployment benefit, 1958 thousand people received Supplementary benefit, 819 thousand people received Sickness and Invalidity benefit and 3794 thousand received Child benefit (prior to 1977 this came under Family Allowance).

In 1983, the corresponding figures (in thousands) were 9326, 406, 906, 4349, 1075, and 6919. In addition 3900 thousand were in receipt of Rent rebate, 1080 in receipt of Rent allowance, and 7530 received Rate rebate — the numbers of people receiving these last three benefits in 1964 is not available.

This information was obtained from the "UK in figures" published by the Government Statistical Service.

You are required to tabulate the data together with any secondary statistics that you think appropriate.

3.4   VISUAL DISPLAY
Rather than present data numerically in the form of a table it can sometimes be better to illustrate the information through the use of graphs, charts, diagrams, and so on. There is virtually no limit to the ways that can be devised to display information but some of the most common methods are mentioned below.

Once again, accuracy and detail are often sacrificed when some form of visual display is used but it is often worthwhile if the salient features of the data can thus be more readily appreciated. A visual display can also be useful in arousing people's interest in a way that numerical data cannot.

The various types of display are sometimes called by different names but they are easily recognised and amongst the most common are:

Simple bar charts
Line charts
Component bar charts
Multiple bar charts
Percentage component bar charts
Floating bar charts
Pie charts
Pictograms, Isotype representation, Ideographs
Venn diagrams
Statistical maps, cartographs
Graphs, scattergraphs
Log graphs
Semi-log graphs
Lorenz curves
Z charts
Break-even charts
Frequency curves
Ogives, cumulative frequency curves
Gantt charts, Network diagrams, flow charts, decision trees etc.

3.4.1 Simple bar chart

A simple bar chart is used to illustrate a frequency distribution (the data will not always be recognisable as a frequency distribution but it usually is a frequency distribution of some description). The length of the bars are proportional to the frequency and the bars are of equal width. The bars may be drawn horizontally (which permits longer titles to be placed against or inside each bar), or vertically, and usually there is a gap between each bar of about $\frac{1}{2}$ bar width.

If possible include the zero in your scale as this will avoid distortion of the relative frequencies. Label all the bars and show the scale clearly. Quote the source of information and make sure the chart has a clear heading. As the bar chart is designed to exhibit the salient features in the data, rather than convey information with absolute accuracy, it is perhaps better not to use graph paper because the grid effect can make the bars indistinct. However, a few scale lines can sometimes be useful as reference points. A practical tip is to draw your chart on graph paper in black and then photocopy — the black copies better than the blue grid of the graph paper and leaves a prominent chart.

Example:

SALES (£m)

	1982	1983	1984	1985
Product X	2	3	4	5
Y	2	$2\frac{1}{2}$	$4\frac{1}{4}$	$4\frac{1}{2}$
Z	2	$2\frac{1}{2}$	$\frac{3}{4}$	$\frac{1}{2}$
Total	6	8	9	10

Source: Company Accounts 1982–83.

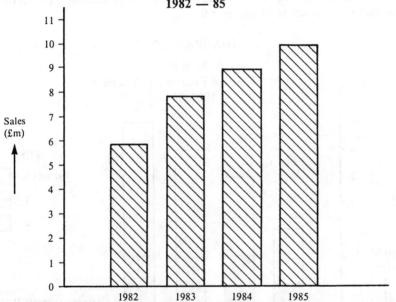

DIAGRAM 3.8
Total Annual Sales of Jackson plc
1982 — 85

Source: Company Accounts 1982-85

The simple bar chart is most common when comparing data which falls into different types of categories, as above the comparison between different years, but it is not unusual to use a bar chart to illustrate a grouped frequency distribution.

Sometimes the bars are reduced to lines when one is representing the values of discrete variables and the result is called a line chart.

N.B. A HISTOGRAM is a development of the bar chart but remember when drawing a histogram it is the **AREA** of each bar which is proportional to the frequency and there are **no gaps** between the bars because the classes are usually arranged so that there are no gaps. In the case of the histogram the height of the bar represents the frequency per class width (frequency density) not the frequency. With equal class intervals the height of the bar will, of course, also represent the frequency.

3.4.1.2 Component bar chart

Component bar charts are simple bar charts with each bar subdivided to show the contributions of the component parts.

Each subdivision of the bar is coloured, or shaded, to distinguish it readily from the other components and a key is necessary to explain the meaning of the shading unless this is signified on the bar itself.

The data in the above example could be presented in the form of a component bar chart, as shown in Diagram 3.9.

DIAGRAM 3.9

Jackson plc
Annual Sales of Products X, Y, and Z
1982–85

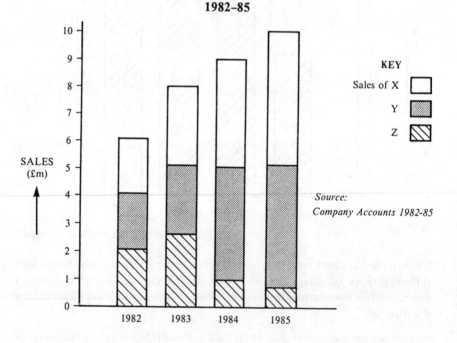

Source:
Company Accounts 1982-85

3.4.1.3 Multiple bar chart

Another way of showing the components is to have separate bars for each component, as illustrated in Diagram 3.10.

DIAGRAM 3.10

**Jackson plc
Annual Sales of Products X, Y, Z
1982–85**

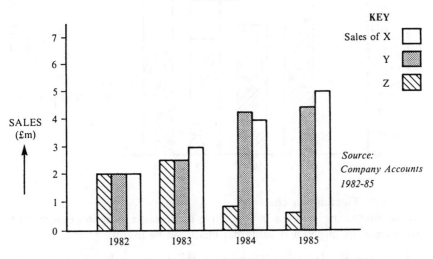

Unlike the component bar chart this diagram does not show the total sales each year, it shows only the values of the components, and this is sometimes a drawback.

It is perhaps better than the component bar chart in showing the relative values of the components but when there are more than three components the multiple bar chart becomes a bit confusing (this is also true of the component bar chart but to a slightly lesser extent).

3.4.1.4 Percentage component bar chart

When the relative proportions of the components are more important than their absolute values a percentage component bar chart may be employed showing what percentage each component is of the overall total.

In this case all the bars are the same height, ie. 100%, as shown in Diagram 3.11.

DIAGRAM 3.11

Jackson plc
Annual Sales of Products X, Y, Z
1982–85

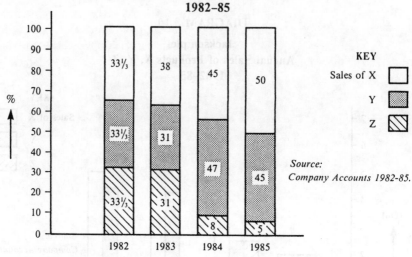

3.4.1.5 Floating bar charts

When comparing changes in a positive or negative direction compared to some base, or target, a floating bar chart can be useful.

So, for example, if we wanted to compare the changes in the sales of product Z between 1982 and 1985 with respect to a target sales figure of £1m we might present the results as below:

DIAGRAM 3.12

Annual Sales of Product Z
1982–85

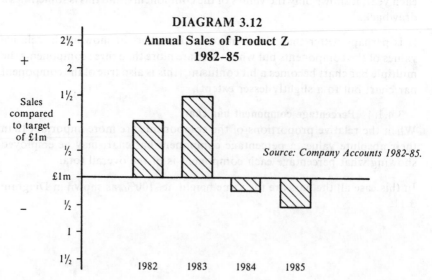

Source: Company Accounts 1982-85.

3.4.2 Pie charts

Pie charts are a popular form of diagram in which the sectors of a circle are used to represent the components of some total figure.

Since the area of a sector of a circle is proportional to the arc of the circle contained by the sector, the circumference of the circle can be divided in proportion to the components represented. To divide up the circumference (or area) of the circle we divide the angle at the centre of the circle (360°). Thus, a component which is P percent of the whole is represented by a sector which has an angle P percent of 360°.

So, if we wished to represent the components of sales in 1985 in our example, we would proceed as follows:

	Sales	Fraction of total	Angle of sector
X	5	½	½ × 360 = 180°
Y	4½	9/20	9/20 × 360 = 162°
Z	½	1/20	1/20 × 360 = 18°

DIAGRAM 3.13

Annual Sales of Products XYZ
1985

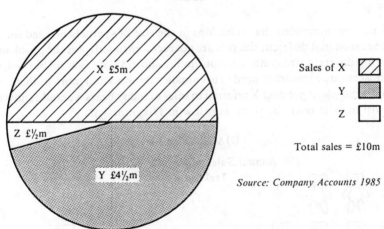

Sales of X

Y

Z

Total sales = £10m

Source: Company Accounts 1985

The pie chart, like the multiple bar chart, is useful to show the relative values or proportions of the components and it has the advantage that more components can be shown.

It is also possible to have more than one pie to show different totals; the pies should be drawn so that the AREAS of the circles are in proportion to the total figures. For example, if we wanted two circles to represent 1982 and 1985 total sales figures then our circles would need to be drawn with areas in the ratio 6:10 and we would need to draw circles with radii of 1.73 and 2.24 inches, or cms, or whatever.

i.e. $\quad \dfrac{\pi\, r_1^{\,2}}{\pi\, r_2^{\,2}} = \dfrac{6}{10}$ $\quad$ where r_1 = radius of circle 1
$\quad\quad\quad\quad\quad\quad\quad\quad$ and r_2 = radius of circle 2

So, $\quad \dfrac{r_1^{\,2}}{r_2^{\,2}} = \dfrac{3}{5}$

and $\quad \dfrac{r_1}{r_2} = \dfrac{\sqrt{3}}{\sqrt{5}} = \dfrac{1.73}{2.24}$

The problem with using pie charts to represent two or more totals is that a circle which is, for example, twice as large as another circle does not really look twice as large — try it and see. The practice is usually best avoided.

3.4.3 Isotype representation, Pictograms
Another popular device is to use pictures to represent the data with differences in frequency indicated by differences in the NUMBER of symbols drawn.

It is not recommended that variations in the size of symbols be used for the same reason that different size pies are not recommended (plus the problem of drawing different size symbols). Nor should a portion of a symbol be used, if a more accurate measure is needed use smaller symbols and more of them. So, in our example, if product X referred to sales of teddy bears we could show the growth in sales over the years as below in Diagram 3.14.

DIAGRAM 3.14

Annual Sales of Product X — Jackson plc

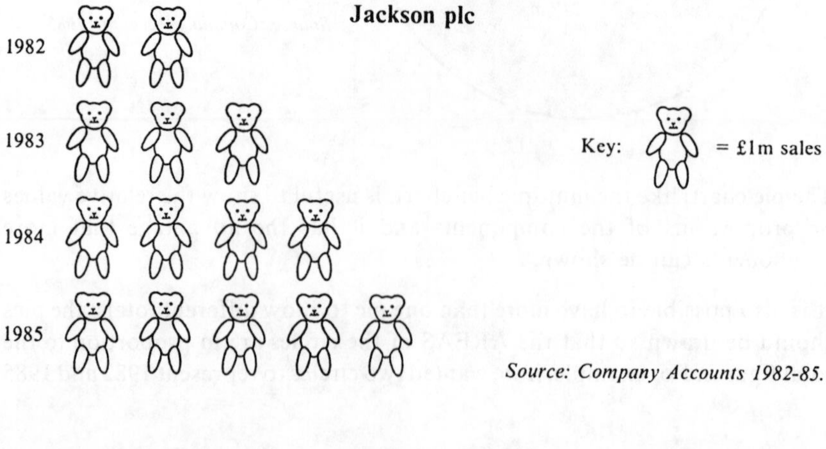

Key: = £1m sales

Source: Company Accounts 1982-85.

3.4.4 Statistical maps or cartograms

A cartogram is used to illustrate data that has some sort of geographical pattern. There are many types of cartogram but the most common is a map of some area with shaded portions representing the density of measurement of some variable in the component parts of the geographical area.

A typical example, with which most people are familiar, is the map of the UK showing the areas of highest unemployment shaded in black — unemployment blackspots.

The example in diagram 3.15 is very similar, showing those areas which qualify for varying degrees of government assistance.

DIAGRAM 3.15

ASSISTED AREAS
(Designated Under Industry Act 1972)

Special Development Areas
Development Areas
Intermediate Areas
Northern Ireland (all incentives + additional assistance)

3.4.5 Venn Diagrams

Venn diagrams are used in the theory of sets and offer a diagrammatic representation of the number of items in various categories.

The diagrams can be useful in describing and understanding situations where the data is confused or incomplete.

Set theory is based upon Boolean algebra which is a little different from the normal number algebra learnt at school. Nevertheless many problems can be solved without resort to the notation and rules of Boolean algebra.

Example: Say out of 265 workers,

120	travel to work by	car;
140	....	bus;
100	....	rail;
38	....	car and bus;
33	....	car and rail;
39	....	bus and rail;
15	....	car, bus and rail.

How many use a car only, bus only, rail only?

If we draw a Venn diagram, as in diagram 3.16, and start with the centre value of 15 (the last mentioned above) then the other figures follow logically. See if you can find the answers.

DIAGRAM 3.16

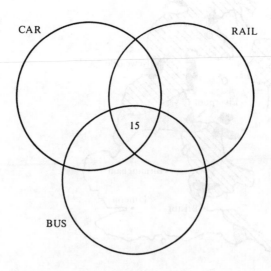

SOLUTION:

    If we denote the number of people using car only as C

                                  car & bus .... CB

                                  car & rail .... CR

                                  car, bus, and rail.. CBR

                                  bus .... B

and so on.

Then $C + CB + CR + CBR = 120$
and substituting the corresponding values we get
$C + (38-15) + (33-15) + 15 = 120$
Therefore $C = 64$

The final solution is:—

DIAGRAM 3.17

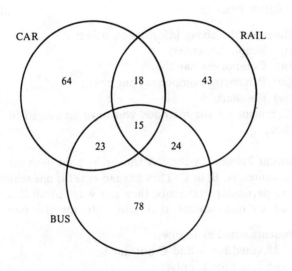

QUESTIONS
*3.7 **Prenton-by-the-Sea University**

Course	Number of students
Professional	
Management	120
Accounting	240
Banking	980
General Business Studies	
BEC National	350
BEC Higher	115
G.C.E. subjects	225
Office Skills	
Typing	220
Shorthand	100
Office Practice	20

(a) Illustrate the above information using:
   (i)   Simple bar chart;
   (ii) Component bar chart;
   (iii) Percentage component bar chart;
   (iv) Pie chart.
(b) Comment on the methods you have employed to illustrate the data.

3.8 Students at Prenton-by-the-Sea University have been asked to vote for three schemes, A, B, or C. They have to vote for one scheme but if they have no particular preference they can vote for all three; if they are opposed to one scheme they can vote for the two they prefer.

200 students voted as follows:
   15 voted for A and C but not B;
   65 voted for B only;
   51 voted for C only;
   15 voted for both A and B;
   117 voted for either A or B or both A and B but not C;
   128 voted for either B or C or both B and C but not A.

How many would vote for:
(a) all three schemes;
(b) only one scheme;
(c) A irrespective of B or C;
(d) A only;
(e) A and B but not C?

3.9 (a) Illustrate the following data by means of a histogram, a frequency polygon, and a cumulative frequency polygon (ogive).

Weekly wage £ £	Number of employees
31 and < 36	6
36 and < 41	8
41 and < 46	12
46 and < 51	18
51 and < 56	25
56 and < 61	30
61 and < 66	24
66 and < 71	14
71 and < 75	6
75 and < 81	3

(b) A large bank in its accounts for the three years showed its profit distribution as follows:

	1978 £m	1977 £m	1976 £m
Profit before taxation	373	295	198
Taxation	135	140	82
Minority interests	12	12	11
Dividends	30	23	20
Retained profit	196	120	85

You are required to present the information given in a visual display form. *(ICMA)*

3.4.6 GRAPHS

Simple graphs can be very useful in illustrating trends but the construction of graphs is open to a great deal of abuse.

The most obvious, but by no means the only, way of distorting a graph is by changing the scale. As can be seen in Diagrams 3.18 and 3.19, if we graph sales of product X in our example, by widening the vertical and narrowing the horizontal scale we can create the impression that sales are expanding more rapidly. Even the 'correctly' drawn graph on the left creates a slightly misleading impression in so far as it appears that sales are increasing at a steady rate when in fact sales are increasing by an equal absolute amount each year but the percentage increase is falling each year. Of course, most graphs and other forms of visual presentation are designed to support some particular argument and one should not be unduly impressed by graphs or charts until they have been subjected to careful scrutiny.

DIAGRAM 3.18   DIAGRAM 3.19

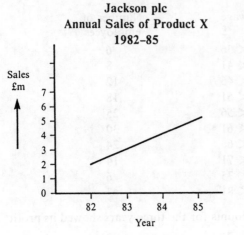

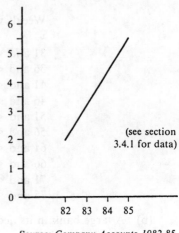

Source: Company Accounts 1982-85.

In the construction of graphs there are certain principles to which reputable statisticians should adhere, viz:

(a) The graph should give the right impression.
     This is the most important principle of graph construction and most of the points mentioned below follow from this. In the above example we would be better advised to use a ratio-scale graph if we were concerned with the rate at which sales were increasing (see later).

(b) The axes must be clearly labelled and the units of measurement stated.

(c) Arrange the scales to use as much of the graph paper as possible.

(d) If it is not practical to start a scale at zero show the zero at the bottom of the scale with a definite break indicated by one of the methods shown in Diagrams 3.20 and 3.21.

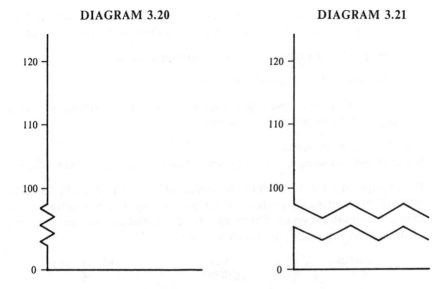

DIAGRAM 3.20   DIAGRAM 3.21

(e) If two curves are plotted on the same chart and they require different scales (either because they are measured in different units or they would otherwise be too far apart) it is acceptable to use a double scale. The two scales would normally be shown on opposite sides, or ends, of the graph paper.

(f) The dependent variable should be plotted on the vertical axis (y-axis, ordinate axis) and the independent variable on the horizontal (x-axis, abscissa) axis. For example, time would always be plotted on the x-axis when plotting time series data and frequency would always be plotted on the y-axis when plotting a frequency distribution.

(g) If a ratio scale is used then this must be clearly shown on the axis along which the ratio scale is measured. If specially constructed graph paper is employed for the purpose (log paper) then the scale will make it clear that the ordinary absolute measure is not being employed. In such cases the heading on the graph or a footnote should make clear the nature and purpose of the graph.

(h) The graph should not be overcrowded with too many curves. This is particularly important if the curves are close together.

(i) The graph should fit its purpose. For example, if the graph is for presentation purposes and designed to illustrate some pattern in the data then the curves need to be clear and distinct and a high degree of accuracy is probably not necessary. On the other hand, if the graph is meant to be read accurately, for example when constructing regression lines or trend lines, the curves must be constructed very carefully and the lines should be as thin as possible so that they can be read accurately.

(j)   The graph must have a clear and unambiguous title.

(k)   The source of data should be quoted.

(l)   If more than one curve is plotted, label each curve clearly or provide a key to indicate which curve is which.

3.4.6.1   Scattergraphs

Scattergraphs are used to show how two variables are related to each other.

For example, if we were given the following information we might decide to plot delivery cost against sales to examine the way in which delivery cost changed with sales revenue. The result would be a plot of a number of points scattered over the graph, as shown in Diagram 3.22.

Month	Sales (£'000s)	Delivery cost £
July	50	340
August	150	400
September	550	700
October	560	650
November	650	760
December	710	750
January	750	800
February	900	900
March	470	600
April	350	450
May	250	500
June	80	330

3.4.6.2   Line Graph

If the points in the scattergraph in Diagram 3.22 are joined up by a series of straight lines we get a line graph as in Diagram 3.23.

However, it seems obvious that the delivery costs increase with the value of sales and that a straight line would provide a close approximation of the relationship between sales and delivery costs. If we draw a **line of best fit** so that the line is as close as possible to as many points as possible we get a result such as in Diagram 3.24.

Because the line of best fit is a straight line we say there is a **linear** relationship and because the line is close to most of the points we say there is a high **correlation** between the variables. As there is a high correlation we can use the curve (even straight lines may be called curves) to read off the delivery cost

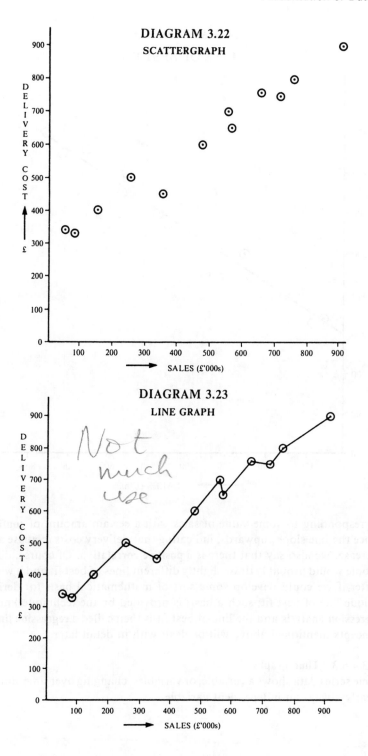

DIAGRAM 3.22
SCATTERGRAPH

DIAGRAM 3.23
LINE GRAPH

DIAGRAM 3.24

LINE OF BEST FIT

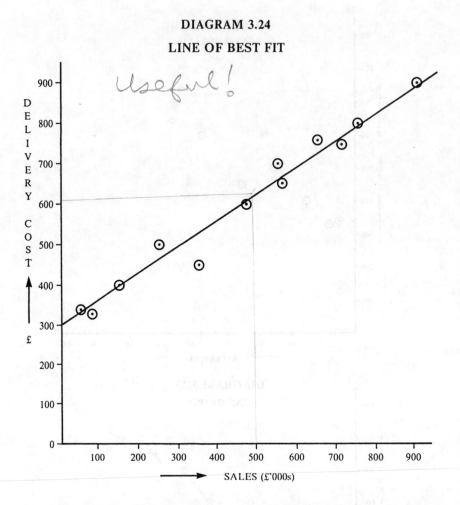

corresponding to some value of sales with a certain amount of **confidence.** Since the line slopes upwards, indicating that delivery costs increase as sales increase, we also say that there is a **positive correlation.** Of course, different people would probably draw slightly different lines of best fit and it would be better if we could develop some sort of mathematical basis for deriving a unique line of best fit; such a basis is provided by the technique known as **regression analysis** and the line of best fit is then called a **regression line.** The concepts mentioned above will be dealt with in detail later.

3.4.6.3 Time graphs
Time series data shows a variable, or variables, changing over time and time is clearly always an independent variable.

A simple time graph shows a series of points representing the value of some variable at different points in time joined by straight lines as in diagram 3.25.

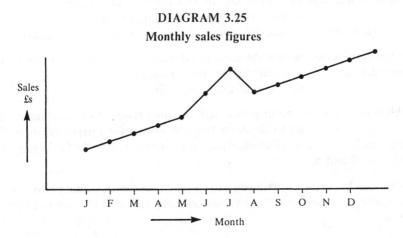

DIAGRAM 3.25
Monthly sales figures

The time graph above indicates clearly that sales are rising, with sales above the general trend in the summer months. We could therefore draw a line of best fit ignoring the seasonal variation in the summer months. Such a line would be called a **trend line** and could be derived through regression analysis, as previously mentioned, or through the method of **moving averages**. Of course the trend line would never be as obvious as in diagram 3.25 and the analysis of time series data is dealt with in some detail later.

3.4.6.4 Band curve charts or layer graphs
A time graph may be refined to show the components that make up the total of a variable as shown in diagram 3.26.

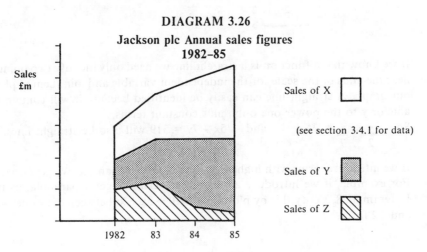

DIAGRAM 3.26
Jackson plc Annual sales figures
1982–85

3.4.6.5 Graphs of functions

Sometimes there may be an exact mathematical relationship between two variables and one variable is said to be a function of the other.

$$y = f(x) \text{ means that y is a function of x.}$$

(Remember y is usually used to denote the dependent variable).

A common relationship is **the linear relationship** $y = a + bx$ where a and b are constants and a = the intercept on the y axis, and

b= the slope of the straight line.

When we know the mathematical relationship between two variables we can easily plot the graph to illustrate the relationship for certain values of the independent variable. For example, let us plot $y = 10 + 3x$ for values of x between 0 and 5.

We begin by preparing a schedule to calculate the corresponding values of the variables and then plot these values on the graph as illustrated in Diagram 3.27.

DIAGRAM 3.27

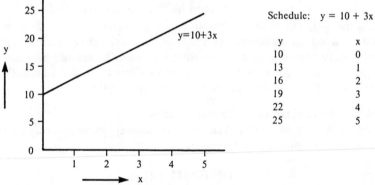

Schedule: $y = 10 + 3x$

y	x
10	0
13	1
16	2
19	3
22	4
25	5

If we know that a function is a straight line we need only identify two points near the ends of the scale for the independent variable and join them to plot our graph. A straight line can easily be identified because it will contain x and/or y to the power one only, plus constant terms.

So, $\dfrac{y}{2} + \dfrac{x}{7} = 35$ and $5x - 7y = 319$ will also be straight lines.

If we introduce terms with higher, or lower, powers than one we get curves. For example, if we introduce an x squared term we get a parabola, as in Diagram 3.28. Verify this by plotting $y = 10 + 3x + x^2$ between the values -5 and $+2$ for x.

DIAGRAM 3.28

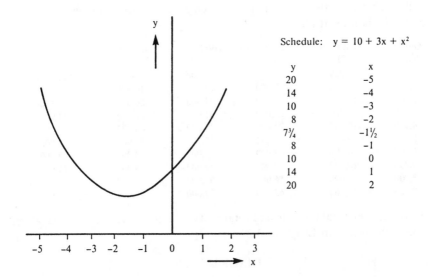

Schedule: $y = 10 + 3x + x^2$

y	x
20	-5
14	-4
10	-3
8	-2
7¾	-1½
8	-1
10	0
14	1
20	2

3.4.6.6 Break-even charts

A common form of graph employed in the business world is the break-even chart. There are many types of break-even chart that employ some of the methods we have already mentioned; the break-even date chart, for example, has similarities with the time graph and the break-even fantail chart uses layers such as in the band curve chart; we shall consider only the simplest form of B/E chart.

The B/E chart shows how Total Sales Receipts (Total Revenue) vary with output (or sales) units and how Total Costs of production vary with output. When the Total Revenue equals the Total Cost we say that the Break-even point has been reached.

EXAMPLE: * Say we have a firm that has a productive capacity of 9,000 units of output. The product sells for £10 per unit and each unit costs £7 to make in terms of direct materials, labour, and other variable expenses.
* Suppose, also, that the firm has fixed costs of £10,000, ie. those costs that do not change with output such as rent, rates, insurance, etc. add up to £10,000 for the period under consideration.
* The sum of all the costs that change with the level of output is the Total Variable Cost per unit (or the Marginal Cost per unit).

To construct our break-even chart it is probably best at this stage to construct a table as below. When you are more familiar with the concepts involved you will be able to draw a B/E chart, for such a simple situation, without doing any calculations at all.

Output (units)	Fixed Cost (£)	Variable Cost (£)	Total Cost (£)	Total Revenue (£)	Profit (Loss) (£)
0	10,000	—	10,000	—	(10,000)
1,000	10,000	7,000	17,000	10,000	(7,000)
2,000	10,000	14,000	24,000	20,000	(4,000)
3,000	10,000	21,000	31,000	30,000	(1,000)
4,000	10,000	28,000	38,000	40,000	2,000
5,000	10,000	35,000	45,000	50,000	5,000
6,000	10,000	42,000	52,000	60,000	8,000
7,000	10,000	49,000	59,000	70,000	11,000
8,000	10,000	56,000	66,000	80,000	14,000
9,000	10,000	63,000	73,000	90,000	17,000

If we plot the total revenue and total costs on a graph we get the Break-Even chart illustrated in Diagram 3.29.

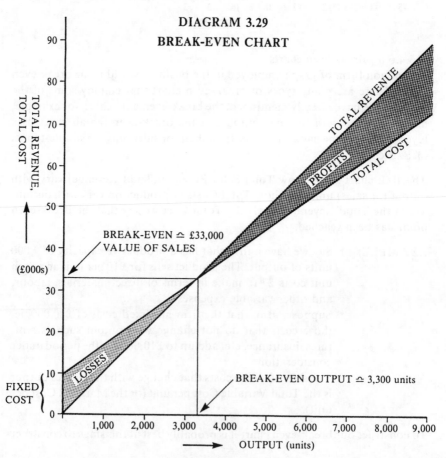

DIAGRAM 3.29
BREAK-EVEN CHART

Now, we can read off from the break-even chart the level of output (3,300 units) or the level of sales (£33,000) at which the firm reaches its break-even point.

If we have drawn the graph with reasonable accuracy, we can judge what profits or losses will be made at various levels of output and we can see what output the firm must achieve to break-even. Such a graph would probably suffice for most practical purposes but, if we wish, we can calculate the exact break-even point by a number of methods. Two possible methods are:

(i) **Simultaneous equations**

The Total Revenue is just the number of units times the selling price per unit.

$$TR = x \times 10 = 10x \quad \text{where } x = \text{number of units of output}$$

The Total Cost is the fixed cost plus the variable cost at that level of output.

$$TC = FC + x \times 7 = FC + 7x$$

When the firm reaches break-even point the Total Revenue and Total Cost will be the same and the level of output, x, will be the break-even output.

So, we can write $TR = TC$ at break-even,
$$10x = FC + 7x$$
$$10x - 7x = FC$$
$$3x = FC$$
$$3x = £10,000$$
$$\underline{x = 3,333 \text{ units}}$$

(ii) **Break-even formula**

Perhaps more simply, we might realise that if every unit sells for £10, but costs £7 to make, then each unit contributes £3 towards the fixed cost.

ie. Contribution = Selling price per unit − Marginal Cost per unit
per unit
$$= SP - MC = £3 \text{ per unit}$$

Once we amass enough £3s to cover the fixed cost the firm will break-even.

So, the break-even output = $\underline{\dfrac{£10,000}{£3} = 3,333 \text{ units}}$

The formula we have used is Break-even output = $\dfrac{\text{Fixed Cost}}{\text{Contribution per unit}}$
in units

which is well known to every student of Cost and Management Accountancy

3.4.6.7 Profit Graph

We said earlier that you should not have too many lines on a graph. The two lines on a break-even chart are obviously not confusing but it is possible to present the information in an even more simple form. The profit graph has just one line and is, in some ways, more revealing than the break-even chart. This is not the place to discuss the merits of the profit graph but it is an alternative way of presenting accounting information and the above information (3.4.6.6) could be shown in the form of the profit graph in Diagram 3.30.

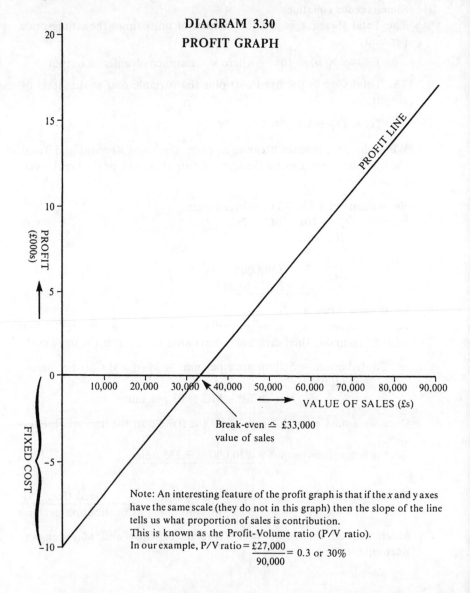

DIAGRAM 3.30

PROFIT GRAPH

Break-even ≏ £33,000
value of sales

Note: An interesting feature of the profit graph is that if the *x* and *y* axes have the same scale (they do not in this graph) then the slope of the line tells us what proportion of sales is contribution.
This is known as the Profit-Volume ratio (P/V ratio).
In our example, P/V ratio = $\dfrac{£27,000}{90,000}$ = 0.3 or 30%

3.4.6.8 Z Charts

Another common type of graph employed in the business world is the Z chart. The Z chart is a special type of time graph usually covering a single year and showing, for some variable, the following:—

     (i)   Individual monthly totals;
    (ii) cumulative monthly totals;
   (iii) the moving annual totals (MAT).

Often a double scale is used in order to accentuate variation in the smaller individual monthly figures, one scale being used for the monthly figures and the other for the cumulative and moving annual totals.

The MAT for any month is the total for the 12 months preceeding the end of the month concerned. Such a total eliminates seasonal variation and allows us to judge the trend in the data. It means, of course, that we must have data covering two years to be able to compute the MAT for each month of the current year.

Example.
Using the data below we can produce the Z chart shown in Diagram 3.31.

Month	Sales (£000s) 1984	Sales (£000s) 1985	MAT 1985	Cumulative Sales 1985
Jan	55	115	1075*	115
Feb	60	120	1135	235
Mar	65	125	1195	360
Apr	70	130	1255	490
May	75	135	1315	625
June	90	150	1375	775
July	100	165	1440	940
Aug	90	150	1500	1090
Sept	95	155	1560	1245
Oct	100	155	1615	1400
Nov	105	150	1660	1550
Dec	110	140	1690	1690
	1015			

*MAT for Jan 1985 = Sum of sales from Feb 84 to Jan 85
          1015 − 55 + 115 = 1075

The Z chart in Diagram 3.31 uses a single scale, in practice a larger scale for the monthly totals would probably be used.

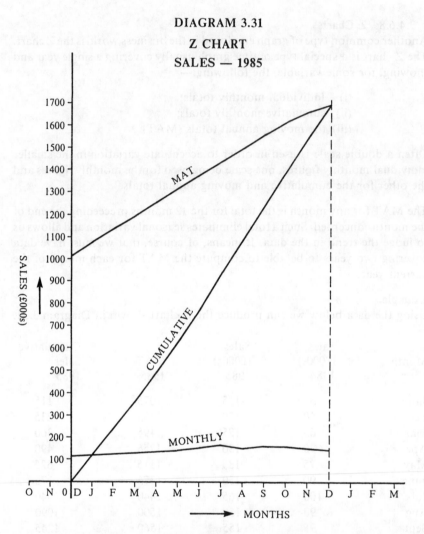

DIAGRAM 3.31

Z CHART

SALES — 1985

N.B. The MAT, cumulative totals, and monthly totals have all been plotted at the end of each month. It is sometimes recommended that the monthly totals are plotted at the middle of the month over which the figures are measured. In examinations, a footnote to indicate that you are aware of the alternatives may be advisable.

The monthly totals show the seasonal increase in June and July and the fall in sales at the end of the year. It is only by reference to previous years that we know the former is seasonal while the latter is not.

The cumulative totals show the sales performance over the year and can be compared to budgeted figures by superimposing a budgeted sales line on the graph.

The MAT compares the current year with the previous year and as long as the line slopes upwards then this year's monthly sales are better than the corresponding figures of the previous year. The slight levelling off in the MAT and the cumulative totals indicate that the increase in sales has not been maintained towards the end of the year and that the fall in the monthly totals is not due to seasonal factors.

It is possible to link a number of Z charts for succeeding years.

3.4.6.9 Lorenz curves

A Lorenz curve is designed to show the inequality in the distribution of some variable between a number of items.

Along both axes the cumulative value, usually in percentage terms, of some variable or item is measured. A 45° line (y=x) showing an exactly even distribution is used to demonstrate the extent to which the actual distribution differs from such a distribution.

A typical use of the Lorenz curve is to show inequalities in the distribution of income and wealth in society.

As an example, let us consider the distribution of income before and after tax in the United Kingdom for 1972.

Range of incomes before tax		Number of tax units (incomes)	Income before tax	Income after tax
Not under £	Under £	(000s)	£m	£m
—	595	4868	2104	2104
595	1000	5674	4593	4471
1000	1500	5139	6404	5801
1500	2000	4644	8082	7086
2000	3000	5633	13615	11616
3000	6000	2084	7891	6295
6000	12000	253	2030	1345
12000	20000	43	634	332
20000 and over		13	411	142
		28,351	45,764	39,192

In order to plot a Lorenz curve we need to calculate the cumulative percentages of the number of tax units and money incomes. The results are as below:—

Pre-tax income range		Number of tax units (incomes)		Income before tax		Income after tax	
		%	Cumulative %	%	Cumulative %	%	Cumulative %
Not under £	Under £						
—	595	17.2	17.2	4.6	4.6	5.4	5.4
595	1000	20.0	37.2	10.0	14.6	11.4	16.8
1000	1500	18.1	55.3	14.0	28.6	14.8	31.6
1500	2000	16.4	71.7	17.7	46.3	18.1	49.7
2000	3000	19.9	91.6	29.8	76.1	29.6	79.3
3000	6000	7.3	98.9	17.2	93.3	16.1	95.4
6000	12000	0.9	99.8	4.4	97.7	3.4	98.8
12000	20000	0.2	100.0	1.4	99.1	0.8	99.6
200000 and over		—	100.0	0.9	100.0	0.4	100.0
		100.0		100.0		100.0	

If we now plot the cumulative percentage of tax units (or number of incomes) against the cumulative percentages of money income we obtain a Lorenz curve as shown in Diagram 3.32. The curve shows that incomes are rather unevenly distributed with, for example, the bottom 70% of incomes covering only 45% of money incomes and, conversely, the top 30% of incomes covering 55% of money income.

If we plot a second Lorenz curve showing post-tax incomes we see that the tax system reduces inequalities (it is a progressive tax system) because the distribution moves closer to the 45° line of equal distribution. However, to get a clearer picture we would need to consider the effect of the various welfare payments that are made out of tax revenue.

The Lorenz curve may lie above or below the 45° line. If we had swopped the axes then our Lorenz curve would have been above the 45° line or if the inequality in the distribution had been in favour of the lower income groups then the result would have been the same. The moral of this is to be careful when you interpret the Lorenz curve!

The degree of inequality in the distribution can be evaluated numerically as the ratio of the area between the Lorenz curve and the line of equal distribution to the area between the line of equal distribution and the axes. This ratio is known as the Gini coefficient.

The main use of the Lorenz curve is for comparative purposes; in our example we used two Lorenz curves to compare the distribution of income before and

DIAGRAM 3.32
LORENZ CURVES

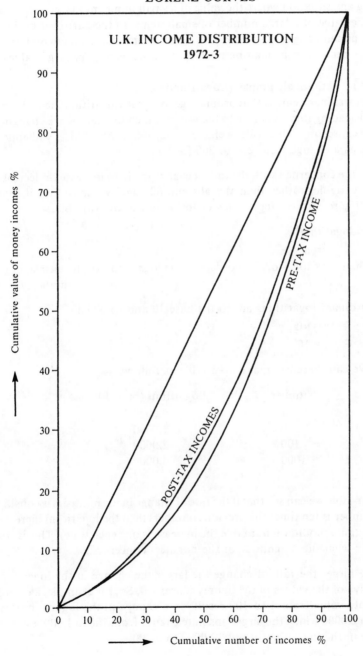

Source: National Income and Expenditure Blue Book.

after tax, we could equally compare distributions over a run of years or between different countries, and so on. The Lorenz curve can be useful in analysing any situation where the value of a small number of large items may exceed the value of a large number of small items. In the narrower business context one can imagine a situation where a firm may have a small number of very large debtors or a small number of stock items of very large value.

3.4.6.10 Ratio-Scale graphs (Logarithmic graphs)

The point was made earlier that ordinary graphs, with an arithmetic scale, can give a misleading impression as to the way in which the figures are changing. This is because, on such a scale, a change from 100 to 200 (100%) will appear the same as a change from 200 to 300 (50%).

When we are concerned with the **rate of change** (be it an increase or decrease) of some variable, rather than the absolute change, we may find it more illuminating to plot the **logarithms** of the values of the variable.

What is a logarithm?

If $y = a^x$

Then $x = \log_a y$ or, in words, x is the logarithm, to the base a, of the number y.

Ordinary logarithms are to the base 10 and so when

$x = \log_{10} y$

$y = 10^x$

We can therefore make up a table as follows:—

Number	Logarithm (base 10)
1	0.0000
10	1.0000
100	2.0000
1000	3.0000
etc.	

From our table we can see that if the rate of change in the numbers is constant (each number is ten times the previous number) then the logarithm increases by a constant amount (in our table the increase is one each time). This is true no matter what the magnitude of the numbers concerned.

Also, the larger the rate of change the larger the change in the logarithm, irrespective of the values of the figures concerned. So, for example, a change in absolute value from 1 to 100 results in a change in the logarithm from 0.0000 to 2.0000 whilst the larger absolute change from 100 to 1,000 results in a change in the logarithm of only 2.0000 to 3.0000.

Thus, if we plot the logarithms of the values of a variable then a constant rate of growth in the arithmetic values will show as a straight line, an increasing rate of growth will be shown as an increasing slope, and a decreasing rate of growth will show as a decreasing slope.

Plotting the logarithms rather than the absolute values has the advantage that a wide range of values can be shown. For example, if we wanted to plot the y values in the above table our scale would need to run from 1 to 1,000 but the x values need only run from 0.0000 to 3.0000. This is very useful because it also means that variables of different magnitude and units may be shown on the same graph with the same scale because the rate of change provides a common basis for comparing two or more sets of figures.

EXAMPLE
Let us plot the following sales figures using
    (i) Absolute values, and
    (ii) Logarithmic values.

YEAR	SALES (£m)	LOG. of Sales
1982	2	0.30
83	4	0.60
84	6	0.78
85	8	0.90
86	10	1.00

The results are shown in diagrams 3.33 and 3.34.

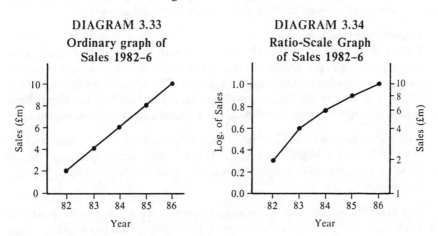

DIAGRAM 3.33
Ordinary graph of
Sales 1982–6

DIAGRAM 3.34
Ratio-Scale Graph
of Sales 1982–6

There are a number of points to observe concerning the two types of graph:—

Arithmetic Scale Graphs
1. Shows the absolute value of the variable.
2. Equal distances represent equal changes in the actual values.

3. Large increases, or decreases, in the value of the variable can be difficult to accommodate.
4. The actual values can be entered on the scale directly.
5. Variables of different magnitudes and units can only be shown by using different scales and comparisons can only be made indirectly.
6. A zero base line can be shown if required.
7. Negative values can be shown.

Ratio-Scale Graphs
1. Shows the rate of change of the variable.
2. Equal distances represent equal proportionate, or percentage, changes.
3. Large changes in the value of the variable can be coped with more easily. For example, if 1987 Sales were £100m the arithmetic scale would need to be increased tenfold while the log scale would only need to be doubled ($\log 100 = 2$).
4. The logs of the values have to be found and plotted. The actual values can be shown as a second scale or the log scale can be erased and the actual figures entered on the scale in the appropriate place.
5. Direct comparisons are possible because the rate of change is independent of magnitude and units.
6. The number zero has no logarithm and so you cannot show the log corresponding to an actual value of zero. Since the distances on a log scale represent rates of change, any change at all from zero would be infinite.
7. Since we cannot show the log corresponding to zero actual value, we cannot show logs corresponding to negative actual values.

Logarithmic-Graph paper
Rather than find the logs of the values we wish to plot and using ordinary graph paper it is far simpler to use graph paper which is designed for the purpose of drawing logarithmic-scale graphs. The advantage of such paper is that you can mark off the axes without having to first find the logarithmic values; it is ruled so that equal distances represent equal percentage changes.

Such paper may have one axis ruled with the normal arithmetic scale and the other axis with a logarithmic scale, this is called semi-logarithmic graph paper. If both axes have a logarithmic scale it is called 'double-log' or 'log-log' graph paper.

The logarithmic scale can be in one or more "cycles" (or blocks or decks). Each "cycle" represents a size range of 10^n to 10^{n+1}. In other words, a single cycle could represent from 1 to 10, or 10 to 100, or 100 to 1,000, or 0.1 to 1.000, etc.

Similarly, "three-cycle" paper could represent from 0.01 to 10, or 1 to 1,000, or 100 to 100,000, etc. If we were using "three-cycle" paper to represent values

DIAGRAM 3.35

LOGARITHMIC-SCALE GRAPH OF SALES 1982–86

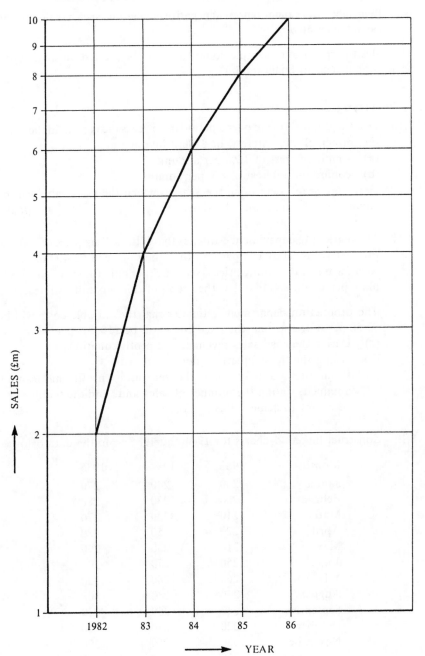

YEAR

from 1 to 1,000 then the first cycle would represent values from 1 to 10, the second from 10 to 100, and the third from 100 to 1,000.

N.B. **Remember you cannot represent negative numbers on such a scale and you cannot start at zero.**

The Sales figures in our example could therefore be plotted on single-cycle semi-log paper as in Diagram 3.35.

QUESTIONS

3.10 Draw a graph showing over a period of 15 years the growth in the value (i.e. principal plus interest) of £100 if invested at:
(a) simple interest of 12% per annum;
(b) compound interest of 8% per annum.
From the graph determine the year in which the total value will be equal under both (a) and (b) above. *(ICMA)*

3.11 The marketing department estimates that if the selling price of the new product A1 is set at £40 per unit then the sales will be 400 units per week, while, if the selling price is set at £20 per unit, the sales will be 800 units per week. Assume that the graph of this function is linear.

The production department estimates that the variable costs will be £7.50 per unit and that the fixed costs will be £10,000 per week.
(a) Derive the cost, sales revenue, and profit equations.
(b) Graph the three equations derived in (a).
(c) From the graph estimate the maximum profit that can be obtained, stating the number of sales units and the selling price necessary to achieve this profit. *(ICMA)*

3.12 Construct linked Z–charts for 1984 and 1985 from the data below:

Month	1983	1984	1985
January	200	240	270
February	200	230	280
March	210	230	270
April	220	250	280
May	210	230	290
June	250	270	300
July	260	280	320
August	250	280	300
September	240	250	220
October	220	240	210
November	230	250	200
December	230	260	200

In the example in the text we plotted the **value** of sales; why might **units** of sales be a better measure of performance and what does the Z–chart reveal about the firm's performance?

* 3.13 You are a member of a company selling computer software services to the accountancy profession. The value of those services sold to the profession throughout a twenty-four month period is shown in the following table.

		Services in £000			Services in £000
1984	Nov	80	1985	Nov	92
	Dec	85		Dec	98
1985	Jan	90	1986	Jan	105
	Feb	70		Feb	85
	Mar	75		Mar	90
	Apr	70		Apr	83
	May	65		May	76
	Jun	60		Jun	72
	Jul	57		Jul	65
	Aug	77		Aug	80
	Sep	82		Sep	93
	Oct	87		Oct	88

Required:
(i) Draw a Z chart plotting the above data.   *(8 marks)*
(ii) Describe the purpose of such a chart, using your own as an illustration, to your immediate superior, who is unfamiliar with this form of presentation.   *(2 marks)*

(Total 10 marks)

(ACA)

3.14 An analysis of the debtors of a firm, at the end of the trading year, yields the following frequency distribution:

Value of debt £	Number of debtors
under 10	4000
10 – under 50	800
50 – under 200	150
200 – under 500	40
500 – under 2000	10

(a) Construct a Lorenz curve from the data.
(b) Comment on the result.

3.15 Plot the following sales figures, for each branch and for the firm as a whole, on semi-log double-cycle scale and comment briefly on what the graph shows.

Sales (£000s)	1979	1980	1981	1982	1983	1984	1985
Branch A	1.4	2.4	4.1	7.0	12.0	20.5	35.0
Branch B	4.2	6.3	9.8	14.0	21.3	31.5	47.0
Total for firm	5.6	8.7	13.9	21.0	33.3	52.0	82.0

*3.16 The following table is an extract from a summary dealing with the Personal Income and Expenditure which appeared in the National Institute Economic Review, dated November 1975.

Year	Quarter	Consumer Price Index (1970=100)
	1st	135.8
1974	2nd	142.1
	3rd	147.6
	4th	152.5
	1st	160.1
1975	2nd	173.6
	3rd estimate	182.0
	4th forecast	188.7

You are required:
(a) to plot, on the standard graph paper provided, the values of the index given above on a ratio (semi-logarithmic) graph;
(b) to plot lines on the same graph representing forecasts predicting annual rates of inflation at 10%, 15%, 20% and 25%, compounded against the 1974 first quarter value of the index;
(c) to state which rate of inflation you consider to be the most realistic forecast;
(d) to comment on the superiority of a ratio scale graph over a natural scale graph for this kind of analysis.   *(ICMA)*

N.B. We have not covered index numbers but in this example the index simply shows by what percentage prices have risen compared to the base date of 1970. For example, by the first quarter of 1974, prices were 35.8% higher than 1970.

Chapter 4
DESCRIPTIVE STATISTICS

We have seen that by classifying, ordering, and grouping data and then presenting it in the form of diagrams, charts and graphs we can make the information more comprehensible. Some of the graphs that we have studied can also be quite useful from an analytical point of view.

It is often useful to summarize data by using numerical measures and such measures are called derived statistics. The use of such statistics enables us to describe the shape and characteristics of distributions and make comparisons in a more precise and objective way than through a visual comparison using diagrams.

To adequately describe a distribution we need three measures, viz:

(a) **MEASURES OF LOCATION**

The most obvious characteristic of a distribution that needs to be described is what sort of size the variable takes. Thus we need some measure that tells us the location or position of the distribution. Clearly the two distributions A and B cover different values but these values are spread out and to find a single figure that represents the location of the distribution is not easy.

An average is an attempt to represent the values that the data take in a single number that is typical or representative of the data. An average is a measure of central tendency because it represents the central value around which the data is clustered but there are several different averages which can be used depending upon the particular aspect of the data that is of interest.

DIAGRAM 4.1

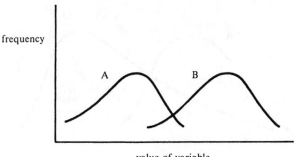

value of variable

(b) **MEASURES OF DISPERSION**
(SPREAD/VARIABILITY/DEVIATION)

It is probably fairly obvious that the two distributions C and D have the same 'central tendency' but the values in distribution D are concentrated around the centre of the distribution to a greater extent than the values in distribution C which are more spread out. Again, there are a variety of measures of dispersion.

DIAGRAM 4.2

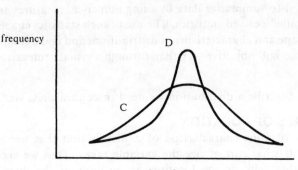

(c) **MEASURES OF SHAPE or SKEWNESS**

When a distribution is skewed we shall see that the different averages that we can calculate will have very different values. We can get an idea as to the shape of the distribution by calculating a number of different types of average and using the differences as a measure of the departure from symmetry.

DIAGRAM 4.3

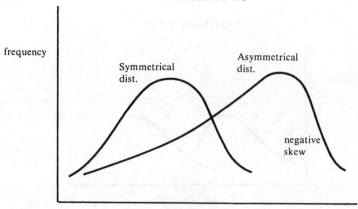

4.1 MEASURES OF LOCATION

An average is an attempt to summarise a set of data in a single measure which is representative or typical of the data as a whole. Because there are a number of ways in which a measure may be representative or typical there are several different types of average and the one we choose will depend on its purpose and the particular aspect of the data which is of interest.

Averages, and indeed all statistical tools, should possess certain desirable properties but different measures will possess these properties to varying extents and no particular average will be best in all circumstances.

Desirable properties of averages

(i)   Rigidly defined
(ii) As simple as possible — easily understood and calculated
(iii) The average should be a function of all the items in the group
(iv) The average should be easily manipulable — for example, the arithmetic mean can be multiplied by the number of items to obtain the total for all items. The mathematical properties of the A.M. make it useful as a basis for further statistical analysis. This is not true of other averages.
(v)   Minimum sampling fluctuation — again the A.M. is better than other averages.

4.1.2 ARITHMETIC MEAN

The arithmetic mean (A.M.) is the most useful measure of location and is what most people understand when the word 'average' is used. The word 'mean' is usually taken to refer to the A.M.; the mean of a sample is usually denoted by the symbol $\bar{x}$ (x-bar) while the population mean is denoted by the Greek letter μ (mu).

Calculation of the mean

(a)   **For ungrouped data**

The A.M. is obtained by adding up all the values of the items and dividing the total by the number of items.

$$\bar{x} = \frac{\Sigma x}{n}$$

So, the A.M. of 10, 10, 20, 20, 20, 30, 30, 30, 40, 40.

$$\bar{x} = \frac{250}{10} = 25$$

It should be noted that the variable never takes the value 25 in the above data so the A.M. is not representative in the sense that it is a typical value. However, consider the deviations from the A.M., they are $-15, -15, -5, -5, -5, +5, +5, +5, +15, +15$ and they sum to zero, ie $\Sigma(x-\bar{x})=0$. It is in this sense that the A.M. is a measure of central tendency.

(b) **For ungrouped frequency distributions**
The above data can be re-arranged into a frequency distribution as below and rather than add up all the values as before we can just multiply the value of the variable by its frequency of occurrence and add together the products to obtain the sum of all the values (Σfx). The number of items (n) is the same as the sum of the frequencies (Σf) and so we can calculate the mean from

x	frequency f	fx
10	2	20
20	3	60
30	3	90
40	2	80
	$\Sigma f=10$	$\Sigma fx=250$

$$\bar{x} = \frac{\Sigma fx}{\Sigma f} = \frac{250}{10} = 25 \text{ as before}$$

(c) **For grouped data**
If the same data were in the form of a grouped frequency distribution then we have to assume that the frequency of occurrences is concentrated around the mid-points of the class (we said in 3.2.3.1 that classes should be chosen so that this is the case). We then follow the same procedure as for ungrouped data using the mid-points of the class intervals as estimates of the value of the variable.

Class	frequency f	Mid-point of class x	fx
5 – under 15	2	10	20
15 – under 25	3	20	60
25 – under 35	3	30	90
35 – under 45	2	40	80
	$\Sigma f=10$		$\Sigma fx=250$

$$\bar{x} = \frac{\Sigma fx}{\Sigma f} = \frac{250}{10} = 25$$

EXAMPLE
To illustrate the effect of grouping data consider the following values for some variable:

10, 12, 14, 22, 26, 28, 30, 35, 36, 37, 42, 44, 46, 47.

(a) Calculate the A.M. from the ungrouped data.

Answer: $= \frac{429}{14} = $ (True A.M.) $= 30.6$

(b) Now group the data into the classes shown below and perform the calculation again.

Class	frequency	Mid-point of class	
	f	x	fx
10 – under 20	3	15	45
20 – under 30	3	25	75
30 – under 40	4	35	140
40 – under 50	4	45	180
	$\Sigma f = 14$		$\Sigma fx = 440$

$$\bar{x} = \frac{\Sigma fx}{\Sigma f} = \frac{440}{14} = 31.4$$

We see that the A.M. calculated from grouped data is not the same as the true A.M. because of the loss of detail in the calculation. However, as long as class intervals are chosen carefully the loss of accuracy should not in most cases be too serious.

4.1.3 DATA TRANSFORMATION
When a large number of measurements are involved and/or the numbers are awkward we can simplify the arithmetic by the process of coding.

We may code the original data by adding or subtracting a constant amount from the values of the variable. Usually we would do this so that one of the values becomes zero which makes calculations even easier.

Similarly, we may divide or multiply the data by a constant and this is particularly useful if very large numbers or fractions are contained in the original data. Neither of these operations will alter the shape of the distribution and so we can perform our calculations on the 'transformed' data and then simply reverse the transformation to find the correct value of whatever statistic we are calculating.

For example, say we decided to transform the data in the example we have been using by dividing by 10 and subtracting 3 so that $X = \frac{x - 3}{10}$

our calculations become:—

Class	frequency	Mid-point of class		
	f	x	X	fX
5 – under 15	2	10	−2	−4
15 – under 25	3	20	−1	−3
25 – under 35	3	30	0	0
35 – under 45	2	40	1	2
	$\Sigma f = 10$			$\Sigma fX = -5$

$$\bar{X} = \frac{\Sigma fX}{\Sigma f} = \frac{-5}{10}$$

When we reverse our transformation we must be careful to do so in the correct order so that

$$\bar{x} = (\bar{X} + 3) \cdot 10$$
$$(\text{NOT } \bar{x} = (10 \cdot \bar{X}) + 3)$$
$$\text{So, } \bar{x} = \left(\frac{-5}{10} + 3\right) \cdot 10 = 25$$

Such transformations give rise to certain formulae for calculating arithmetic means and standard deviations (see later) that involve "assumed means" and "deviations from assumed means", the latter being in terms of classes or original units depending upon whether the distribution has equal or unequal class intervals. Such formulae are often quoted on the formulae sheets used in examinations in Statistics but they are quite complicated and tricky to use. Moreover, they are completely unnecessary and they are not quoted here. If the numbers need simplifying then transform the data to make the calculations as simple as possible and then proceed in the normal way.

EXAMPLE

Consider the following frequency distribution of weights of 150 bolts:—

Weight (ounces)		frequency
5.00 and less than 5.01		4
5.01	5.02	18
5.02	5.03	25
5.03	5.04	36
5.04	5.05	30
5.05	5.06	22
5.06	5.07	11
5.07	5.08	3
5.08	5.09	1

Calculate the arithmetic mean of the weights of bolts to three decimal places.

Answer:

Mid-point of class x	X	f	fX
5.005	0	4	0
5.015	1	18	18
5.025	2	25	50
5.035	3	36	108
5.045	4	30	120
5.055	5	22	110
5.065	6	11	66
5.075	7	3	21
5.085	8	1	8
		150	501

Transformation $X = (x - 5.005) \times 100$

$$x = \frac{X}{100} + 5.005$$

> If we had chosen to make one of the middle classes zero, it would have made the multiplication a bit easier but the subtractions would have been a little more difficult and we would have had some negative fX values.

$$\bar{X} = \frac{501}{150}$$

$$\bar{x} = \left(\frac{501}{150} \times \frac{1}{100} \right) + 5.005 = 5.005 + 0.0334 = 5.0384 = 5.038 \text{ to three d.p.}$$

4.1.4 MEDIAN

The median is the **value of** the middle item in a distribution when the items are arranged in order of size. Therefore, half of the items in the distribution have a value greater than or equal to the median and half have a value less than or equal to the median and this is the sense in which the median is a measure of central tendency. If there are n observations then the median item is the one which is in the $\frac{n+1}{2}$ th position when the items are arranged in size order.

If there are an odd number of items then the median will correspond to a particular item but if there are an even number then the median item will be a fractional figure.

Although not used a great deal in more advanced statistical work, the median is widely used in demographic studies and because it is not affected by extreme values it is useful when a distribution has open-ended classes. It is also very useful when one is testing a number of items to failure because the median time to failure is known once half the items have failed and one does not need to wait for all the items to fail before obtaining a measure of the average time to failure.

Calculation of the median

(a) **For ungrouped data**

First rank the data and then find the value of the item half way through the data.

EXAMPLE

What is the median of 10, 12, 14, 22, 26, 28, 30, 35, 36, 37, 42, 44, 46, 47?

There are 14 items so we want the one in the $\frac{14+1}{2} = 7\frac{1}{2}$ th position

(they are already in rank order)

By convention we take the A.M. of the 7th and 8th items
So, the median is $\frac{30+35}{2} = 32.5$

Because there are an even number of items the median does not correspond to an actual value taken by the variable.

(b) **For an ungrouped frequency distribution**

Again we simply find the value of the item in the half-way position.

(c) **For grouped data**

Again, calculating the median from a grouped frequency distribution is more of a problem and we may not be able to determine it exactly. We can only determine the class in which the median lies with total confidence. We have to assume that the values in the median class are evenly distributed within that class and we can then determine the median graphically or by calculation.

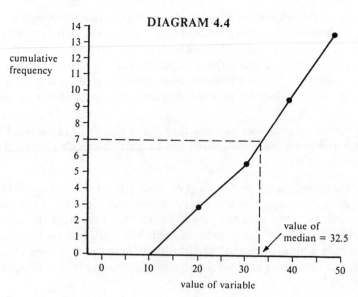

DIAGRAM 4.4

(i) Graphically

If we plot the cumulative frequency curve, or ogive, as in Diagram 4.4, we can read off the value of the item in the n/2 position.

It is the n/2 position rather than the n+1/2 position because the vertical scale runs from 0 and so the half-way point is when the cumulative frequency has reached n/2.

The median is also known as the 50 percentile. Percentiles are the values of the variable that divide the distribution into hundredths. For obvious reasons the 25 percentile is known as the first or lower quartile and the 75 percentile is the upper or third quartile. These values may also be read off the ogive.

(ii) By calculation

Class	frequency	cumulative frequency
10 – under 20	3	3
20 – under 30	3	6
30 – under 40	4	10
40 – under 50	4	14

We want to know the value of the item half-way through the distribution. This value occurs when the cumulative frequency has reached n/2 = 7. This is somewhere in the 30 – under 40 class, but where?

There are 4 items in the median class and we want the value when we are one item into that class. By linear interpolation (i.e. assuming the value of the variable increases in direct proportion to the frequency) the value of the median item will be

$$30 + \frac{1}{4} \times 10 = 32.5$$

The formula if you need it is

$$\text{Median} = L_m + \frac{c_m \left(\frac{1}{2}N - F_{m-1}\right)}{f_m}$$

where L_m = lower limit of median class

c_m = class interval of median class

N = number of observations

F_{m-1} = cumulative frequency up to median class

f_m = frequency of median class

QUESTION

4.1 Find the median wage of the following sample of workers.

(a) Graphically;

(b) By calculation.

Wage £ p.a.	Frequency
0 – 2000	40
2001 – 4000	20
4001 – 5000	126
5001 – 6000	184
6001 – 7000	232
7001 – 8000	110
8001 – 10000	37
10001 – 15000	21
15001 – 20000	10

Handwritten annotations: Class fx, 3000.5 600l0, 4500.5 567063

4.1.5 MODE

The mode is the value that occurs most frequently. If there is no value that occurs more frequently than the rest then the distribution has no mode, if two values occur more frequently than the rest then the distribution is bi-modal, and so on.

The mode is representative of the data in that it is the most typical value that occurs and it is a measure of central tendency in the sense that it is the value where most of the occurrences are clustered.

The mode is the average that people are usually referring to when they say things like "the average man . . . .". While it may be more accurate to say that the average couple have 2.2192 children, the mode might be a more sensible statistic to quote.

Although the mode is little used except for its descriptive properties it is the most appropriate average in many situations. For example, if we were comparing the earnings of two different groups the model wage would be an appropriate measure because it would tell us what most people in each group earns while the arithmetic mean might be affected by extreme value; the median might also be useful but this would depend on the shape of the distribution as we shall see later. Similarly, it would be useful to a housebuilder to know the modal family size so that he knows how many bedrooms are required to appeal to the greatest number of potential purchasers.

Calculation of the mode

(a) **For ungrouped data** and
(b) **For ungrouped frequency distributions**

In both cases it is only necessary to find the value (or values) that occurs most frequently.

(c) **For grouped data**

Again the situation is more complicated when we have to deal with a grouped frequency distribution.

If we draw a histogram, the modal class will be the one with the highest frequency density. This will not necessarily be the class with the highest frequency because when we draw a histogram it is the **area** of the rectangle that is proportional to the frequency and so the tallest rectangle represents the highest frequency per class width, i.e. frequency density. Of course, the modal class will depend upon how it was originally decided to group the data but if we want a single value for the mode we may again find it graphically or by calculation.

(i) Graphically, as in Diagram 4.5.

DIAGRAM 4.5

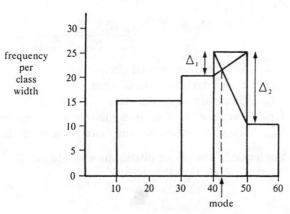

Value of variable

In the histogram in diagram 4.5 the modal class is 40–50. To find an actual value for the mode we assume that the mode is more likely to be to the left of the mid-point in the modal class because the frequency in the class 30–40 is more than that in the 50–60 class. We therefore estimate how far the mode is into the modal class by reference to the differences between the frequency of the modal class and the frequencies of the two classes adjacent to the modal class. As shown in the diagram, we draw the diagonals to the adjacent corners of the rectangles on either side of the modal class and the mode is the value of the variable corresponding to the intersection of the diagonals.

We have in fact divided the modal class in the ratio Δ_1 to Δ_2 so that

$$\text{Mode} = L + \left(\frac{\Delta_1}{\Delta_1 + \Delta_2} \right) c$$

where L = true lower limit of modal class;
Δ_1 = difference between frequency of modal class and the frequency of the class immediately below the modal group
Δ_2 = difference between frequency of modal class and the frequency of the class immediately above the modal group
c = class interval of modal group

The method requires that the classes immediately above and below the modal class have equal class intervals.

(ii) By calculation
Rather than construct the histogram (or part of it) we can calculate the mode from the formula:

$$\text{Mode} = L_m + \frac{c_m (f_m - f_{m-1})}{2f_m - (f_{m-1} + f_{m+1})}$$

where L_m = lower limit of modal class
c_m = class interval of modal class
f_m = frequency of modal class
f_{m-1} = frequency of class immediately below modal class
f_{m+1} = frequency of class immediately above modal class

Thus, the mode in the above distribution would be

$$\frac{40 + 10 (25-20)}{(2 \times 25) - (20+10)} = 42.5$$

QUESTION
4.2   Repeat question 4.1 but this time find the modal wage (a) graphically and (b) by calculation.

4.1.6   Other averages
There are two other less important averages that we should mention.

(a)   Geometric mean
   The GM of the values $x_1, x_2, x_3, \ldots . x_n$.

$$GM_x = \sqrt[n]{x_1 . x_2 . x_3 . \ldots . x_n}$$

So the GM of 10, 24, 27, 125 = $\sqrt[4]{10\times24\times27\times125}$ = 30

If the product of the values is large the calculation can be simplified by taking logarithms.

The Geometric mean is not used very often but it can be useful in connection with economic statistics where there is some form of geometric progression and the percentage change is more important than the change in absolute values, e.g. population growth, price indexes.

(b) **Harmonic mean**
The HM is the reciprocal of the arithmetic mean value of the reciprocals of a set of values. The HM of $x_1, x_2, x_3, \ldots . x_n$

$$HM_x = \frac{n}{\sum \frac{1}{x}}$$

So the HM of 2, 3, 4 = $\dfrac{3}{(\frac{1}{2}+\frac{1}{3}+\frac{1}{4})}$ or $\dfrac{1}{\frac{1}{3}(\frac{1}{2}+\frac{1}{3}+\frac{1}{4})}$ = $\dfrac{36}{13}$ = 2.77

The HM is of little importance in statistical work but is of use when averaging rates.

For example, Say a car travels equal distances at 20 mph and 40 mph. The average speed is not the arithmetic mean of 30 mph but the harmonic mean of 26.67 mph. If the car had travelled for equal periods of time the average speed would have been the arithmetic mean, which is 30 mph.

4.1.7 Features of averages
We said earlier that averages ought to possess certain properties, let us consider the three main averages:

ADVANTAGES
Arithmetic Mean
1. Rigidly defined.
2. Easy to understand.
3. Easy to calculate but more trouble than others.
4. Easily manipulable and is used in further statistical analysis.
5. Uses every value in distribution.
6. AM of samples will usually show less fluctuation than other averages.

Mode
1. Not affected by extreme values.
2. Will be an actual value when dealing with discrete data.

3. Can be calculated even if all the values in the distribution are not known due to open-ended classes.
4. Easily understood and calculated.

Median
1. Not affected by extreme values.
2. Can be calculated even if all values in distribution not known.
3. Takes an actual value for discrete data (except if middle two are averaged).

DISADVANTAGES
Arithmetic Mean
1. Can be affected by extreme values.
2. May be inaccurate if open-ended classes are involved.
3. May take a value that does not correspond to an actual value in the data.

Mode
1. A distribution may have more than one mode.
2. Cannot be readily manipulated.
3. Somewhat inexactly defined in the case of grouped distributions.
4. Not suitable for further statistical analysis.
5. Not a function of all values.
6. Data has to be arrayed or grouped.

Median
1. More than one item may take median value.
2. Not rigidly defined for grouped data.
3. Not suitable for manipulation or further statistical treatment.
4. Data has to be arrayed/grouped.
5. Not a function of all values.

4.1.8 Choice of average

The average, or averages, that we decide to use to summarise the data will depend upon the reason for calculating the average. If we intend to use the measure for further statistical analysis then the arithmetic mean will be the obvious choice but if we are looking for a 'typical' value then the median or mode may be preferred.

If we are confronted by data with open-ended classes we may find it difficult to estimate the mid-points of those classes. Usually this will not matter too much but in some cases, for example in the case of distributions of income or wealth, this will prohibit the use of the mean and we will be forced to use one of the other averages.

Remember at all times, an average is a summary measure and so involves a loss of information. Only the original data contains all the information.

EXAMPLE
Consider the following situations and say what average you would use.

(a) If we are interested in the value of a retail organisation that has a number of outlets, would AM sales/outlet, M_d sales/outlet, or M_o sales/outlet be best?
Answer: AM because you can find value of sales for whole organisation.

(b) If we want to assess the standard of living in a country what would be the best measure?
Answer: Mode because it is typical.

(c) If we want to know which of two communities with the same total income could best support a government expenditure programme financed by a rise in direct progressive taxation would it be best to find AM income per head of population, Median or Modal income per head of population?
Answer: AM because being affected by extreme values is an advantage in this case.

(d) An office survey shows that the AM of stated preferences for certain temperatures is 68°, the median is 70°, and the mode is 71°. Which of these do we take if we wish to:—
(i) avoid as much discomfort as possible?
Answer: Median because the variation is less around the median than any other value.
(ii) give the greatest number satisfaction?
Answer: Mode because most people say this temperature.

(e) As a factor in your choice of different careers, what is the best guide the mean wage for different jobs, the median, or the modal wage?
Answer: The mode because that is what you are most likely to end up earning.

(f) Which average did the journalist have in mind when he made the sensational announcement "Half the population is below average intelligence?
Answer: The median is the half-way value.

Hopefully the above examples emphasise the point that the particular average we choose will depend upon its purpose and the particular aspect of the data that is of interest.

4.2 MEASURES OF DISPERSION
If someone said "the arithmetic mean depth of this river is 2 feet" would you wade across? Having studied the arithmetic mean you would probably be reluctant because you would realise that the arithmetic mean can be affected

by extreme values and tells us nothing about the dispersion of data around the average; the river might be about 2 feet deep right across or it might be 20 feet deep in some parts and ½ inch deep in others.

We need some measures of the scatter, dispersion, variation, spread, deviation — all terms meaning the same thing — of the data around the average. Again, there are several different measures of dispersion which may be useful in different situations.

4.2.1. The Range

DIAGRAM 4.6

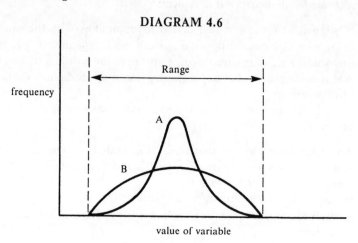

This is the simplest measure of spread in a set of values and is simply the difference between the largest and smallest values in the set of data. It is useful for comparing the variability in samples of the same size but it relies only on the two extreme values and so tells us nothing about the way the rest of the data is dispersed. Hence, both distributions A and B in Diagram 4.6 would have the same range.

4.2.2 Partition values or fractiles

To overcome the problem of extreme values we can consider only the range in some central part of the distribution rather than over the whole of the distribution. Partition values are the values which are some given proportion of the way through the distribution and we can define the range of values contained within any two partition values. The most common partition values are:—

Quartiles

Q_1, the first or lower quartile is the **value** of the item one-quarter of the way through the distribution.

Q_2, the second quartile is the value of the item one-half of the way through the distribution (the Median).

Q_3, the third or upper quartile is the value of the item three-quarters of the way through the distribution.

Deciles

Deciles divide the distribution into tenths, so the first decile is the value of the item one-tenth of the way through the distribution.

Percentiles

Percentiles divide the distribution into hundredths, so the first percentile is the value of the item one hundredth of the way through the distribution.

$$\text{5th decile} = 50\% \text{ ile} = Q_2 \text{ (Median)}$$

Calculating partition values

Partition values are calculated in the same way as described for the median.

(a) For ungrouped data

Rank the data and find the value of the item in the appropriate position.

So the first quartile, Q_1, is the value of the item in the $\dfrac{n+1*}{4}$ position.

(b) For grouped data

(i) Graphically

Plot the cumulative frequency curve, or ogive, and read off the value of the item in the appropriate position.

So the first quartile, Q_1, is the value of the item $\dfrac{n*}{4}$ of the way through the distribution, as shown in Diagram 4.7.

The difference was explained in 4.14.

DIAGRAM 4.7

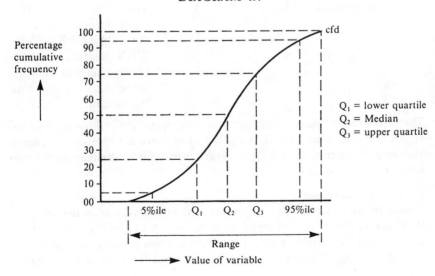

Q_1 = lower quartile
Q_2 = Median
Q_3 = upper quartile

(ii) By calculation

The value of any partition value can be calculated by the method shown earlier for the median.

This means that one must estimate how far into the class containing the partition value one needs to go to and then by linear interpolation find the partition value. A formula would take the following form:

$$\text{Partition value} = L_p + c_p \cdot \frac{F_p - F_{p-1}}{f_p}$$

where L_p = lower boundary of class containing partition value
c_p = class interval of class containing partition value
f_p = frequency of class containing partition value
F_p = cumulative frequency of required partition value
F_{p-1} = cumulative frequency up to class containing partition value.

Measuring the dispersion

Once we have calculated the appropriate partition values the range of any given part of the distribution can be defined.

For example, the 90% range, the range of the central 90% of the distribution, is the difference between the values of the 5%ile and the 95%ile as above.

The two most common ranges quoted are:

Inter-quartile range $= Q_3 - Q_1$ i.e. the range of values covered by the middle 50% of the distribution.

Semi-inter-quartile range $= \dfrac{Q_3 - Q_1}{2}$ The semi-inter-quartile range is sometimes called the QUARTILE DEVIA-TION because it is the average amount by which the quartiles differ from the median.

These two ranges, and others, are useful because they exclude the extreme values and this is particularly valuable when there are open-ended classes. However, this strength is also a weakness because it means they do not take account of all the data.

4.2.3 Mean deviation

A measure of dispersion which does use all the data is the mean deviation. As the name implies, the mean deviation is the average of the differences between the values of the variable and their arithmetic mean. However, we said earlier that the arithmetic mean is a measure of central tendency just because the deviations from the arithmetic mean sum to zero. Therefore, the mean deviation is taken as the arithmetic mean of the **absolute** deviations from the mean (with the signs being ignored).

$$\text{Mean deviation} = \frac{\Sigma |(x - \bar{x})|}{n} \qquad \text{for ungrouped data}$$

$$= \frac{\Sigma f|(x - \bar{x})|}{\Sigma f} \qquad \text{for frequency distributions}$$

where $|(x - \bar{x})|$ is the modulus of the deviation of the value from the arithmetic mean.

$\bar{x}$ = arithmetic mean

n = number of observations = Σf

and the mid-points of the classes are used if one is dealing with a grouped frequency distribution. If the population mean, μ, is known then this replaces the sample mean, $\bar{x}$, in the formulae.

The mean deviation is a very useful measure of dispersion; it uses all the data, is not unduly affected by extreme values, and is easily calculated and understood. However, the mean deviation is not so easily calculated when large amounts of data are involved and because of the modulus sign it is difficult to manipulate algebraically. It is not therefore used in more advanced statistical analysis. It is worth noting that the mean deviation is at a minimum when measured from the median rather than the mean.

QUESTION

4.3   A fruit and vegetable chain has ten shops in an area. The shops are 5, 14, 16, 19, 26, 32, 45, 56, 62, and 68 miles from the wholesale market.
   (i)   Calculate the mean deviation of the distances from the mean distance from the market.
   (ii) Calculate the mean deviation of the distances from the median distance from the market.
   (iii) Calculate the mean deviation of the distances from 26 and 32 miles.
   (iv) If one of the shops is to serve as a distribution depot, which one should it be, and why?

4.2.4   Variance and Standard deviation

The problem with using deviations from the mean as a measure of dispersion is that, by the property of the mean, the deviations add up to zero. The mean deviation overcomes this by summing the moduli of the deviations. Unfortunately, this makes the mean deviation cumbersome to deal with algebraically.

An alternative approach is to square the deviations and this again gets over the problem of the signs of the deviations. The resultant measures of dispersion are called the variance and the standard deviation. Both these measures are very important for further statistical analysis and are more easily manipulated than the mean deviation. The meaning of these two measures in terms of the original data is not quite so clear but their other advantages far outweigh this drawback.

Variance

The variance is the **mean of the squared deviations** and the symbol for the variance of the population is σ^2 (the lower case of the Greek letter sigma). If one is dealing with a sample, as is usually the case, the symbol s^2 is used for the variance of the sample and s^2 is, of course, an estimate of σ^2.

For ungrouped data

$$\sigma^2 = \frac{1}{n} \Sigma(x - \mu)^2 \qquad \text{where } n = \text{number of observations}$$
$$\mu = \text{population arithmetic mean}$$

$$s^2 = \frac{1}{n} \Sigma(x - \bar{x})^2 \qquad \text{where } \bar{x} = \text{sample arithmetic mean}$$

Strictly speaking, $s^2 = \frac{1}{n-1} \Sigma(x - \bar{x})^2$. The reason for the difference in the denominator is rather technical and concerns the loss of one 'degree of freedom' because $\bar{x}$ has to be used as an estimate of the value of μ. However, if n is reasonably large n–1 will be virtually the same as n and so the divisor n will usually be used.

For grouped data and frequency distributions

$$\sigma^2 = \frac{1}{n} \Sigma f(x - \mu)^2$$

where f = frequency of occurrence
$n = \Sigma f$

$$s^2 = \frac{1}{n} \Sigma f(x - \bar{x})^2$$

and x = mid-point of class if frequency distribution is grouped.

Calculating variance

The definitional formulae above are rather tiresome to use but, with some not too complicated algebra, it is possible to derive computational formulae that are easier to use for calculations. The formulae are shown below and the derivation is shown as follows for those who are interested.

Ungrouped data	Grouped data and frequency distributions

$$s^2 = \frac{\Sigma x^2}{n} - \left(\frac{\Sigma x}{n}\right)^2 \qquad\qquad s^2 = \frac{\Sigma f x^2}{n} - \left(\frac{\Sigma f x}{n}\right)^2$$

i.e. mean x^2 – (mean x)^2 in both cases.

Taking the sample variance for ungrouped data and being a little more precise, we have that

$$s^2 = \frac{1}{n} \sum_{i=1}^{i=n} (x_i - \bar{x})^2$$

$$(x_1 - \bar{x})^2 = x_1^2 + \bar{x}^2 - 2x_1\bar{x}$$
$$+ \quad (x_2 - \bar{x})^2 = x_2^2 + \bar{x}^2 - 2x_2\bar{x}$$
$$+ \qquad \cdot \qquad \cdot \qquad \cdot \qquad \cdot$$
$$+ \qquad \cdot \qquad \cdot \qquad \cdot \qquad \cdot$$
$$+ \qquad \cdot \qquad \cdot \qquad \cdot \qquad \cdot$$
$$+ \quad (x_n - \bar{x})^2 = x_n^2 + \bar{x}^2 - 2x_n\bar{x}$$

$$\sum_{i=1}^{i=n} x_i^2 + n\bar{x}^2 - 2\bar{x}\sum_{i=1}^{i=n} x_i$$

$$\therefore \quad s^2 = \frac{1}{n}\sum_{i=1}^{i=n} x_i^2 + \bar{x}^2 - \frac{2\bar{x}}{n}\sum_{i=1}^{i=n} x_i$$

$$\text{But} \quad \frac{1}{n}\sum_{i=1}^{i=n} x_i = \bar{x}$$

$$\therefore \quad s^2 = \frac{1}{n}\sum_{i=1}^{i=n} x_i^2 + \bar{x}^2 - 2\bar{x}\bar{x}$$

$$= \frac{1}{n}\sum_{i=1}^{i=n} x_i^2 - \bar{x}^2 = \text{mean } x^2 - (\text{mean } x)^2$$

Example

Let us use some very simple data to compare the definitional and computational formulae. Say a variable takes the values 5, 6, 8, 10, 12, and 14. Calculate the variance.

(a) Using definitional formula

x	x−x̄		(x−x̄)²
5	5−9.17 =	−4.17	17.4
6	6−9.17 =	−3.17	10.0
8	8−9.17 =	−1.17	1.4
10	10−9.17 =	0.83	0.7
12	12−9.17 =	2.83	8.0
14	14−9.17 =	4.83	23.3

$$\bar{x} = \frac{5+6+8+10+12+14}{6} = 9.17$$

$$\Sigma(x-\bar{x})^2 = 60.8$$

$$s^2 = \frac{1}{n}\ \Sigma(x-\bar{x})^2 = \frac{60.8}{6} = 10.13$$

$S =$ Standard deviation is 3.18

(b) Using computational formula

x	x²
5	25
6	36
8	64
10	100
12	144
14	196

$$\Sigma x^2 = 565 \qquad s^2 = \frac{\Sigma x^2}{n} - \left(\frac{\Sigma x}{n}\right)^2 = \frac{565}{6} - (9.17)^2 = 10.17$$

If you have a calculator with statistical functions (and you can use it properly!) the difference between the formulae does not matter. Otherwise, the computational formula should save time.

Transforming the data

We have already mentioned that there are some more complicated formulae designed to simplify calculations. Again, they are not quoted here and the recommendation is that if the arithmetic is messy transform the data as described in 4.1.3. before using the computational formula.

However, when dealing with variance even more care is required when reversing your transformation. The best method is to write down your transformation and then do some simple algebra to check on the way to reverse the transformation.

Say, for example, you decide to subtract a from each x value and then divide by b to get your transformed value t.

Then, $t = \dfrac{x - a}{b}$ and $x = bt + a$ and $\bar{x} = b\bar{t} + a$

This is fairly straightforward but the variance demands a little more care:

$$s^2 = \frac{1}{n}\Sigma(x - \bar{x})^2 = \frac{1}{n}\Sigma[bt + a - (b\bar{t} + a)]^2$$

$$= \frac{1}{n}\Sigma(bt - b\bar{t})^2 = \frac{1}{n}\Sigma[b(t - \bar{t})]^2$$

$$= b^2 . \frac{1}{n}\Sigma(t - \bar{t})^2$$

So, to get the correct variance you have to multiply the answer from your transformed data by b^2. N.B. The adding or subtracting of the constant, a, has no effect on the variance because it does not affect the absolute values of the deviations at all.

The algebra is not very difficult and you should be able to work out what to do from first principles of necessary. If you do find it difficult then just remember that if you transform the original data by subtracting a (or adding (–a)) and then divide by b (or multiply by $\frac{1}{b}$) then to find the mean you multiply by b and **then** add a. To find the variance you multiply by b^2.

i.e. If $t = \dfrac{x - a}{b}$ then $\bar{x} = b\bar{t} + a$ and $s_x^2 = b^2 . s_t^2$

It really is a lot less trouble than spending time trying to understand and use the more complicated formulae. In any case, you will only need to transform the data before carrying out your computations if the data contains large numbers or decimals that your calculator cannot accommodate.

Properties of the variance

A very useful property of the variance is that if you combine two distributions by adding pairs of measurements then the new distribution has a variance equal to the sum of the variances of the two original distributions.

i.e. $\sigma^2 = \sigma_1^2 + \sigma_2^2$

A disadvantage of the variance as a measure of dispersion is that it is measured in units that are the square of the units of the original data. To get over this problem we can take the square root of the variance to get a measure of dispersion in the same units as the original data known as the standard deviation.

Standard deviation

The standard deviation is the "root mean squared deviation" and is found by taking the square root of the variance. As we shall see the standard deviation is a very important statistic and is particularly useful in the theory of sampling. It has the slight drawback as a measure of dispersion in that by squaring the deviations it gives a lot of weight to extreme values but it uses every value in the distribution and its other advantages in further statistical analysis far outweigh this slight disadvantage.

The various formulae are as described for the variance but with the square root taken. For example, the computational formula for grouped data becomes:

$$s = \sqrt{\frac{\Sigma fx^2}{n} - \left(\frac{\Sigma fx}{n}\right)^2}$$

If we carried out the transformation described above for the variance then you would, of course, only have to multiply by b to get the correct standard deviation because the standard deviation is in the units of the original data.

Coefficient of variation

Say we were interested in the deviation in the weights of adult male fleas as compared to that of elephants. The standard deviation would not tell us a great deal because the absolute values would be somewhat different. The answer to the problem is to compare the standard deviations to the arithmetic means.

$$\text{Coefficient of variation} = \frac{s}{\bar{x}} \text{ or } \frac{\sigma}{\mu} \quad (\text{x } 100\%)$$

The coefficient of variation enables us to compare the variability in data of different magnitudes or units provided the scale of measurement begins at zero.

N.B. If the mean is measured from an arbitrary zero (e.g. temperature) the coefficient of variation is meaningless.

Rough check

For reasonably symmetrical unimodal distributions the range should be roughly six standard deviations and the arithmetic mean will lie towards the centre of the distribution. So, Range $\simeq \bar{x} \pm 3s$ provides a rough check on your answers.

4.3 MEASURES OF SHAPE AND SKEWNESS

A frequency distribution may be discrete or continuous; the variable may take only a certain set of specific values or it may take any value on a continuous scale in some specified interval. The observations can be shown in the form of a histogram, with the **area** of each rectangle proportional to the frequency, and in the case of continuous data as more and more observations are taken in smaller class intervals the histogram becomes a smooth curve known as a frequency curve (see 3.2.3.5 and 3.4.1.1).

In passing it is worth mentioning that if the height of a histogram is standardised, by dividing the frequency per class width (frequency density) by the total frequency, so that the total area of the histogram is unity, we can obtain a relative frequency histogram. The area above any given class width then gives the **probability** that the variable will take a value in that interval. When more and more observations in smaller class intervals are taken the curve obtained is a **probability curve**. If the height of the probability curve at some point x is given by f(x) then this function f(x) is known as the probability density function (pdf) and the probability that the variable x may take a value in the interval x_1 to x_2 can be found from the area under the curve between these two points which is given by the integral of the curve between the two points.

$$\text{i.e. probability } (x_1 \leqslant x \leqslant x_2) = \int_{x_1}^{x_2} f(x)dx.$$

The frequency distribution can take on many different shapes and some distributions such as the Binomial, Poisson, Rectangular, exponential, hypergeometric, and normal are well defined mathematically. We will need to study some of these theoretical distributions in some detail and the normal distribution is very important for more advanced statistical analysis. In practice, a distribution may well conform to one of these theoretical distributions or may be some combination of two or more of them and it is worth mentioning some of the common patterns that data may take.

N.B. The distributions below are shown as continuous curves but discrete distributions such as the binomial or Poisson can also take similar shapes.

4.3.1 Types of distribution
(a) J-shaped distribution

DIAGRAM 4.8

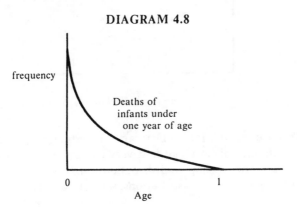

The 'backward J-shaped' distribution, as in Diagram 4.8, is positively skewed with the mode to the left of the centre of the distribution and the tail to the right. The distribution of the size of firms in many industries approximates to this type of distribution and the economist's demand curve is another example although the economist reverses the axes.

DIAGRAM 4.9

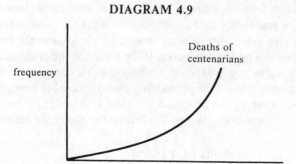

The ordinary J-shaped distribution, in Diagram 4.9, is negatively skewed with the mode to the right of the centre of the distribution and the tail to the left.

(b) **U-shaped distribution**

DIAGRAM 4.10

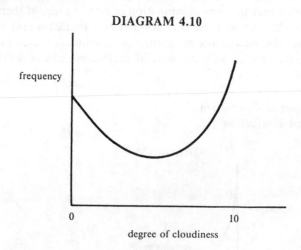

The U-shaped distribution, in Diagram 4.10, is bimodal; in the example, the two extremes of no cloud and very cloudy are the most frequent occurrences. The U-shaped distribution can often be the result of combining two J-shaped distributions; for example, if we combined the two J-shaped distributions above to obtain a distribution for mortality rates amongst the very young and very old the result would be a U-shaped distribution.

The U-shaped average total cost curve in economics is obtained by combining the J-shaped average variable and average fixed cost curves although they are not frequency distributions in the normal sense.

(c) **Rectangular or Uniform distribution**

DIAGRAM 4.11

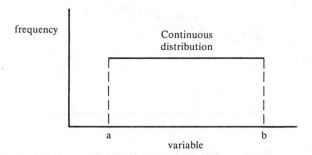

The rectangular, or uniform, distribution occurs, as in Diagram 4.11, when the frequency is constant between certain values, say a and b, and so the probability of the variable taking a certain value (if data is discrete) or between two values (if continuous) is constant and equals $(\frac{1}{b-a})$. Such a distribution has no mode and by symmetry the mean and median are both $\frac{b-a}{2}$.

DIAGRAM 4.12

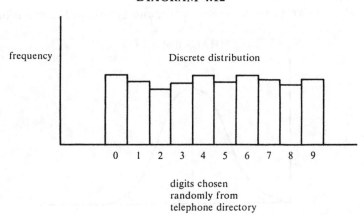

An approximately uniform distribution (discrete) would be obtained if a large sample of telephone numbers were taken and the occurrences of the various digits plotted, as in Diagram 4.12.

(d) **Bivariate or 'two-way' distributions**

DIAGRAM 4.13

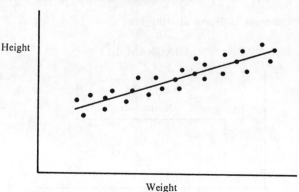

So far we have mentioned only frequency distributions with one variable (univariate distributions). It is of course possible to consider two variables (or more) at the same time and to plot the pairs of values on a scatter graph. Sometimes it will be possible to fit a straight line or curve to the data and this is known as the regression line or curve, as in Diagram 4.13. An associated problem is to decide how well the estimated regression line fits the data by calculating a correlation coefficient.

(e) **Normal distribution**
(also known as the Gaussian, error, and bell-shaped distribution).

DIAGRAM 4.14

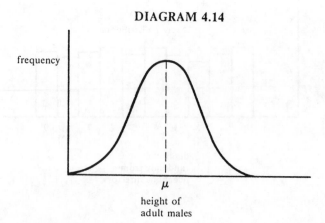

The normal distribution illustrated in Diagram 4.14 is the most important of all the distributions because it has so many practical applications. It is a univariate continuous distribution to which many physical distributions correspond. The normal distribution can often be used as an approximation to non-normal distributions to give reasonably accurate results. The normal distribution is of great importance in sampling theory because it can be shown, by the central limit theorem, that the means of a series of samples form a normal distribution even if the population from which the samples are drawn is not normal. The normal distribution is symmetric about the point $x = \mu$ which is the mean, median, and mode.

DIAGRAM 4.15

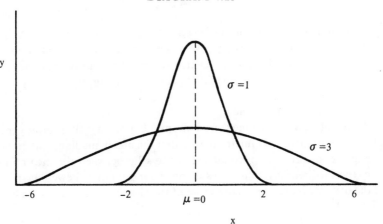

$$y = \frac{1}{\sigma \sqrt{2\pi}} \; e^{-(x-\mu)^2 / 2\sigma^2}$$

The normal distribution may be very flat or very pointed, it depends upon the value of the standard deviation. The two normal distributions in Diagram 4.15 have the same mean of zero but one has a standard deviation of 1 and the other a standard deviation of 3. However, no matter what values the mean and standard deviation take, the normal distribution is such that only about 1 in 20 observations will lie more than 2 standard deviations from the mean.

Do not be frightened by the complicated formula for the height of the normal curve. We shall be concerned only with the area under the curve which is well tabulated!

(f) Skewed distributions

DIAGRAM 4.16

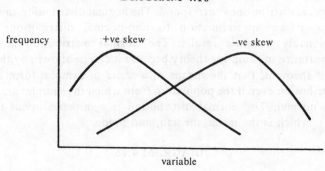

A unimodal distribution is skewed when the mode is not at the centre of the distribution. A distribution is said to be positively skewed if the mode is to the left of the centre of the distribution and negatively skewed when it is to the right, as shown in Diagram 4.16.

4.3.2 Measures of skewness

The degree of skew can be measured in a number of ways that employ the fact that a departure from symmetry means that the mean, median, and mode will no longer coincide. The median will always lie between the mean and the mode (the median may sometimes lie on the mode) in a skewed distribution and the order will denote the direction of the skew, as can be seen in Diagram 4.17 and 4.18.

DIAGRAM 4.17   DIAGRAM 4.18

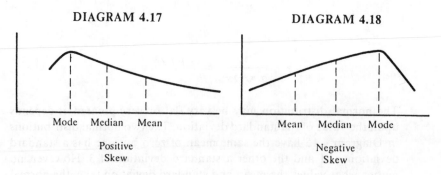

The more skewed a distribution is, the more spread out the three averages will be and the differences can thus be used as a measure of skew.

(i) Pearson's Coefficient of Skewness (Sk_p)

$$Sk_p = \frac{\text{Mean} - \text{Mode}}{\text{Standard deviation}} \quad \text{or} \quad \frac{3(\text{Mean} - \text{Median})}{\text{Standard deviation}}$$

(ii) The second formula may have to be used when the mode is difficult to calculate but the two formulae are roughly the same because for symmetric and moderately skewed data   Mean – Mode $\simeq$ 3(Mean – Median).

Dividing by the standard deviation means that the measure is independent of units of measurement and so different distributions can be compared.

Sk_p can take values between +3 and –3 and the sign corresponds to the direction of the skew. A symmetric distribution will give an answer of zero and moderately skewed data will give answers between +1 and –1.

(ii) **Quartile measure of skewness**
In a symmetrical distribution the upper and lower quartiles will be equidistant from the median and so these different distances provide a measure of skewness. The measure is again standardised, this time by dividing by the quartile deviation.

$$Sk_q = \frac{(Q_3 - Md) - (Md - Q_1)}{(Q_3 - Q_1)/2}$$

Again the measure takes the sign that indicates the direction of the skew and symmetric distributions will obviously take the value of zero. The measure can take values between ± 1.

4.3.2.1   Why measure skewness?
The reason for measuring skewness is the same as that for calculating averages, standard deviations, or other summarising measures; unless we present the data in full or plot the frequency curve or histogram we need statistics to summarise the data. Averages provide a measure of the location of the distribution, the various measures of dispersion indicate the spread in the data, and measures of skew give us an indication of the shape of the distribution. Also, if we know that a distribution is only slightly skewed we may be able to assume that the distribution is approximately normal and this can greatly simplify further analysis.

QUESTIONS
4.4   The following is a distribution of earnings of semi-skilled workers for one week in 1977:—

Weekly earnings £		Number of workers
20 and under 30		5
30	40	26
40	50	41
50	60	58
60	70	48
70	80	18
80	90	4

You are required to:
(a) Calculate from the distribution given:
    (i) the median;
    (ii) coefficient of variation.
(b) Explain the meaning of the median and the coefficient of variation related to the above example.   *(ICMA)*

4.5 Your company manufactures components for use in the production of motor vehicles. The number of components produced each day over a forty day period is tabulated below:

   553 523 532 528 524 533 541 519 526 538 554 523 512 519
   535 530 521 546 517 510 525 521 531 549 528 524 549 555
   543 536 551 518 538 544 512 545 532 534 535 531

You are required to:
(a) Group the data into five classes.
(b) Draw the histogram of the frequency distribution that you have obtained in (a).
(c) Establish the value of the mode of the frequency distribution from the histogram.
(d) Establish the value of the mean of the distribution.
(e) Establish the value of the standard deviation of the distribution.
(f) Describe briefly the shape of the frequency distribution, using the values you obtain in (c), (d) and (e).   *(ACA)*

4.6 The distribution of gross annual earnings for 200 operatives in an engineering company is shown below.

Range of earnings £		Number of operatives
At least	Less than	
	3,000	7
3,000	4,000	30
4,000	5,000	37
5,000	6,000	51
6,000	7,000	32
7,000	8,000	25
8,000	10,000	14
Over 10,000		4
		Total 200

You are required to:
(a) Draw a cumulative (less than) frequency distribution on squared paper.
(b) Use your diagram to find estimates of the median, upper quartile, lower quartile, highest decile, and quartile deviation, and interpret the results.

(c) Without performing any further calculations, estimate the value of the arithmetic mean and justify your choice.

(ICMA)

*4.7 (a) Your company is in the course of preparing its published accounts and the Chairman has requested that the assets of the Company be compared in a component bar chart for the last five years. The data for this task is contained in the following table.

Asset	1978 £'000s	1979 £'000s	1980 £'000s	1981 £'000s	1982 £'000s
Property	59	59	65	70	74
Plant and Machinery	176	179	195	210	200
Stock and work-in-progress	409	409	448	516	479
Debtors	330	313	384	374	479
Cash	7	60	29	74	74

You are required to:
You are required to:
(i) Construct the necessary component bar charts. *(4 marks)*
(ii) Comment upon the movements in the assets over the five year period. *(3 marks)*

(b) The company has a Canadian subsidiary. During this year the Finance Director has monitored weekly the exchange rate of the Canadian dollar to the £, after each Monday's trading. His findings are summarized in the following table.

Rate of Exchange Canadian Dollars to £1	Number of Weeks
1.80 but less than 1.85	1
1.85 but less than 1.90	8
1.90 but less than 1.95	2
1.95 but less than 2.00	6
2.00 but less than 2.05	3
2.05 but less than 2.10	5
2.10 but less than 2.15	6
2.15 but less than 2.20	10
2.20 but less than 2.25	10
2.25 but less than 2.30	1

You are required to:
(i) Plot the cumulative frequency diagram (ogive) from this data. *(4 marks)*
(ii) Determine the median exchange rate from the ogive. *(2 marks)*

     (iii) Determine the semi-interquartile range of the exchange rate using the ogive. *(3 marks)*

     (iv) Determine the mean exchange rate to the nearest cent, that is to two decimal places. *(4 marks)*

(Total 20 marks)

* 4.8   The production of each manufacturing department of your company is monitored weekly to establish productivity bonuses paid to the members of that department.

250 items have to be produced each week before a bonus will be paid. The production in one department over a forty week period is shown below:

382	367	364	365	371	370	372	364	355	347
354	359	359	360	357	362	364	365	371	365
361	380	382	394	396	398	402	406	437	456
469	466	459	454	460	457	452	451	445	446

You are required to:

(a) Form a frequency distribution of five groups for the number of items produced per week. *(5 marks)*

(b) Construct the ogive or cumulative frequency diagram for the frequency distribution established in (a). *(5 marks)*

(c) Establish the value of the median from the ogive. *(2 marks)*

(d) Establish the value of the semi-interquartile range. *(4 marks)*

(e) Interpret the results that you obtain in (c) and (d). *(2 marks)*

(f) Compare the use of the median and the mean as measures of location. *(2 marks)*

(Total 20 marks)
(ACA)

4.4 INDEX NUMBERS

Continuing the theme of summarising measures we turn to the concept of index numbers. An index number is a single number which gives the average value of a set of related items expressed as a percentage of their average value at some base period.

For example, if the average earnings of a group of workers were as shown on the following page we could calculate index numbers to represent the earnings showing the percentage changes compared to the first year.

	Year 1	Year 2	Year 3
Average weekly earnings	£200	£220	£240
Index Number	100	110	120

If we take year 1 to be the **base** period, against which we will compare future levels of earnings, then we may assign earnings during that period an arbitrary value of 100. The number 100 is chosen so that future values show the percentage change that has occurred since the base date (or period) but any number might be used and a few indexes do use different numbers for technical reasons. If we do use the number 100 to represent earnings of £200 per week then earnings of £220 are represented by the number 110 which shows a 10% increase $(\frac{220}{200} \times 100)$. Note that the year 3 index shows the percentage increase compared to the base year not year 2 although this could easily be calculated as $\frac{10}{110} \times 100\%$.

Historically, index numbers were first developed to measure changes in price levels and so the purchasing power of money. Index numbers have since been extended to cover many other variables and some well known indexes include the Index of Industrial Production which measures the **volume** of industrial output, Index of Retail Sales which measures the **value** of retail sales, Index of wages, FT Ordinary Share Index, Trade-Weighted Index of the value of Sterling, and so on.

The index which most people are aware of is the Retail Price Index formerly known as the Cost of Living Index. There are reasons why it is not strictly correct to speak of a cost of living index but setting these aside for the moment let us consider how we might go about constructing such an index.

4.4.1 Weighted Aggregative Index

Suppose there are just three goods in the shopping 'basket' of a 'typical' family and their prices have changed as indicated below.

	Quantity purchased during base year i.e. Year 1	Prices Year 1	Year 2	Year 3
Bread	200 loaves	20p	30p	40p
Newspapers	200	10p	20p	25p
Shoes	2 pairs	£20	£20	£30

One way of calculating how much the cost of living had increased between the years would be to find out how much a simple average of prices had increased over the years.

So, arithmetic mean price in year $1 = \frac{1}{3}(20p+10p+£20) = £6.77$
and arithmetic mean price in year $2 = \frac{1}{3}(30p+20p+£20) = £6.83$

In percentage terms this is an increase on the mean level in year 1 of $\frac{0.06 \times 100}{6.77} = 0.9\%$ so although bread has gone up by 50% and newspapers have doubled in price the average shows an increase of less than 1%.

This is not very satisfactory because it ignores the amount of expenditure on the different items and the average is dominated by the price of shoes which has not changed. A better approach is to compare the amount that the 'basket' costs in year 1 to what the same basket would cost in years 2 and 3.

So, the cost of the basket in year 1 $= 200 \times 20p + 200 \times 10p + 2 \times £20 = £100$
and the cost of the same basket year 2 $= 200 \times 30p + 200 \times 20p + 2 \times £20 = £140$
and the cost of the same basket year 3 $= 200 \times 40p + 200 \times 25p + 2 \times £30 = £190$

If we let the cost of the basket in year 1, the base year, be represented by 100 then we can calculate the corresponding price index numbers for years 2 and 3. These are price indexes because the change in the cost of the basket is purely due to price changes since we kept the quantities bought the same in each year.

	Year 1	Year 2	Year 3	
Cost of basket	£100	£140	£190	N.B. Index for Yr 2 =
Price Index	100	140	190	Index for Yr 3 =

This more realistic measure of the change in the cost of living results from giving more importance, or "weight", to the changes in the prices of bread and newspapers because, even though they do not cost very much, they account for a great deal of expenditure. Since we have kept the quantity of each item fixed, the index shows how the cost of the basket of goods has changed as a result of price changes.

We have in fact calculated a Laspeyre's, or base-weighted, index of prices.

$$\text{Laspeyre's Price Index} = \frac{\Sigma p_n q_o}{\Sigma p_o q_o} \times 100$$

where, p_o = price of item during base period
p_n = price of item during period n
q_o = quantity during base period

Alternative method using price relative indexes
In practice the above calculation is more usually performed using price relative indexes which show the percentage change in price of each item in the index since the base year. These price relatives are then weighted according to the **expenditure** on each item in order to calculate an expenditure relative index for each item and then the overall increase in the cost of the 'basket' is calculated by adding up the expenditure relative indexes and dividing by the total weight.

In our example the expenditure in the base year on the three items was:

$$\text{Bread } 200 \times 20p = £40$$
$$\text{Newspapers } 200 \times 10p = £20$$
$$\text{Shoes } 2 \times £20 = £40$$

and so we weight the price changes in the ratio 4:2:4 which conveniently totals to 10. If the expenditures had not summed to such a convenient figure I could make the weights add up to whatever figure I wished, say k, by multiplying each expenditure by k/j where j is whatever they add up to, and the weights would still be in the same proportions as the original expenditures.

	Weight	Price	Price relative Index	Expenditure Relative Index	Price	PRI	ERI	Price	PRI	ERI
			Year 1			Year 2			Year 3	
Bread	4	20p	100	400	30p	150	600	40p	200	800
Newspapers	2	10p	100	200	20p	200	400	25p	250	500
Shoes	4	£20	100	400	£20	100	400	£30	150	600
Total weight	10			1000			1400			1900
Index for all items = $\dfrac{\text{ERI}}{\text{TOTAL WEIGHT}}$				100			140			190

The answer is the same as before because what we have done above is to calculate

$$\frac{\sum 100 \cdot \dfrac{p_n}{p_o} \cdot p_o \, q_o}{\sum p_o q_o}$$

which if we cancel the p_os in the numerator is the same as $\dfrac{\sum p_n q_o}{\sum p_o q_o} \times 100$

So remember,
if you use actual prices you use actual quantities to weight the index and
if you use price relatives you use expenditures to weight the index.

It is worth spelling out what we have done in this method. First we let each of the base year prices and the overall index of prices be represented by a PRI of 100 and the effect of this is to make each price of equal importance in the overall index. The PRIs for the following years show the change in the prices of the individual items and this is quite useful. Next we weighted the PRI according to the expenditure (price × quantity) in the base year on each item to calculate Expenditure relative indexes for each item and an overall index indicating the change in the cost of the 'basket' of goods year by year assuming the 'basket' always consists of base year quantities.

4.4.2 Laspeyre's and Paasche's Price Indexes

As we have seen the Laspeyre's Price Index weights the price changes according to the base year quantities. An alternative approach is to use current year quantities to weight the index in which case we calculate a Paasche Price Index. Thus,

$$\text{Laspeyre's Price Index} = \frac{\Sigma\, p_n q_o}{\Sigma\, p_o q_o} \times 100 \qquad \text{(base-weighted)}$$

$$\text{Paasche's Price Index} = \frac{\Sigma\, p_n q_n}{\Sigma\, p_o q_n} \times 100 \qquad \text{(current-weighted)}.$$

A problem with Laspeyre's Price Index is that it may over-estimate the effect of increases in prices because if demand for a product falls as its price rises the base-weighted index will still assume that the same quantities are bought as in the base year. Conversely, the Paasche Price Index will tend to under-estimate the effect of price rises because the current weighted index will take the latest quantities for the weights. The reverse will of course be true when prices fall.

If a Laspeyre's index is calculated then only the weights for the base period need to be calculated but a Paasche index requires the weights to be re-calculated for each period and this can be time-consuming and expensive; Laspeyre's indexes are therefore often preferred.

The Paasche Price Index has the advantage that it is based upon current expenditure patterns and it is variations in the cost of maintaining current standards of living that really concerns people. An additional complication here is that current consumption patterns may include expenditure on items that did not even exist some years ago and the quality of goods may also have changed. This is the basic index number problem — comparing like with like — and it is no more relevant to compare the costs of a 'basket' that is typical of today's family expenditure than to compare a 'basket' typical of family purchases some years ago. The problem is overcome to some extent by the use of a chain base.

4.4.3 Chain base and chain linked Index numbers

A chain base index shows the changes in price compared to the period immediately before and so gets over the problem of new items appearing in the index.

	1984	1985	1986	1987
Chain base index	100	110	105	120

The above chain base index shows that prices in 1985 were 10% higher than in 1984, prices in 1986 were 5% higher than in 1985, and prices in 1987 were 20% higher than those in 1986.

Thus, if we are calculating a current-weighted index using the chain base method we need only compare prices in the current period with prices of the same 'basket' one period before.

If we want to compare prices to some fixed base period we can convert the chain base index into a chain-linked index quite easily. If we wanted to convert the above chain base index into a chain linked index with 1984 as the fixed base period the result would be as below. We know that prices rise by 10%, 5%, and 20% in successive years but these increases refer to percentage changes on the previous year and we want the percentage changes on the base year of 1984.

	1984	1985	1986	1987
Chain base index	100	110	105	120
Chain linked index	100	110	115.5[1]	138.6[2]

[1] Chain linked index for 1986 is $110 \times \dfrac{105}{100}$ i.e. 115.5 which is 5% higher than the index for 1985.

[2] Chain linked index for 1987 is $115.5 \times \dfrac{120}{100}$ i.e. 138.6 which is 20% higher than the index for 1986.

Chain linking is useful because it facilitates constant up-dating of weights to reflect current expenditure patterns and the introduction of new items into the index when prices are known only for a short while back. However, it does not overcome the basic index number problem of comparing like with like except over the short-run during which consumer expenditure patterns can be assumed to change very little. As the gap between the base period and the current period increases the 'basket' of goods will be increasingly different and eventually comparisons become meaningless.

4.4.4 The Index of Retail Prices

On page 111 is a copy from a recent Annual Abstrct of Statistics of the Index of Retail Prices, monthly changes in the index are produced in the Monthly Digest of Statistics which is eagerly awaited as a measure of the success of the government's anti-inflation policies.

The RPI has developed from an index first published just after the First World War and descriptively entitled "Index of the cost of maintaining a standard of living of the same level as in 1914 in working-class households". The present index is somewhat different from the old index, it is a chain-linked index and as can be seen the base year has been changed several times. When the base year is changed the index number for that year based on the old series is published so that one can link back if necessary.

The weights are based upon the results of the Family Expenditure Survey which provides information on the spending patterns of about 11,000 randomly selected households. From the details of their expenditure it is possible to allocate the weights to the eleven broad groups as shown and to various subdivisions of these groups. In our example we had only three items and a total weight of 10, the RPI covers about 350 items and has a total weight of 1,000, the weighting being revised annually.

The prices of a 'representative' group of items are measured each month in a variety of ways for a variety of outlets and these prices are expressed as chain-linked index numbers showing the percentage change in prices for each group and sub-group of items since the base year. These price relative index numbers are then weighted using the weights based upon the previous year's Family Expenditure Survey to arrive at the General Index of Retail Prices which shows the weighted average increase for all the items included in the index since the base year.

The RPI has been in the public eye for many years as a measure of the inflation rate; towards the end of 1973 it received even more attention when, as part of the government's statutory incomes policy, pay increases were linked directly to changes in the RPI. Naturally, people became more concerned about what was included in the index and what was not, how far the index reflected their cost of living, and so on. One result of this increased concern was that in 1975 mortgage interest payments were included as a measure of the cost of owner-occupation, previously this had been measured by an imputed rent based upon rateable values. Other indexes were also produced such as the pensioner's index, the tax price index, etc.

4.4.4.1 Purchasing Power Index

As prices rise the purchasing power of money falls. It is a simple matter to calculate, for example, what £1 is worth today compared to some years ago. Let us use the RPI opposite to compare the purchasing power of the £ in December 1983 as compared to January 1962.

	1962	1974	1983
		100 ——————— 342.8	
RETAIL PRICE INDEX	100 ——————— 191.8		

The RPI indicates that between 1962 and 1974 prices rose by 91.8% and then between 1974 and 1983 by 242.8%.

First we need to find the 1983 Price Index with a 1962 base year and this is 191.8 × $\frac{342.8}{100}$ = 657.49 showing that prices have risen by 557.49%

So, £1 in 1962 would buy the same as £6.5749 in 1983 and therefore £1 in 1983 would buy the same as $\frac{1.00}{6.5749}$ in 1962 giving the Purchasing Power Index of £0.15 which shows that the £ in 1983 will buy the same as 15p in 1962.

INDEX OF RETAIL PRICES

	All items	Food	Alcoholic drink	Tobacco	Housing	Fuel and light	Durable household goods	Clothing and footwear	Transport and vehicles	Miscellaneous goods	Services	Meals bought and consumed outside the home
	17 January 1956 = 100											
Weights 1956 to 1961	1 000	350	71	80	87	55	66	106	68	59	58	
1962 January 16	117.5	110.7	108.2	123.6	140.6	130.6	102.1	106.6	126.7	128.2	130.1	
	16 January 1962 = 100											
Weights												
1966	1 000	298	67	77	113	64	57	91	116	61	56	
1967	1 000	293	67	72	118	62	59	92	118	61	58	
1968	1 000	263	63	66	121	62	59	89	120	60	56	41
1969	1 000	254	64	68	118	61	60	86	124	66	57	42
1970	1 000	255	66	64	119	61	60	86	126	65	55	43
1971	1 000	250	65	59	119	60	61	87	136	65	54	44
1972	1 000	251	66	53	121	60	58	89	139	65	52	46
1973	1 000	248	73	49	126	58	58	89	135	65	53	46
1974	1 000	253	70	43	124	52	64	91	135	63	54	51
Annual averages												
1966	116.5	115.6	121.7	120.8	128.5	120.9	107.2	109.9	109.9	112.5	120.5	
1967	119.4	118.5	125.3	120.8	134.5	124.3	109.0	111.7	112.2	113.7	126.4	
1968	125.0	123.2	127.1	125.5	141.3	133.8	113.2	113.4	119.1	124.5	132.4	126.9
1969	131.8	131.0	136.2	135.5	147.0	137.8	118.3	117.7	123.9	132.3	142.5	135.0
1970	140.2	140.1	143.9	136.3	158.1	145.7	126.0	123.8	132.1	142.8	153.8	145.5
1971	153.4	155.6	152.7	138.5	172.6	160.9	135.4	132.2	147.2	169.1	169.6	165.0
1972	164.3	169.4	159.0	139.5	190.7	173.4	140.5	141.8	155.9	168.0	180.5	180.3
1973	179.4	194.9	164.2	141.2	213.1	178.3	148.7	155.1	165.0	172.6	202.4	211.0
1974	208.2	230.0	182.1	164.8	238.2	208.8	170.8	182.3	194.3	202.7	227.2	248.3
1974 January 15	191.8	216.7	166.0	142.2	225.1	188.6	158.3	166.6	175.0	182.2	212.8	229.5
	15 January 1974 = 100											
Weights												
1974	1 000	253	70	43	124	52	64	91	135	63	54	51
1975	1 000	232	82	46	108	53	70	89	149	71	52	48
1976	1 000	228	81	46	112	56	75	84	140	74	57	47
1977	1 000	247	83	46	112	58	63	82	139	71	54	45
1978	1 000	233	85	48	113	60	64	80	140	70	56	51
1979	1 000	232	77	44	120	59	64	82	143	69	59	51
1980	1 000	214	82	40	124	59	69	84	151	74	62	41
1981	1 000	207	79	36	135	62	65	81	152	75	66	42
1982	1 000	206	77	41	144	62	64	77	154	72	65	38
1983	1 000	203	78	39	137	69	64	74	159	75	63	39
Annual averages												
1974	108.5	106.1	109.7	115.9	105.8	110.7	107.9	109.4	111.0	111.2	106.8	108.2
1975	134.8	133.3	135.2	147.7	125.5	147.4	131.2	125.7	143.9	138.6	135.5	132.4
1976	157.1	159.9	159.3	171.3	143.2	182.4	144.2	139.4	166.0	161.3	159.5	157.3
1977	182.0	190.3	183.4	209.7	161.8	211.3	166.8	157.4	190.3	188.3	173.3	185.7
1978	197.1	203.8	196.0	226.2	173.4	227.5	182.1	171.0	207.2	208.7	192.0	207.8
1979	223.5	228.3	217.1	247.6	208.9	250.5	201.9	187.2	243.1	236.4	213.9	239.9
1980	263.7	255.9	261.8	290.1	269.5	313.2	226.3	205.4	288.7	276.9	262.7	290.0
1981	295.0	277.5	306.1	358.2	318.2	380.0	237.2	208.3	322.6	300.7	300.8	318.0
1982	320.4	299.3	341.0	413.3	358.3	433.3	243.8	210.5	343.5	325.8	331.6	341.7
1983	335.1	308.8	366.5	440.9	367.1	465.4	250.4	214.8	366.3	345.6	342.9	364.0
1983 March 15	327.9	302.4	357.0	432.9	349.7	465.6	249.2	213.8	356.5	339.5	337.8	356.5
June 14	334.7	308.8	368.2	444.0	364.0	461.8	251.2	213.7	366.3	345.7	342.7	363.5
September 13	339.5	313.0	371.8	443.5	376.7	466.0	251.6	215.8	373.1	348.6	344.7	368.9
December 13	342.8	318.5	373.2	450.0	381.6	469.0	253.0	217.1	371.7	353.4	350.0	375.7

1. The index of retail prices replaced the interim index from January 1956 (indices of the interim index of retail prices for the period 1952 to January 1956 were last published in *Annual Abstract of Statistics* No. 103, 1965). A new set of weights was introduced, based on ascertained expenditure in 1953–54, valued at January 1956 prices. Between January 1962 and January 1974 the weights have been revised each January on the basis of ascertained expenditure in the three years ended in the previous June, valued at prices obtaining at the date of revision. From 1975 the weights have been revised on expenditure for the latest available year.

Source Department of Employment

4.4.4.2 Averaging rates of change of prices

	Year		
	1	2	3
RPI	100	120	132

From the above table we can see that between year 1 and year 3 prices have risen by 32 **points**. Also, we can see that in year 2 prices rose by 20% on year 1 and in year 3 prices rose by 10% on year 2. What then is the average rate of increase in prices? Or put another way, what constant rate of increase would lead to an increase of 32% between year 1 and year 3?

You might well say that the answer is the arithmetic mean of 20% and 10%, i.e. 15%, but this is not quite correct.

If we take the average rate as 15% and the initial price level to be 100 then the price level in year 3 should be

$$100 \ \times \ \frac{115}{100} \ \times \ \frac{115}{100} \ = \ 132.25 \text{ which is 0.25 out.}$$

The correct method is to take the Geometric Mean.

Geometric Mean $= \sqrt{120 \times 110} = 114.89125$

showing that the average rate of increase $= 14.89\%$

and checking $\quad 100 \ \times \ \dfrac{114.89}{100} \ \times \ \dfrac{114.89}{100} \ = \ 131.997$ which is correct except for rounding error.

Another way of calculating the rate of increase is to think of it in terms of a compound interest calculation (see later) where

$$A_n = P(1 + r)^n \quad \text{and } A_n = \text{Amount after n years}$$
$$P = \text{Principal}$$
$$n = \text{number of years}$$
$$r = \text{compound rate of interest}$$

So, $132 = 100(1 + r)^2 \quad$ giving $r = 14.89125\%$ again.

4.4.4.3 Using index numbers to 'deflate' a series

A common use of index numbers is to compare changes in some variable whilst another variable is held constant. So, for example, we often hear such statements as "The output of industry ABC has increased by x% at 19XX prices".

The most familiar use of index numbers in this context is to evaluate earnings in 'real' terms. In other words, we wish to know how earnings have changed not in money terms but in terms of what those wages will buy.

Say we had the figures overleaf for the average earnings of a group of workers and we wish to calculate the real earnings in each of the years.

Year	Average weekly earnings (£)
1972	45.30
1973	55.20
1974	65.75
1975	75.85
1976	95.90
1977	120.00
1978	130.00
1979	150.00
1980	180.00
1981	210.00
1982	230.00
1983	250.00

Consulting our copy of the RPI, we see that we have a slight problem because there was a change of base at 15 January 1974. The easiest way of dealing with this is to convert the figures for the first two years to a base of January 1974.

i.e. Average value of index for 1972 $= 164.3 \times \dfrac{100}{191.8} = 85.7$
with 15 Jan 74 as base date

Average value of index for 1973 $= 179.4 \times \dfrac{100}{191.8} = 93.5$
with 15 Jan 74 as base date

Having done this we may now use our Price Index to 'deflate' the actual earnings. So, for example, Real Weekly Earnings for 1983 at Jan 74 prices $= 250 \times \dfrac{100}{335.1} = £74.60$

Year	Average Weekly Earnings (£)	Avg. Value of Index of Retail prices over the year (1962 base)	(1974 base)	Price Index with Jan 74 as base date	Real Weekly earnings at Jan 74 prices (£)
1972	45.30	164.3		85.7	52.85
1973	55.20	179.4		93.5	59.04
Index at 15 Jan 74		191.8	100		
1974	65.75	208.2	108.5	108.5	60.60
1975	75.85		134.8	134.8	56.27
1976	95.90		157.1	157.1	61.04
1977	120.00		182.0	182.0	65.93
1978	130.00		197.1	197.1	65.96
1979	150.00		223.5	223.5	67.11
1980	180.00		263.7	263.7	68.26
1981	210.00		295.0	295.0	71.19
1982	230.00		320.4	320.4	71.78
1983	250.00		335.1	335.1	74.60

When we see the value of wages at constant prices it is obvious that wages have risen faster than prices in every year except 1975 and so real wages have increased in every year except 1975.

QUESTION
4.9   Construct an Index of Real Wages using 1973 as the base year.

4.4.5   Quantity or Volume Indexes

If we are interested in changes in quantity, or volume, rather than price changes, quantity indexes may be constructed in a similar way. The weighting will often be according to prices and the index numbers would be calculated as:

$$\text{Base weighted quantity index (Laspeyre)} = \frac{\Sigma p_o q_n}{\Sigma p_o q_o} \times 100$$

$$\text{Current weighted quantity index (Paasche)} = \frac{\Sigma p_n q_n}{\Sigma p_n q_o} \times 100$$

Here we are holding prices constant, at either base or current levels, and so any change in expenditure must be due to changes in quantity.

4.4.6   Expenditure or Value Indexes

If we are simply interested in the change in the value of expenditure (price × quantity) on a group of items the question of base or current weighting does not arise. Only one index can be constructed.

$$\text{Expenditure index} = \frac{\Sigma p_n q_n}{\Sigma p_o q_o} \times 100$$

4.4.7   Fisher's 'Ideal' Index

We have said that Laspeyre's base weighted index will tend to overstate the effect of price rises on expenditure because as price rises demand falls but the base weighted index assumes that the quantities stay the same as in the base year. This means that the reduced importance in the 'basket' of items whose price has risen will not be reflected in the index.

Similarly, we have argued that Paasche's current weighted price index will tend to understate the effect of price rises because the current weights will recognise the reduced importance of the items whose quantities have fallen as a result of price rises.

Again, for similar reasons, the base weighted volume index will tend to overstate the effect of volume changes upon expenditure because it will weight the volume changes according to base year prices; so if volume has increased because price has fallen the weight will not be reduced in line with the reduced importance, in terms of expenditure, resulting from the price reduction. Conversely, if volume has fallen because price has risen, the extra importance of this item in the cost of the 'basket' as a result of its higher price will not be taken into account.

The current weighted volume index will take account of the changes in price and so will attach more importance to those items whose price has risen and whose quantities have therefore fallen thus understating the effect of the changes in volume upon expenditure. Similarly, less importance will be attached to those items whose volume has risen as a result of price reductions.

Fisher suggested that the 'true' index (price or quantity) would be the Geometric Mean of Laspeyre's and Paasche's indexes.

i.e.   Fisher's Index $= \sqrt{\text{Laspeyre's index} \times \text{Paasche's index}}$

Whereas Laspeyre's index overstates the effect of price and quantity changes upon expenditure and Paasche's index understates the effect, Fisher's price and quantity indexes taken together correctly predict the effect upon expenditure. This can be shown by some quite simple algebra,

$$\text{Fisher's Price Index} = \sqrt{\frac{\Sigma p_n q_o}{\Sigma p_o q_o} \times \frac{\Sigma p_n q_n}{\Sigma p_o q_n}}$$

$$\text{Fisher's Quantity Index} = \sqrt{\frac{\Sigma q_n p_o}{\Sigma q_o p_o} \times \frac{\Sigma q_n p_n}{\Sigma q_o p_n}}$$

Fisher's Expenditure Index = Price index $\times$ Quantity index

$$= \sqrt{\frac{\Sigma p_n q_o}{\Sigma p_o q_o} \times \frac{\Sigma p_n q_n}{\Sigma p_o q_n} \times \frac{\Sigma q_n p_o}{\Sigma q_o p_o} \times \frac{\Sigma q_n p_n}{\Sigma q_o p_n}} = \frac{p_n q_n}{p_o q_o}$$
which is, of course, the expenditure index.

So, unlike Laspeyre's and Paasche's indexes, Fishers indexes taken together correctly predict the effect upon expenditure. This does not mean we have solved the index number problem — we cannot compare like with like — but by taking the average we are getting a better indicator of the effect upon expenditure of price or volume changes.

4.4.8 Geometric Index
The index numbers mentioned so far have been weighted arithmetic means. It is also possible to calculate the geometric mean and the Financial Times Industrial Ordinary Share Index, the top 30 index, is a practical example. The FT Index of 30 top companies chosen as being representative of industrial shares generally and 1st July 1935 is the base date.

It is possible to calculate a weighted geometric mean and the formula would be

$$\text{Geometric Mean} = \sqrt[n]{p_1^{w_1} \times p_2^{w_2} \times p_3^{w_3} \ldots \ldots p_n^{w_n}}$$

where w is the weight, p is the variable, and n is the sum of the weights. Calculation is simplified by taking logs.

4.4.9 EXAMPLE

As a means of revising the methods of calculating the various indexes let us calculate the various indexes for another simple example involving only three commodities.

	Base year prices and quantities		Current year prices and quantities	
	p_0	q_0	p_n	q_n
Bread	20p	200 loaves	30p	200 loaves
Newspapers	10p	200 papers	25p	150 papers
Shoes	£20	2 pairs	£15	3 pairs

(a) Laspeyre's Price Index $= \dfrac{\Sigma p_n q_0}{\Sigma p_0 q_0} = \dfrac{140}{100} = 1.4$ ($\times$ 100 if you want the increase as %)

(b) Laspeyre's Volume Index $= \dfrac{\Sigma q_n p_0}{\Sigma q_0 p_0} = \dfrac{115}{100} = 1.15$

(c) Paasche's Price Index $= \dfrac{\Sigma p_n q_n}{\Sigma p_0 q_n} = \dfrac{142.5}{115} = 1.24$

(d) Paasche's Volume Index $= \dfrac{\Sigma q_n p_n}{\Sigma q_0 p_n} = \dfrac{142.5}{140} = 1.02$

(e) Expenditure Index $= \dfrac{\Sigma p_n q_n}{\Sigma p_0 q_0} = \dfrac{142.5}{100} = 1.425$

(f) Fisher's Price Index

$= \sqrt{\text{Laspeyre's Price Index} \times \text{Paasche's Price Index}} = \sqrt{1.4 \times 1.24}$
$= 1.32$

(g) Fisher's Volume Index

$= \sqrt{\text{Laspeyre's Volume Index} \times \text{Paasche's Volume Index}} = \sqrt{1.15 \times 1.02}$
$= 1.08$

(h) Fisher's Expenditure Index

$= \text{Fisher's Price Index} \times \text{Fisher's Volume Index} = 1.32 \times 1.08$
$= 1.4256$

or, more accurately,

$\sqrt{\dfrac{140}{100} \times \dfrac{142.5}{115} \times \dfrac{115}{100} \times \dfrac{142.5}{140}} = 1.425$ which corresponds to the expenditure index in (e).

(i) Base-weighted Geometric
     Price Index

$$= \frac{\sqrt[402]{0.3^{200} \times 0.25^{200} \times 15^2}}{\sqrt[402]{0.2^{200} \times 0.1^{200} \times 20^2}} \times 100$$

But the above calculation is not possible on most calculators and it is easier to use logarithms. It will simplify matters further if we use price relatives and weight according to base year **expenditure.**

ITEM	WEIGHT	PRI for current year	Log.PRI	Weight × Log.PRI
Bread	4	150	2.176	8.704
Newspapers	2	250	2.398	4.796
Shoes	4	75	1.875	7.500
	10			21.000

$$\text{Log Index} = \frac{\Sigma \text{ Weight} \times \text{Log.PRI}}{\Sigma \text{ Weights}} = \frac{21.000}{10} = 2.1$$

Index = 125.89   i.e. the number whose log is the log.index, or the antilog of the log.index.

Alternatively, we could calculate the weighted geometric mean of the price relatives as $\sqrt[10]{150^4 \times 250^2 \times 75^4}$ which most calculators can cope with.

4.4.10 Problems in the construction of index numbers

(a) TIME PROBLEM

As we have noted, in the case of price indexes, consumer spending patterns change with the passage of time and this illustrates the 'index number problem' — it is not possible to compare like with like. To some extent this can be overcome by the use of a chain base index and linking but as weights change and new products are included in the index comparisons between the current year and a base year in the distant past have little real meaning.

(b) SAMPLE PROBLEM

Indexes usually relate only to a sample. For example, the RPI collects prices of only about 350 items and the weightings are based upon a random sample of some 11,000 households but excluding very high income groups. Strictly, then, the index relates only to those people who spend their income in a certain way upon a certain selected range of goods. In other words, the index is an average with all the limitations that this implies.

(c) ACCURACY

There may, of course, be errors in the collection of information. The Department of Employment takes elaborate precautions in collecting information on prices for the construction of the RPI but the price of, say, fresh vegetables may vary even in the same town and price competition between various supermarkets and large stores is a further complication. Information for the weightings in the RPI is derived from the Family Expenditure Survey of the previous year and covers about 11,000 households. The weighting given to certain items, e.g. cigarettes is subject to correction and certain items which are known to be important, such as gambling, are excluded because they are so difficult to estimate. So, the weightings are averages and do not include all items — this is not a serious criticism because an index including all items would be meaningless — but it is a limitation that has to be recognised. Likewise, the prices are averages and may not be representative of the prices in a particular area.

(d) BASE DATE PROBLEM

It is often said that it is desirable to choose a base year in which the variable is behaving 'normally'. This is not because it has any particular significance in itself, after all we have seen that we can quite easily change the base year to any year we wish by multiplying by the appropriate ratio. The reason we need to take care is because of the effect upon the weighting given to different items. For example, if we chose a year of rapid inflation as the base year for a price index, and used base weighting, the quantities and prices, and hence weights, of particular items might behave abnormally.

For example, it would not make a lot of sense to choose 1984 as the base year for an index of coal production because the miners' strike reduced production to well below the normal level in some pits but not in certain pits that did not take part in the strike. So any weighting based upon output in that year could create a misleading impression as to how the industry as a whole was performing.

The base date for an index is periodically updated because small % changes tend to be more easily understood and because people find it easier to relate to more recent changes.

Index numbers, then, are useful indicators as to the behaviour of the average value of a certain set of items. But they are only averages, subject to all the limitations of averages, and we need to be aware of these limitations when we interpret their meaning.

QUESTIONS

4.10 A basic food price index (F.P.I.) comprises the undermentioned items, weighted for the average family taking a normal diet as follows:

	Price	Weighting
Bread	20p/loaf	7 loaves
Potatoes	12p/lb.	20 lbs.
Milk	8p/pint	15 pints
Eggs	40p/dozen	2 dozen
Meat	80p/lb.	10 lbs.

It is expected that during the next year the cost of bread will rise by 10%, potatoes will rise by 25%, milk will fall by 10%, eggs will fall by 5% and meat will increase by 30%.

Required:
(a) Calculate the F.P.I. expected in one year's time, if the present F.P.I. is 112.
(b) Calculate the F.P.I. expected in three years' time if prices continue to change at the same average rate.
(c) Suppose that it is predicted that people will spend rather more on milk and eggs and somewhat less on meat during the coming year. In what way would you expect your answer to part (a) to be affected, if a current weighted index were used?
(d) Why could a current weighted F.P.I. be unsatisfactory?

(20 marks)
(ACA)

4.11 Recently the following information was published by a large retail group.

Year	Sales £m	Pre-tax profits £m	Net capital employed £m	Number of employees
1979–80	888	57.25	615.6	41,500
1978–79	823	52.61	307.5	41,770
1977–78	724	46.52	279.7	43,867
1976–77	665	40.59	268.8	47,498
1975–76	573	36.10	268.6	49,121

(a) As management accountant you are to select any set of figures or combination of figures given above and present them in a visual display form. The objective of your display is to aid employees to understand the information presented.

The following information is also given:

General index of retail prices

Year	Index	Increase on previous year %
1975	100.0	24.2
1976	116.5	16.5
1977	135.0	15.8
1978	146.2	8.3
1979	165.8	13.4

Marks will be awarded for effective and imaginative use of the information provided.

(b) Explain why you consider your presentation should help the reader understand the figures more easily. *(ICMA)*

4.12 A factory produces togs, clogs and pegs, each of these three products having a different work content. The proportions of these products vary from month to month and the factory requires an index for assessing productivity changes. Each tog, clog and peg produced is to be weighted according to its work content, these weights being 6, 8 and 5 respectively. Also, because some months contain more working days than others, the index should offset the effect of this.

Data for the months of May, June and July are as follows:

	May	June	July	
No. of working days	23	22	16	(due to factory closure for 2 weeks)
Output (thousands)				
togs	19	16	10	
clogs	12	20	15	
pegs	22	15	10	

It is intended that May should be the base month for comparison, with a productivity index of 100.

Required:

(a) Design a simple productivity index, calculate its value for June and July, and comment briefly on the results.

(b) Now, due to a change in the type of peg produced, a new weight is required. Production data are shown below for two days when productivity was judged to be about equal.

Output	Day 1	Day 2
togs	921	811
clogs	800	747
new pegs	1042	1206

Use these data to estimate a suitable weight for the new pegs, to 1 decimal place, assuming that the weightings of 6 for togs and 8 for clogs are as before. *(ACA)*

4.13 A survey of household expenditure shows the following changes over the same week in each of three years for an average family in the South of England.

	1973			1974			1975		
	Price in pence	Unit	Quantity pur-chased	Price in pence	Unit	Quantity pur-chased	Price in pence	Unit	Quantity pur-chased
Sugar	10	2 lb	4 lb	11	2 lb	4 lb	29	2 lb	3 lb
Bread	11	loaf	4	12	loaf	4	16	loaf	4
Tea	8	$\frac{1}{4}$lb	$\frac{1}{2}$lb	9	$\frac{1}{4}$lb	$\frac{3}{4}$lb	10	$\frac{1}{4}$lb	1 lb
Milk	5	pint	20	5	pint	21	$5\frac{1}{2}$	pint	19
Butter	9	$\frac{1}{2}$lb	$1\frac{1}{2}$lb	10	$\frac{1}{2}$lb	$1\frac{1}{2}$lb	13	$\frac{1}{2}$lb	1 lb

(a) Using 1973 as base, calculate index numbers for 1974 and 1975 using the Laspeyre base weighted formula.

(b) State, with reasons, whether a survey based on these items represents a reasonable assessment of changes in the cost of living over the three years. *(ICMA)*

4.14 Prodco PLC manufactures an item of domestic equipment which requires a number of components which have varied as various modifications of the model have been produced.

The following table shows the number of components required together with their price over the last three years of production.

Component	1981		1982		1983	
	Price	Quantity	Price	Quantity	Price	Quantity
	£		£		£	
A	3.63	3	4.00	2	4.49	2
B	2.11	4	3.10	5	3.26	6
C	10.03	1	10.36	1	12.05	1
D	4.01	7	5.23	6	5.21	5

Required:

(a) Establish the base weighted price indices for 1982 and 1983 based on 1981 for the item of equipment. *(8 marks)*

(b) Establish the current weighted price indices for 1982 and 1983 based on 1981 for the item of equipment. *(8 marks)*

(c) Using the results of (a) and (b) as illustrations compare and contrast Laspeyres and Paasche price index numbers.*(4 marks)*

(Total 20 marks) (ACA)

*4.15 Your company Manco p.l.c. is about to enter wage negotiations with its Production Department. Below are tabulated the average weekly earnings and hours worked of the full-time manual workers 21 years of age and over in the Department. Also included in the table is the General Index of Retail Prices (in some countries known as the Consumer Price Index) for the years 1974 to 1981.

Year	Average Weekly Earnings £	Average Hours Worked	Retail* Price Index (1975 = £100)
1974	40.19	44	80.5
1975	52.65	45	100.0
1976	62.03	45	116.5
1977	70.20	46	135.0
1978	76.83	46	146.2
1979	91.90	46	165.8
1980	107.51	45	195.6
1981	121.95	43	218.9

Source: Economic Trends – HMSO.

Required:

(a) Assuming that normal time for the Production Department has been 40 hours for the period covered, tabulate the year, average weekly earnings, average hours worked and add the normal weekly rate to the table. You may also assume that overtime is paid at time and a half, i.e. one and a half times the basic hourly rate of pay. *(5 marks)*

(b) Plot the figures for the Retail Price Index on a semi-logarithmic (ratio scale) graph, by plotting the logarithm of the Retail Price Index against time. *(5 marks)*

(c) What characteristic does this graph demonstrate about the Retail Price Index? *(2 marks)*

(d) Deflate the Normal Weekly Rate by the Retail Price Index and show this in tabulated form against the Normal Weekly Rate and the year. *(4 marks)*

(e) What is the significance of the deflated series with regard to the wage negotiations? *(4 marks)*

(Total 20 marks)

(ACA)

*4.16 Your company, based in the United Kingdom, has subsidiaries in seven countries. The table below shows the Bank of England Index of Currency Movements (that is the Trade Weighted Index) as at recent date for the eight countries in the corporate operation.

Currency	Bank of England Index
Sterling	91.7
U.S. Dollar	122.1
Canadian Dollar	90.1
Deutsche Mark	125.2
Swiss Franc	145.3
Dutch Guilder	117.1
French Franc	72.2
Japanese Yen	130.2

Base average 1975 = 100
Source: Financial Times

Required:

(a) Present the above data on a suitably labelled bar chart and interpret it as for a layman. *(6 marks)*

(b) Explain the usefulness of a weighted index number, using the above data for illustrative purposes. *(3 marks)*

(c) Contrast the use of a base weighted index number with the use of a current weighted index number. *(4 marks)*

(d) As the company may be setting up another subsidiary in another country shortly, describe the main published sources of economic, accounting and business data to which you would turn for background information about that country. (Belgium may be taken as a suitable example of that other country if you wish.)
(7 marks)
(Total 20 marks)
(ACA)

Chapter 5
THEORY OF PROBABILITY

Most people have a good grasp of probability from various games of chance such as poker, dice, roulette, even tossing a coin.

Sometimes our estimates of probability are based upon previous experience, or experiment, and this is known as the RELATIVE FREQUENCY approach. For example, if I recorded how long it takes me to get to work in the morning I might get a frequency distribution such as Diagram 5.1.

DIAGRAM 5.1

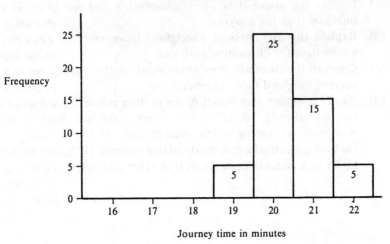

Journey time in minutes

From the frequency distribution I can calculate the probability of my journey taking 20 minutes (or more exactly between $19\frac{1}{2}$ and $20\frac{1}{2}$ minutes) as 25/50 or 0.5. In other words, there is a 50% chance that my journey will take 20 minutes. Of course, the bigger the sample I take the better will be my estimate of the probability and I must ensure that my sample is representative of the population — for example, it would not be a good idea to include observations during the school holidays when the roads are less crowded because I would really be sampling from two populations.

On other occasions our estimates of probability are based upon theoretical considerations. For example, if you were asked the probability of throwing a number greater than four with a true die you would reply $2/6 = \frac{1}{3}$ or 0.33 because you would assume that each number has an equal chance of being thrown and there are two numbers greater than four. This notion of equally likely events provides us with a definition of probability.

Equally likely events

If in n trials one event occurs r_1 times and another event occurs r_2 times the two events are equally likely if

$$\lim_{n \to \infty} \frac{r_1}{n} = \lim_{n \to \infty} \frac{r_2}{n}$$

In other words, if we tossed a coin a number of times then as the number of throws grew very large the proportion of heads would tend to get closer and closer to the proportion of tails.

Definition of probability

If out of a total of n equally likely events r are deemed favourable, then the probability of a favourable event, p, is given by

$$p = \frac{r}{n}$$

In other words, the probability of an event occurring is the proportion of occurrences of that event in a long series of experiments.

If an event cannot possibly occur then its probability is zero but if it must occur then its probability is 1. The probability of an event must fall somewhere between zero and unity.

So, the probability of "a pig flying" is zero while the probability of "a little rain falling into every life" is unity.

The next step is to build up some rules for calculating the probabilities of more complex events. But first let us define some terms.

5.1 TYPES OF EVENT

(a) **Mutually exclusive events**

If two, or more, events are mutually exclusive it means that only one of them can occur in a single trial, the occurrence of one excluding the occurrence of all the others.

Example: If we throw a die, then the occurrence of one number excludes the possibility of all the others.

(b) **Non-mutually exclusive events**

If events are not mutually exclusive it means that two, or more, events can occur together. In this situation the events may be independent or dependent.

(i) **Independent events**

Two, or more, events are said to be independent if the occurrence, or non-occurrence, of one has no effect on the probability of occurrence of any of the others.

Example: If we consider the tossing of a coin, it makes no difference that the coin has turned up heads on, say, the last seven occasions. The probability of it turning up heads again is still 0.5.

(ii) **Dependent events**

Conversely, two or more events are dependent if the occurrence, or non-occurrence, of one event does have an effect on the probability of occurrence of the others.

Example: If we consider the probability of drawing an ace from a pack of cards, on two draws, where the first card is **not** replaced. The probability of drawing an ace on the second draw is either $\frac{3}{51}$ or $\frac{4}{51}$ **depending** on whether an ace was drawn first time. These are **conditional** probabilities because the probability of drawing an ace on the second draw changes according to the result of the first draw.

(c) **Joint events**

When two, or more, events occur together we refer to joint events. The probability of joint events occurring will depend upon whether the events involved are dependent or independent.

Example: The probability of drawing two aces from one pack of cards is slightly different from the probability of drawing two aces from two packs of cards, they are both joint events but in the first case they are dependent events and in the second case independent. In the first case the probability of drawing an ace on the second draw is affected by what happens on the first draw, but in the second case the probability of drawing an ace from one pack is not affected by whether or not an ace is drawn from the other pack.

We have tried where possible to make our examples relevant to the business world. The above examples, involving dice and cards, have little direct relevance to business but they are simple ways of introducing ideas which, as we shall see, can be useful in a business context.

5.2 THE RULES OF PROBABILITY

(a) **The Addition Rule**

(i) **Mutually exclusive events**

The probability that **any one** of several mutually exclusive events will occur is the sum of the probabilities of the separate events.

i.e. P(A) or B or C . . .) = P(A) + P(B) + P(C) . . . . (see footnote)

Footnote: P(A or B) is sometimes written P(A+B) or P(A ∪ B).

For example, the probability of throwing an odd number with a die is

$$P(\text{odd}) = P(1) + P(3) + P(5) = \frac{1}{6} + \frac{1}{6} + \frac{1}{6} = \frac{3}{6} = \frac{1}{2} = 0.5$$

We could, of course, have got this more directly from our definition of probability as r/n which in this case gives probability of odd $= 3/6 = 0.5$.

(ii) Non-mutually exclusive events
If we are interested in the probability that **any one** of several events may occur, then if the events are not mutually exclusive we have to be a little more careful.

For example, say a menswear department finds that 50% of its customers buy a shirt and 60% buy a tie, what percentage buy either a shirt or tie? The above rule suggests that
$$P(\text{shirt or tie}) = P(\text{shirt}) + P(\text{tie}) = 0.5 + 0.6 = 1.1 \text{ or } 110\%$$
but this is obviously WRONG! We are forgetting that some customers buy both a shirt and a tie; say that 25% of customers buy both a shirt and a tie then it is fairly obvious that the probability of a customer buying a shirt or a tie, or a shirt and a tie, is $50\% + 60\% - 25\% = 85\%$ or 0.85, as illustrated in Diagram 5.2.

DIAGRAM 5.2

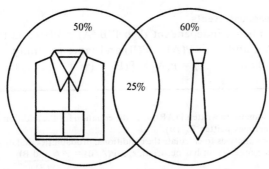

So, for non-mutually exclusive events we have to modify the addition rule such that
$$P(A \text{ or } B) = P(A) + P(B) - P(AB)$$
where $P(AB)$ is the probability of the joint occurrence of the two events (See footnote)

The general form for the addition rule is then as we have just shown $P(A \text{ or } B) = P(A) + P(B) - P(AB)$ but if the events are mutually exclusive $P(AB) = 0$ and we have the rule as in (i).

Footnote: $P(A \text{ or } B \text{ or } C \dots)$ is more complicated and involves all the joint probabilities.

$$P(E_1 \text{ or } E_2 \text{ or } \dots E_n) = \sum_{i=1}^{i=n} P(E_i) - \sum_{i \neq j} P(E_i \text{ and } E_j) + \sum_{i \neq j \neq k} P(E_i \text{ and } E_j \text{ and } E_k) \dots$$

$(-1)^{n-1} P(E_1 \text{ and } E_2 \text{ and } \dots E_n)$

If you draw a Venn diagram for the three event case you will realise why the signs change.

(b) **The Multiplication Rule**

As we said earlier, the probability of a joint event (A **and** B) depends upon whether the events involved are dependent or independent, i.e. whether the occurrence, or non-occurrence, of one has an effect on the probability of occurrence of the other(s).

(i) **Dependent events**

To calculate the probability of a joint occurrence of two events A and B, multiply the probability of A by the conditional probability of B, given that A has occurred.

i.e. $P(A \text{ and } B) = P(A) \times P(B/A)$ (see footnotes (1) and (2))

where $P(B/A)$ is the probability of B given that A has occurred.

Also, $P(A \text{ and } B) = P(B) \times P(A/B)$ (see footnotes (3) and (4)).

For example, what is the probability of picking 2 white bills from a bag containing 3 white and 7 black balls when the first ball chosen is not replaced?

Prob (White on first pick) = 3/10

Prob (White on second pick) = 2/9 or 3/9 depending on whether first ball was white. The probability of the second event is conditional on the outcome of the first event.

P(2 whites) = P(white on first pick) × P(white on second pick given that first pick resulted in white).

$$= 3/10 \times 2/9 = 1/15.$$

(ii) **Independent events**

If the events are independent then $P(B/A) = P(B)$ and the equation is simply $P(A \text{ and } B) = P(A) \times P(B)$ and more generally

$P(A \text{ and } B \text{ and } C \ldots) = P(A) \times P(B) \times P(C) \ldots \ldots$ (see footnote (5)).

Footnotes:
(1) $P(A \text{ and } B)$ is sometimes written $P(AB)$, as in the equation for the addition rule, or $P(A \cap B)$.
(2) $P(B/A)$ is sometimes written $P_A (B)$.
(3) These equations allow us to calculate the conditional probabilities that one event will occur given that some other event has occurred, e.g. $P(A/B) = \dfrac{P(A \text{ and } B)}{P(B)}$
(4) Combining the two equations $P(A \text{ and } B) = P(A) \times P(B/A) = P(B) \times P(A/B)$ gives
$P(B/A) = \dfrac{P(B) \times P(A/B)}{P(A)}$ which is Bayes' theorem in a simple form.
(5) $P(A \text{ and } B \text{ and } C \ldots) = P(A) \times P(B/A) \times P(C/AB) \times P(D/ABC) \ldots \ldots$ for dependent events.

To summarize for the two event case:—

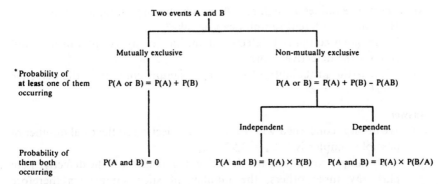

*For non-mutually exclusive events this means either one or both of them occur. For mutually exclusive events it means one or the other because, by definition, both cannot occur.

5.3 Permutations and Combinations

When calculating the probability of an event we often need to consider the number of 'favourable' outcomes compared to the number of possible (equally likely) outcomes. In such situations a knowledge of permutations and combinations can be helpful.

Permutations

The number of ways that r items can be chosen from n distinct items taking notice of the order of selection is denoted by ^nP_r.

$$^nP_r = \frac{n!}{(n-r)!}$$

where $n! = n(n-1)(n-2)(n-3) \ldots 3.2.1$
and $(n-r)! = (n-r)(n-r-1) \ldots \ldots \ldots 3.2.1$
and n! is referred to as n factorial.

Combinations

The number of ways that r items can be chosen from n distinct items disregarding the order of selection is denoted by ^nC_r

$$^nC_r = \frac{n!}{(n-r)!\,r!}$$

So, $^nP_r = {}^nC_r \times r!$ because r items can be arranged in r! permutations. For example, the letters abc can be arranged in 3! permutations: abc, acb, bac, bca, cab, cba.

5.4 Total possible outcomes of joint events

If an event has w_1 possible outcomes and another event has w_2 possible outcomes then the two events taken together have $w_1 \times w_2$ possible outcomes. Similarly, three events have $w_1 \times w_2 \times w_3$ possible outcomes, etc.

For example, the number of possible outcomes when two dice are thrown is $6 \times 6 = 36$.

Example:

An inspector examines a batch of 100 items by testing a sample of four items.
(a) How many different samples can he take?
(b) If the batch contains 1 defective item, how many samples of four will contain the defective item?
(c) What is the probability of selecting a sample containing the defective item?

Answer:
(a) We are not concerned with the order of selection so the total number of possible samples is $^{100}C_4 = 3,921,225$.
(b) Each sample containing the defective item consists of the defective item plus any three others, the number of such samples is therefore $^{99}C_3 = 156,849$.
(c) The probability of selecting a sample containing the defective item is

$$= \frac{\text{Number of samples containing defective item}}{\text{Total number of possible samples}} = \frac{156,849}{3,921,225} = \frac{4}{100} = 0.04$$

N.B. We could in fact have arrived at the answer to part (c) directly by observing that each item has a probability of $\frac{4}{100}$ of appearing in the sample and so the probability that the defective item will appear in the sample is 0.04.

Likewise, from the addition rule of probability, the probability that **any one** of the four items in the sample is defective is

$$\frac{1}{100} + \frac{1}{100} + \frac{1}{100} + \frac{1}{100} = \frac{4}{100}$$

5.5 WORKED EXAMPLES:

Example 1

Suppose that a batch of 30 items contains 3 items that are defective. If a sample of 2 items is taken, what is:
(a) Probability that both are defective;
(b) Probability that only one is defective;
(c) Probability that neither of the items is defective?

(a) Number of possible samples $= {}^{30}C_2 = \dfrac{30 \times 29}{2}$
Number of samples with 2 defectives $= {}^3C_2 = 3$
Probability of sample containing 2 defectives

$$= \frac{\text{Number of samples with 2 defectives}}{\text{Total number of possible samples}} = \frac{3}{\dfrac{30 \times 29}{2}} = \frac{1}{145}$$

OR Prob (A and B) = P(A) $\times$ P(B/A)

Prob (1st item defective **and** 2nd item defective) $= \dfrac{3}{30} \times \dfrac{2}{29} = \dfrac{1}{145}$

(b) Number of samples with only one defective $= 3 \times {}^{27}C_1 = 3 \times 27 = 81$
Probability of sample containing only one defective $= \dfrac{81}{\dfrac{30 \times 29}{2}} = \dfrac{27}{145}$

OR Prob $\begin{pmatrix} \text{1 defective} \\ \text{in sample} \end{pmatrix} = P \begin{pmatrix} \text{1st is defective} \\ \text{and 2nd is OK} \end{pmatrix} + P \begin{pmatrix} \text{1st is OK} \\ \text{and 2nd is defective} \end{pmatrix}$

$= P \begin{pmatrix} \text{1st defective} \end{pmatrix} \times P \begin{pmatrix} \text{2nd is OK} \\ \text{given} \\ \text{1st defective} \end{pmatrix}$

$+ P \begin{pmatrix} \text{1st is OK} \end{pmatrix} \times P \begin{pmatrix} \text{2nd is defective} \\ \text{given} \\ \text{1st is OK} \end{pmatrix}$

$= \dfrac{3}{30} \times \dfrac{27}{29} + \dfrac{27}{30} \times \dfrac{3}{29} = \dfrac{27}{145}$

N.B. We do not need to deduct the joint probability because these are mutually exclusive since if the first is defective and 2nd OK, the first cannot be OK or the second defective.

OR Why not $P(A \text{ or } B) = P(A) + P(B) - P(AB)$ for non-mutually exclusive dependent events.

$P \begin{pmatrix} \text{1st is defective or 2nd is defective} \\ \text{or both} \end{pmatrix} = \dfrac{3}{30} + \dfrac{3}{30} - \dfrac{1}{145}$

But we want

$P \begin{pmatrix} \text{1st defective or 2nd defective} \\ \text{but \textbf{not} both} \end{pmatrix} = \dfrac{3}{30} + \dfrac{3}{30} - \dfrac{1}{145} - \dfrac{1}{145} = \dfrac{27}{145}$

$\therefore$ we need to deduct $P \begin{pmatrix} \text{both being} \\ \text{defective} \end{pmatrix}$ again

(c) $P \begin{pmatrix} \text{Neither is defective} \end{pmatrix} = P \begin{pmatrix} \text{1st OK} \end{pmatrix} \times P \begin{pmatrix} \text{2nd OK} \\ \text{given 1st OK} \end{pmatrix} = \dfrac{27}{30} \times \dfrac{26}{29} = \dfrac{117}{145}$

OR $\dfrac{{}^{27}C_2}{{}^{30}C_2} = \dfrac{117}{145}$ or $1 - \text{Prob} \begin{pmatrix} \text{1 defective or 2 defective} \end{pmatrix}$

$= 1 - \left(\dfrac{27}{145} + \dfrac{1}{145} \right) = \dfrac{117}{145}$

Check: Total Prob. of all possible events $= \dfrac{1}{145} + \dfrac{27}{145} + \dfrac{117}{145} = 1$

The above example illustrates the consistency of the laws of probability and how the same problem can be solved by a variety of methods.

Example 2

A batch contains 12 items, four of which are defective. One item is chosen and tested and then put back in the batch before a second item is chosen and tested.

What is

(a) The probability of both items being defective;

(b) The probability of only one being defective;

(c) The probability of neither being defective?

(a) $P(A \text{ and } B) = P(A) \times P(B)$ since the item is put back the events are mutually exclusive.

$$= \frac{4}{12} \times \frac{4}{12} = \frac{1}{9}$$

(b) $P\left(\begin{array}{c} A \text{ or } B \\ \text{or both} \end{array}\right) = P(A) + P(B) - P(AB)$ but we want only A or B

So, $P(A \text{ or } B) = P(A) + P(B) - 2P(AB)$

$$= \frac{1}{3} + \frac{1}{3} - \frac{2}{9} = \frac{4}{9}$$

(c) $P(A \text{ and } B) = P(A) \times P(B)$

$$P\left(\text{neither defective}\right) = \frac{8}{12} \times \frac{8}{12} = \frac{4}{9}$$

Check: $\dfrac{1}{9} + \dfrac{4}{9} + \dfrac{4}{9} = 1$

Example 3

Three boxes each contain 100 items, there are 10 defectives in the first box, 5 in the second, and 8 in the third. One item is chosen from each box, what are the probabilities that

(a) at least one is defective;

(b) none are defective?

(a) $P(A) = \dfrac{1}{10}$, $P(B) = \dfrac{1}{20}$, $P(C) = \dfrac{2}{25}$

$$P\left(\begin{array}{c} A \text{ or } B \text{ or } C \\ \text{or all of them} \end{array}\right) = P(A) + P(B) + P(C) - P(AB) - P(AC) - P(BC) + P(ABC)$$

$$= \frac{1}{10} + \frac{1}{20} + \frac{2}{25} - \frac{1}{10} \times \frac{1}{20} - \frac{1}{10} \times \frac{2}{25} - \frac{1}{20} \times \frac{2}{25} + \frac{1}{10} \times \frac{1}{20} \times \frac{2}{25} = \frac{1067}{5000}$$

OR $P\left(\begin{array}{c} \text{at least} \\ 1 \text{ defective} \end{array}\right) = 1 - P\left(\text{no defectives}\right)$

$$= 1 - \left[\frac{9}{10} \times \frac{19}{20} \times \frac{23}{25}\right] = \frac{1067}{5000}$$

(b) $\quad P \left(\text{no defectives} \right) \quad = 1 - \dfrac{1067}{5000} = \dfrac{3933}{5000}$

5.6 Decision Trees

A decision tree is a diagram that shows the sequence of decisions which have to be made in a business situation and the possible outcomes of those decisions.

Probabilities are attached to the various outcomes which are envisaged, and estimated monetary values of these outcomes are weighted by the probabilities to calculate the 'expected values' of the various decisions.

These expected values can then be "rolled back" in order to compare the expected values of the initial decisions, the decision which yields the highest expected value being the preferred course of action.

5.6.1 Expected Values

The expected value of a variable is denoted by $E(x)$ and can be calculated from the probabilities.

$$E(x) = \Sigma x_i\, p_i \qquad \text{where } x_i = \text{value of variable}$$
$$\text{and } p_i = \text{probability that the variable}$$
$$\text{will take the value } x_i.$$

For example, if we estimated the probabilities of various levels of sales over a period as below:

SALES (£)	Probability
10,000	0.2
15,000	0.7
20,000	0.1

The expected value of sales over the period would be $10{,}000 \times 0.2 + 15{,}000 \times 0.7 + 20{,}000 \times 0.1 = £14{,}500$.

5.6.2 Decision Tree Analysis

To illustrate the use of decision trees let us consider a simplified example.

Suppose a firm is considering large scale capital investment to expand its production capacity. Demand for the firm's product may turn out to be high, average, or low. It may then have to decide whether to continue to market its product on a regional basis or go national. If the firm does not expand its production capacity, there is of course no point in marketing the product nationally.

The various decisions and possible outcomes are, therefore, as shown overleaf and the estimated monetary value of the outcomes might be those shown in the final column.

Initial decision	Demand for product	Marketing decision	Demand for product	Estimated monetary value (£k)
Do not invest	High			12,000
✓	Average			10,000
✓	Low			6,000
Invest	High	Stay regional	High	7,000
✓	✓	Go national	High	20,000
✓	✓	✓	Average	15,000
✓	✓	✓	Low	5,000
✓	Average	Stay regional	Average	5,000
✓	✓	Go national	High	18,000
✓	✓	✓	Average	12,000
✓	✓	✓	Low	3,000
✓	Low	Stay regional	Low	1,000
✓	✓	Go national	High	15,000
✓	✓	✓	Average	8,000
✓	✓	✓	Low	-1,000

The situation can now be shown in the form of a decision tree with decisions shown by triangles and outcomes by circles. If we can assign probabilities, shown in brackets, to the various outcomes then we can use these probabilities to calculate the expected monetary values of the various branches of the tree as shown in Diagram 5.3.

The expected monetary values at decision points D2, D3, and D4 are:

Decision point	Expected monetary value (£k)
D2	17,500
D3	12,000
D4	2,400

At each point we assume that the decision-taker will choose that course of action which gives the highest expected monetary value. For example, at point D2 going national gives an expected monetary value of $(20,000 \times 0.7) + (15,000 \times 0.2) + (5,000 \times 0.1) = £17,500\,k$. Whilst staying regional gives an expected monetary value of $(7,000 \times 1.0) = £7,000\,k$.

These expected monetary values can now be "rolled-back" to find the expected monetary value of point D1 which is £13,790k $[(17,500 \times 0.5) + (12,000 \times 0.4) + (2,400 \times 0.1)]$ given by the "invest" branch of the tree compared to the £10,600k $[(12,000 \times 0.5) + (10,000 \times 0.4) + (6,000 \times 0.1)]$ given by the "do not invest" branch.

So, the weighted averages of the various outcomes indicate that the decision should be to undertake the investment in this case.

DIAGRAM 5.3

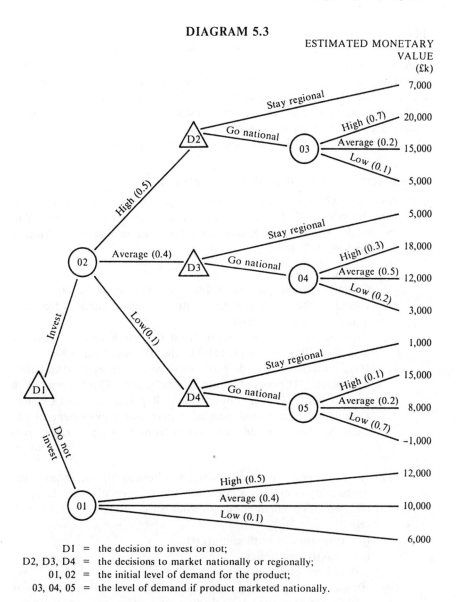

ESTIMATED MONETARY
VALUE
(£k)

D1 = the decision to invest or not;
D2, D3, D4 = the decisions to market nationally or regionally;
01, 02 = the initial level of demand for the product;
03, 04, 05 = the level of demand if product marketed nationally.

All of this depends, of course, upon accurate assessments of probabilities and estimated monetary values. But there is a more basic problem concerning the use of expected value as a decision criterion; the expected value is the result that could be expected on average in a long series of trials. When we are faced with a one-off decision, such as a large capital investment, the project may have a favourable expected value but the risk of loss may be a more important consideration.

In our example, the worst situation envisaged is for the firm to invest, find that demand is low, try to overcome this through a national marketing campaign, but find that demand remains low. The probability of this happening is thought to be low (0.1×0.7) but if it does happen the firm faces an estimated £1m loss. If such an outcome could bankrupt the firm, it may well be decided not to undertake the investment. The decision, in practice, would probably depend upon the decision-taker's attitude to risk and the ability of the firm to withstand such a loss on the project.

QUESTIONS — THEORY OF PROBABILITY

5.1　A large batch of items comprises some manufactured by process X and some by process Y. There are twice as many items from X as from Y in the batch. Those from X contain 9% defectives and those from Y contain 12% defectives.

You are required to:
(1)　Calculate the proportion of defective items in the batch.
(2)　Calculate the probability that 3 items taken at random from the batch contain 1 defective.
(3)　An item is taken at random from the batch and found to be defective. What is the probability that it came from Y?
(4)　It is found that 50% of defective items cannot be repaired and must be replaced. The cost of repairing a defective is £2 if it comes from process X and £3 if it comes from Y. Replacements cost £7 each. Calculate the expected cost of repair and replacement of the defectives found in 300 items taken from the batch. *(20 marks)*
(ACA)

5.2　(a)　An insurance agent finds that on following up an enquiry the probability of making a sale is 0.4. If on a particular day the agent has two independent enquiries what is the probability that he will sell:
(i)　insurance to both enquirers;
(ii)　exactly one policy;
(iii) at least one policy?
(b)　An oil company drilling in the North Sea reckoned that there was a 60% chance of success of finding oil in economic quantities in a particular field. After a first test drilling had been completed the results were favourable.
If the probability is 0.3 that the test drilling would give a misleading result, what would be the revised probability, using Bayes' theorem, that a find of oil in economic quantities would occur?
(ICMA)

5.3 (a) You are required, for two events, A and B, to express $P(A \cup B)$ in terms of $P(A)$ and $P(B)$ only, when:
(i) the events A and B are mutually exclusive;
(ii) the events A and B are independent. *(6 marks)*
[Note: $P(A \cup B)$ is also written as $P(A$ or $B)$.]

(b) A manufacturer has three main suppliers of fuses. The table below shows the quantities of colour-coded fuses held in stock by the manufacturer. As part of a quality control check a sample of boxes of fuses is to be tested. Boxes of fuses are of identical size, each box containing 100 fuses.

Number of boxes of fuses in stock

Colour code	Red	White	Green	Blue	Totals
Supplier					
X	100	90	110	100	400
Y	40	60	50	50	200
Z	10	50	190	150	400
Totals	150	200	350	300	1,000

You are required:
(i) if a sample of 100 boxes is to be checked for quality, to state how you would recommend the sample to be selected. (You may assume that fuses cost equal amounts to check.); *(2 marks)*
(ii) if *one* box is to be selected randomly from the total, to state the probability of it being:
1 red;
2 from Supplier X;
3 red and from Supplier X;
4 red or from Supplier X; *(6 marks)*
(iii) if *two* boxes are to be chosen randomly from the total, to state the probability that they will both be from the same supplier;
(4 marks)
(iv) one box having been selected randomly from the total and given that it has been identified as having come from Supplier Y, to state the probability it contains fuses that are *not* red. *(2 marks)*
(ICMA)

5.4 A company manufactures items using a maximum of three different operations: shaping, plating and finishing. A defect can arise in an item during any operation which it undergoes and it may be classified as minor or major. The following table gives the probabilities of a defect arising during each of the three operations, which are independent.

Operation	No defect	One minor defect	One major defect
Shaping	0.70	0.20	0.10
Plating	0.70	0.10	0.20
Finishing	0.65	0.20	0.15

Required:

(1) What is the probability that an item which has gone through all three operations contains

 (i) no defects?

 (ii) one minor defect and two major defects?

 (iii) two defects of unspecified type?

(2) Consider now only items which undergo shaping and finishing but which are not plated. Any minor defect which occurs is repaired at an average cost of £1 each and a major defect at an average cost of £5 each. Calculate the average repair cost incurred per item produced of this type. *(20 marks)*

(ACA)

5.5 (a) Define the term 'conditional probability', illustrating your answer with an example.

 (b) One of the products your company manufactures and sells has a stable selling price of £30 per unit but the monthly sales volume is uncertain. The fixed cost is stable at £6,000 per month but the variable cost per unit is also subject to uncertainty.

Based on past experience, management has developed the following probability distribution of sales and variable cost per unit.

Sales per month units	Probability
400	0.3
500	0.4
600	0.3

Variable cost per unit £	Probability
10	0.2
15	0.5
20	0.3

 (i) Calculate the expected profit in total for the product;

 (ii) Analyse the profit in (i) above into its constituent parts attributable to each possible combination of sales and variable costs. *(ICMA)*

5.6 (a) An item produced by a company is susceptible to two types of defect, A and B. The probability that an item has defect A is $\frac{1}{6}$.

The probability that it has defect B is $\frac{1}{8}$, independent of whether it has defect A.

Required:
(1) Calculate the probability that an item has:
   (i)   both A and B defects;
   (ii) one defect only, A or B;
   (iii) no defect.
(2) What simple relationship is there between your answers to part (1)?

(b) Suppose now, in addition to the above defects, the item is susceptible to a third type of defect C. The probability that an item contains C depends on whether it has the other defects. If it has neither A nor B then there is a probability of $\frac{1}{10}$ that it has C. If it has one of A or B the probability of having C is $\frac{2}{10}$, and if it has both A and B the probability of having C is $\frac{3}{10}$.

Required:
(1) Show the probability that an item has

   (i)   none of the three defects is $\frac{315}{480}$

   (ii) one of the three defects is $\frac{131}{480}$

(2) If items with 1 defect can be repaired at a cost of £10 but those with 2 or more defects are scrapped at a cost of £30, determine the total cost of repair and scrapping associated with the production of 480 items.   *(ACA)*

*5.7 A component goes through five operations before it is completed. Information relative to production is given below:
Basic units of raw material introduced 3,200
Rejects:

   1st operation.........................136
   2nd operation........................126
   3rd operation 56
   4th operation 48
   5th operation 12

(a) (i) What is the probability that a basic unit of raw material will become a finished component?

(ii) What is the probability of a basic unit of raw material getting beyond the second operation?

(iii) If a further 600 finished components are required how many basic units of raw material should be introduced?

(b) The inter-relationship of events is of fundamental importance in probability theory.

Explain what is meant by the following two events and illustrate each with an example:
(i) independent events;
(ii) mutually exclusive events. *(ICMA)*

*5.8 A company has the opportunity of marketing a new package of computer games. It has two possible courses of action: to test market on a limited scale or to give up the project completely. A test market would cost £160,000 and current evidence suggests that consumer reaction is equally likely to be 'positive' or 'negative'. If the reaction to the test marketing were to be 'positive' the company could either market the computer games nationally or still give up the project completely. Research suggests that a national launch might result in the following sales:

Sales	Contribution £ million	Probability
High	1.2	0.25
Average	0.3	0.5
Low	−0.24	0.25

If the test marketing were to yield 'negative' results the company would give up the project. Giving up the project at any point would result in a contribution of £60,000 from the sale of copyright etc to another manufacturer. All contributions have been discounted to present values.

You are required to:
(a) draw a decision tree to represent this situation, including all relevant probabilities and financial values; *(8 marks)*

(b) recommend a course of action for the company on the basis of expected values; *(8 marks)*

(c) explain any limitations of this method of analysis. *(4 marks)*
(Total 20 marks)
(ICMA)

5.7 PROBABILITY DISTRIBUTIONS

At the beginning of this chapter we referred to the RELATIVE FREQUENCY approach to probability where our estimates of probability are based upon previous experience or experiment. A frequency distribution can easily be turned into a probability distribution by changing the frequencies into relative frequencies.

Suppose I recorded how long it took me to get to work in the morning and the result was the frequency distribution below:

Journey time (minutes)	col. 1 frequency	Class width	col. 2 frequency density	col. 3 Relative frequency density or probability density
19 to under 20	5	1	5	0.1
20 to under 21	25	1	25	0.5
21 to under 22	15	1	15	0.3
22 to under 24	5	2	2.5	0.05
	$\Sigma f = 50$			

To represent this data in the form of a histogram, I need first to calculate the frequency density (col. 2) so that the area of each rectangle represents the frequency.

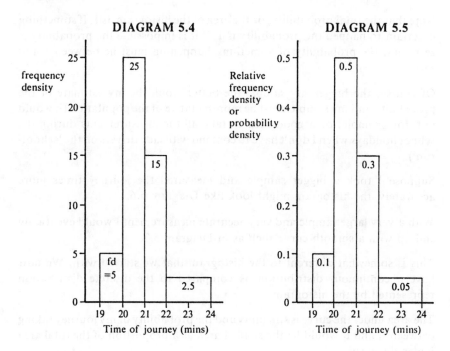

DIAGRAM 5.4 DIAGRAM 5.5

From this distribution, illustrated in Diagram 5.4, I can now derive the relative frequency density by dividing each frequency density by the total frequency of 50 (col. 3).

This relative frequency density shows the proportion of times my journey takes between certain lengths of time, i.e. the probability that my journey will take between those lengths of time.

The area of each rectangle in Diagram 5.5 now represents the probability that my journey will take a certain length of time (some time interval to be precise).

In fact, all that has happened is that we have changed the vertical scale but let us now calculate the probabilities of my journey taking the given lengths of time, as shown in Diagram 5.5.

Time mins.	Probability (area of rectangle)
19 to under 20	0.1
20 to under 21	0.5
21 to under 22	0.3
22 to under 24	0.1 [2 × 0.05]
	1.0

Note that the total probability, or the area of the histogram, is 1. If something is certain to happen the probability is 1, if it is impossible the probability is zero, and the probability of something happening must lie between 1 and zero.

Of course, the bigger my sample the better would be my estimate of the probability and my sample must be representative of the population (it would not, for example, be a good idea to take all the measurements during the school holidays when I don't have to contend with lady drivers on the 'school-run').

Suppose I took a bigger sample and measured the journey times more accurately, the histogram might look like Diagram 5.6.

With a very large sample and very accurate measurement I would eventually end up with a smooth curve such as in Diagram 5.7.

This is somewhat different to the histogram that we started with. We now have a continuous distribution as compared to the discrete distribution represented by the histogram.

The area under the curve is still unity and the probability of my journey taking between t_1 and t_2 would be the shaded area as a proportion of the total area under the curve.

DIAGRAM 5.6

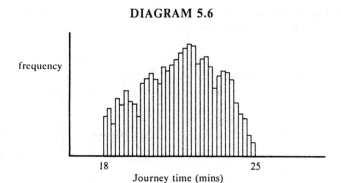

Journey time (mins)

DIAGRAM 5.7

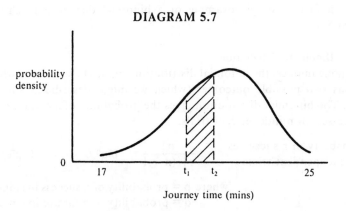

Journey time (mins)

Very often we can describe such curves by mathematical equations known as probability density functions and the area under the curve between certain values (the probability of the variable taking a value in that range) can be found by integration.* Fortunately, we don't usually have to do this because many distributions have been tabulated so that all we need do is decide upon the appropriate distribution and simply look up the probability.

5.8 THEORETICAL PROBABILITY DISTRIBUTIONS

There are a number of 'tailor-made' theoretical probability distributions which we can often use to fit particular situations.

As an example of how such a theoretical distribution can be built up, consider the situation when 3 coins are tossed simultaneously. There are 8 possible ways the coins may fall, viz:

1st coin	H	H	H	H	T	T	T	T
2nd coin	H	H	T	T	H	H	T	T
3rd coin	H	T	H	T	H	T	H	T

*See chapter 11.

Thus, we may derive a probability distribution for the number of heads by looking at the possible combinations.

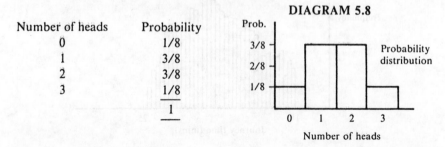

Number of heads	Probability
0	1/8
1	3/8
2	3/8
3	1/8
	$\overline{1}$

DIAGRAM 5.8

This is, in fact, a simple example of a binomial distribution, shown in Diagram 5.8.

5.8.1 Binomial distribution

As the name implies, the binomial distribution applies to situations where an event has two possible outcomes (which we might describe as success or failure). The binomial distribution gives the probability of a certain number of 'successes' in n independent trials.

$$\frac{\text{Probability of r successes}}{\text{in n independent trials}} = \frac{n!}{r! \ (n-r)!} \quad p^r q^{n-r} \quad \text{or} \quad {}^nC_r p^r q^{n-r}$$

where p = probability of a success in single trial
q = probability of a failure in single trial
and q = 1−p because, of course, there are only two possible outcomes, a success or a failure.
n = number of independent trials.

Consider the above example and let p = probability of a head (success) and q = probability of a tail (failure), n=3 the number of independent trials.

The probabilities of the various outcomes are then:

	HHH	HHT	HTH	HTT	THH	THT	TTH	TTT
Probability	ppp	ppq	pqp	pqq	qpp	qpq	qqp	qqq
=	p^3	p^2q	p^2q	p^2q	pq^2	pq^2	pq^2	q^3

So, we can see the probability of no heads $= q^3$
probability of one head $= 3q^2p$
probability of two heads $= 3qp^2$
probability of three heads $= p^3$

These probabilities sum to one, so $q^3 + 3q^2p + 3qp^2 + p^3 = 1$ and each successive term in the expression on the left hand side of the equation gives the probability of 0 successes, 1 success, 2 successes, 3 successes.

The left hand side of the equation is the expansion of the binomial expression $(q+p)^3$.

More generally,
$$(q+p)^n = q^n + nq^{n-1}p + \frac{n(n-1)q^{n-2}p^2}{1\times2} + \frac{n(n-1)(n-2)q^{n-3}p^3}{1\times2\times3} + \ldots + p^n$$

There are (n+1) terms in the expansion and the probability of r successes in n trials is given by the (r+1)th term in the expansion. So the first term gives the probability of no successes, the second term the probability of one success, and so on.

There is, however, no need to remember the expansion. The general expression for the (r+1)th term is as given above:

$$\frac{n!}{r!(n-r)!}\ p^rq^{n-r} \qquad \text{or} \qquad {}^nC_rp^rq^{n-r}$$

From this expression we can calculate the required probabilities so, for example, the probability of 2 heads in 3 independent trials where the probability of a head is $\frac{1}{2}$ is

$$\frac{3!}{2!(3-2)!}\ (\tfrac{1}{2})^2(1-\tfrac{1}{2})^{3-2} = 3/8$$

When the value of n is small, calculating the probabilities is simple but as n increases it becomes tedious. Statistical tables of binomial probabilities have been produced but we can in any case usually use other distributions which approximate to the binomial when n is large (Poisson and Normal — see later).

Mean of the binomial distribution
Successive terms in the binomial expansion give the probabilities that the variable will take values 0,1,2,3,...n. The mean, or expected, value of the variable (i.e. the mean number of successes) is $\mu = np$

For example, if we tossed a coin 10 times the average number of heads would be $10 \times 0.5 = 5$. Of course, if we tossed a coin only ten times we could get any number of heads from 0 to 10, but if we repeated the experiment a large number of times we would expect about half to be heads and our sample mean $\bar{x}$ would provide a good estimate of the theoretical, or true, population mean μ .

The mean, or expected, value of a variable is denoted by E(x) and may be calculated from the probabilities:

$$E(x) = \Sigma x_i p_i$$

where x_i = the value of the variable

p_i = the probability that the variable will take the value x_i

In our example involving the tossing of three coins:

$$E(x) = 0 \times \frac{1}{8} + 1 \times \frac{3}{8} = + 2 \times \frac{3}{8} + 3 \times \frac{1}{8} = 1.5 \,(= np = 3 \times 0.5)$$

Standard deviation of the binomial distribution

It can be shown that the standard deviation of the binomial distribution is given by:

$$\sigma = \sqrt{npq} \qquad \text{or} \quad \sqrt{np(1-p)}$$

σ^2 is the true population variance which, as we know, is a measure of the spread of the data around the mean. The sample variance, s^2, is an estimate of the true population variance, σ^2.

EXAMPLE

In a large batch of components, 10% are defective. What are the probabilities of getting 0,1,2,3,4 defectives in a sample of size 4 taken from the batch?

N.B. Because it is a large batch we can assume that the probability of picking a defective is constant, i.e. each pick is independent of what happened on the other picks.

Answer:

From first principles we could say that the probability of an item being defective, $p = 0.1$ and of it not being defective, $q = 0.9$. Since the batch is large we can assume that the result for each item is independent of the other items in the sample.

So,

Probability (no defectives) $= 0.9 \times 0.9 \times 0.9 \times 0.9 = (0.9)^4$

Probability (1 defective) $=$ Probability (1st defective and rest not defective)

+ P (2nd defective and rest not defective)

+ P (3rd defective and rest not defective)

+ P (4th defective and rest not defective)

$= (0.1 \times 0.9 \times 0.9 \times 0.9) + (0.9 \times 0.1 \times 0.9 \times 0.9)$

$+ (0.9 \times 0.9 \times 0.1 \times 0.9) + (0.9 \times 0.9 \times 0.9 \times 0.1)$

$= 4 \times 0.1 \times 0.9^3$

etc.

It is, however, much easier to simply write down the binomial probabilities, viz:

$$P\,(0) \;=\; \frac{4!}{0!\;4!} \qquad 0.1^0 \quad 0.9^4 \;=\; 0.9^4 \qquad\qquad =\; 0.6561$$

$$P\,(1) \;=\; \frac{4!}{1!\;3!} \qquad 0.1^1 \quad 0.9^3 \;=\; 4 \times 0.1 \times 0.9^3 \;=\; 0.2916$$

$$P\,(2) \;=\; \frac{4!}{2!\;2!} \qquad 0.1^2 \quad 0.9^2 \;=\; 6 \times 0.1^2 \times 0.9^2 \;=\; 0.0486$$

$$P\,(3) \;=\; \frac{4!}{3!\;1!} \qquad 0.1^3 \quad 0.9^1 \;=\; 4 \times 0.1^3 \times 0.9^1 \;=\; 0.0036$$

$$P\,(4) \;=\; \frac{4!}{4!\;0!} \qquad 0.1^4 \quad 0.9^0 \;=\; 0.1^4 \qquad\qquad =\; 0.0001$$

TOTAL 1.0000

5.8.2 Poisson Distribution

When n is large and p very small [$n > 30$ approx., $p \leqslant 0.1$], the binomial distribution is approximated by the Poisson distribution.

$$P(x) = \frac{e^{-\lambda}\,\lambda^x}{x!}$$ where $e = 2.7183$
λ = average number of occurrences
x = number of occurrences on a
particular occasion.

The mean and variance of the Poisson distribution both equal λ and the standard deviation is therefore $\sqrt{\lambda}$.

The Poisson distribution provides a good approximation to the Binomial for a rare event in a large number of trials and applies in many situations such as:— fire brigade callouts per day in a large town, heart attacks per day in a large city, typing errors per page in a manuscript, faults per short length in yarn or wire, bomb fragments per small subdivision of large area, goals per small time interval in a football match, number of calls arriving at a telephone exchange per short period of time, etc. etc.

EXAMPLE

A manufacturer of electronic components produces 1% defective items which are randomly distributed throughout his production.

The components are in packs of 250 and the manufacturer guarantees to provide an additional pack, free of charge, if any pack contains more than 4 defective components.

If annual sales are forecast to be 100,000 packs and each pack costs £50 to produce, how much will the guarantee cost the manufacturer?

Answer:
Each pack is a sample of size 250 from a large batch where the probability of a defective item is 0.01.

We need to know the probability of a pack containing more than 4 defective components and this is best calculated as:—

$$P(x > 4) = 1 - \{ P(x=0) + P(x=1) + P(x=2) + P(x=3) + P(x=4) \}$$

We could calculate the binomial probabilities of a pack containing 0,1,2,3,4 defectives in the way previously described but since n is large and p small it is acceptable to use the Poisson distribution making the calculations a little less tedious.

The mean number of defectives, using the binomial mean (μ =np), is 250 × 0.01 = 2.5 and this will serve as our estimate of λ , the average number of occurrences.

$$\therefore \ P(x) = \frac{e^{-2.5} \, 2.5^x}{x!}$$

$$P(x>4) = 1 - \left\{ \frac{e^{-2.5} \, 2.5^0}{0!} \quad \frac{e^{-2.5} \, 2.5^1}{1!} \quad \frac{e^{-2.5} \, 2.5^2}{2!} \right.$$
$$\left. + \frac{e^{-2.5} \, 2.5^3}{3!} + \frac{e^{-2.5} \, 2.5^4}{4!} \right\}$$

$$= 1 - \{ e^{-2.5} (1 + 2.5 + 3.125 + 2.604 + 1.628) \}$$
$$= 1 - \{ 0.082085 \, (10.857) \}$$
$$= 1 - 0.8912 = 0.1088$$

This means that 10.88% of the packs will contain more than 4 defective components and with annual sales of 100,000 packs 10,880 free packs will have to be supplied.

The cost of the guarantee will thus be 10,880 × £50 = £544,000.

This is obviously expensive, if the guarantee applied to packs containing more than 5 defective components the cost falls to £210,105 — check it for yourself — which might be more acceptable.

5.8.3 Normal distribution
The Binomial and Poisson were examples of discrete distributions where the variables could only take certain specific values. If a distribution is continuous the variable can take any value on a continuous scale and as long as we take a sufficiently large number of observations with sufficient accuracy the frequency polygon will become a smooth curve.

As with a histogram for discrete distributions, the area of the 'block' will represent the frequency with which the variable takes a value in that class interval, as in Diagram 5.9.

DIAGRAM 5.9

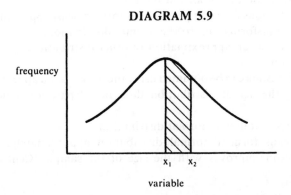

variable

Similarly, the area of the block as a proportion of the total area under the curve represents the probability that the variable will take a value in that class interval.

The area under the curve can be made equal to one by dividing the frequency for each class interval by the total frequency. Of course, the class intervals are infinitesimally small if the curve is smooth and the probability of observing a particular value is infinitesimally small, so when we are dealing with continuous distributions we can only find the probability of observing a value within a certain range, as in Diagram 5.10.

DIAGRAM 5.10

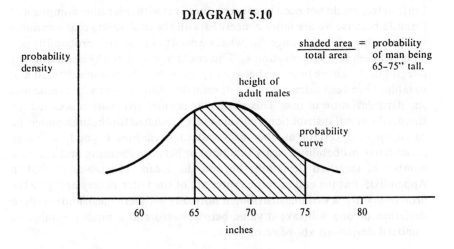

inches

Because it has so many practical applications the most important distribution is the Normal distribution. The Normal distribution is continuous and is also known as the Gaussian, error, and bell-shaped distribution.

Normal distribution
The normal distribution is important because:
(i)   Many distributions found in practice conform, at least approximately or after some transformation, to the normal distribution.
(ii) It can be used as an approximation to other distributions.
(iii) It is easy to use.
(iv) Reasonable results can be obtained using the norma as an approximation as long as the actual distribution does not depart too much from normal.
(v)   Random errors follow a normal distribution.
(vi) Sample means form a normal distribution approximately, and the approximation improves with the size of the sample (Central Limit Theorem).

The normal distribution is bell-shaped, symmetric about the point μ which is the mean, median and mode, and has a standard deviation σ. We often write that $x \sim N(\mu, \sigma^2)$ which means the variable x is distributed normally with a mean μ and standard deviation σ

The height of the normal curve is given by

$$\frac{1}{\sigma \sqrt{(2\pi)}} \exp\left[-\frac{1}{2}\left(\frac{x-\mu}{\sigma}\right)^2\right]$$

and the area under a curve with this probability density function is equal to one for all values of μ and σ.

Fortunately we do not need to concern ourselves with this rather complicated formula because we are more concerned with the probability that a variable will lie within a certain range. So, what we need to know is the probability of x lying between two values x_1 and x_2. This could be calculated by evaluating the integral of the above function between x_1 and x_2 but this is quite difficult and so tables have been calculated for a normal distribution with a zero mean and standard deviation of one. This particular normal distribution is called the standard normal distribution and values are tabulated for the area under the curve up to a certain number of standard deviations beyond the mean (cumulative probability density function) or between the mean and a certain number of standard deviations beyond the mean. The tables printed in Appendix 5.1 at the end of this chapter are of the latter variety and give the probability that a variable distributed normally with zero mean and standard deviation of one will take a value between zero and a certain number of standard deviations above zero.

Location and shape of the normal distribution
The location of the normal distribution is governed by its mean.

The shape of a normal distribution is governed by its standard deviation, the larger the standard deviation the more dispersed will be the distribution.

Shaded areas in Diagram 5.11 represent the areas between the mean and a point 2 standard deviations above the mean. In both cases about 48% of the total area under the curve is contained between these two points.

No matter what the value of σ, the probability of a value lying between the mean and a point a certain number of standard deviations above (or below because the distribution is symmetrical) the mean is constant if the variable is normally distributed.

DIAGRAM 5.11

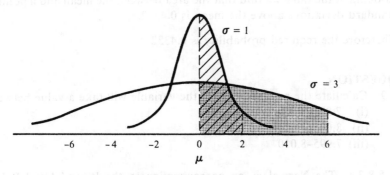

$$\frac{2}{3} \text{ rds of distribution is contained} \atop \text{in the area between the mean and}} \quad \pm 1 \, \sigma$$

95% . . . . $\pm 2 \, \sigma$

99.8% . . . . $\pm 3 \, \sigma$

Using the tables
Say we know that a variable is distributed normally with a mean of 8 and a standard deviation of 0.01 and we want to know the probability that the variable will take a value between 8 and 8.015.

i.e. $\mu = 8$
$\sigma = 0.01$ and we want to know the area between $x_1 = 8$ and $x_2 = 8.015$, the shaded area in Diagram 5.12.

DIAGRAM 5.12

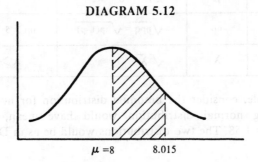

$\mu = 8$ 8.015

First we have to find out how many standard deviations away from the mean the point 8.015 lies.

Let z = the number of standard deviations above the mean that the point lies.

Then $z = \dfrac{8.015-8.000}{0.01} = 1.5$

i.e. $z = \dfrac{x - \mu}{\sigma}$ this is called the 'z-score' or standardized variable.

Looking at the table we find that the area between the mean and a point 1.5 standard deviations above the mean is 0.4332.

Therefore the required probability is 0.4332.

QUESTION
5.9 Calculate the probability that the variable will take a value between:
   (i)   7.875–8.000;
   (ii) 8.005–8.015; and
   (iii) 7.995–8.010

5.8.3.1 The Normal as an approximation to the Binomial and Poisson distributions

We mentioned earlier that calculating binomial or Poisson probabilities can become tedious. If we know the mean and standard deviation of a binomial, or Poisson, distribution we can use these as the parameters for the normal distribution and use the corresponding normal distribution to calculate the required probabilities.

The conditions under which it is reasonable to use a normal approximation are as follows:—

	Mean	Standard Deviation	Conditions for using a normal approximation
Normal	μ	σ	
Binomial	np	$\sqrt{npq} = \sqrt{np(1-p)}$	$np \geqslant 5$, $p > 0.1$ approx.
Poisson	λ	$\sqrt{\lambda}$	$\lambda > 10$ approx.

As an example, consider the binomial distribution for n=10, p=0.5. The corresponding normal distribution would have mean, μ =np=5 and $\sigma = \sqrt{npq} = 1.58$. The two distributions would be as in Diagram 5.13.

DIAGRAM 5.13

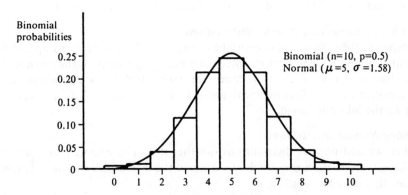

Binomial probabilities for n=10, p=0.5	
r	Prob.
0	0.0001
1	0.0098
2	0.0439
3	0.1172
4	0.2051
5	0.2461
6	0.2051
7	0.1172
8	0.0439
9	0.0098
10	0.0001

Consider, say, the binomial probability of 4 defectives in a sample of 10 where probability of defective is 0.5

$$\text{Binomial probability} = \frac{10!}{4!\ 6!}\ 0.5^4\ 0.5^6 = 0.2051$$

The normal distribution is continuous while the binomial is discrete, so we take 4 defectives as applying to the range 3.5 to 4.5 on the continuous scale. To find the required probability, we proceed as follows:—

$$Z_1 = \frac{3.5-5.0}{1.58} = -0.95 \quad : \quad A_1 = 0.3289$$

$$Z_2 = \frac{4.5-5.0}{1.58} = -0.32 \quad : \quad A_2 = 0.1255$$

The required probability is therefore $0.3289 - 0.1255 = 0.2034$.

So, the normal provides a good approximation to the binomial with the probability only differing at the third decimal place in this instance.

5.8.3.2 Combining Normal distributions

It can sometimes be useful to combine normal distributions; for example, if a number of jobs have to be performed sequentially and we know the mean and standard deviation of the time taken for each job then by combining the distributions we can find the mean and standard deviation of the time taken for all the jobs combined.

Adding Normal distributions:

When we add normal distributions together the mean and variance of the resultant distribution are simply the sums of the means and variances of the individual distributions.

$$\text{i.e.} \quad \mu = \mu_1 + \mu_2 + \mu_3 + \cdots$$

$$\text{and,} \quad \sigma^2 = \sigma_1^2 + \sigma_2^2 + \sigma_3^2 + \cdots.$$

Subtracting Normal distributions

When we subtract one normal distribution from another the mean of the resultant distribution is the difference between the individual means but the variance is the sum of the individual variances.

$$\text{i.e.} \quad \mu = \mu_1 - \mu_2$$

$$\sigma^2 = \sigma_1^2 + \sigma_2^2$$

These rules make sense if we consider a simple example.

Suppose we have a box containing steel rods with lengths distributed normally with a mean of 5′ and variance of 0.4′, and diameters distributed normally with a mean of 5″ and variance of 0.4″.

Suppose we also have another box containing rods with lengths distributed normally with a mean of 6′ and variance of 0.4′, and diameters distributed normally with a mean of 6″ and variance of 0.4″.

Now, suppose the rods are selected at random and one rod from one box is welded to one from the other box. The new rods would have lengths distributed normally with a mean of 5′ + 6′ = 11′ and variance of 0.4′ + 0.4′ = 0.8′. The differences in the diameters would again be distributed normally with a mean of 6″ – 5″ = 1″ and variance of 0.4″ + 0.4″ = 0.8″. In both cases, the variances have to be added. This is reasonably obvious in the case of the lengths but not in the case of the differences in the diameters.

To prove the point, consider two distributions with the characteristics mentioned above:—

Distribution 1		Distribution 2	
frequency	diameter (inches)	frequency	diameter (inches)
f	x	f	x
2	4	2	5
6	5	6	6
2	6	2	7

$\mu_1 = 5''$

$\sigma_1^2 = 0.4''$

$\mu_2 = 6''$

$\sigma_2^2 = 0.4''$

In a long series of trials, we would expect the following distribution to occur if we combined the two distributions:—

Combination	Number of ways combination can occur	Difference in diameters		
	f	x	fx	fx²
4 & 5	4	1	4	4
4 & 6	12	2	24	48
4 & 7	4	3	12	36
5 & 5	12	0	0	0
5 & 6	36	1	36	36
5 & 7	12	2	24	48
6 & 5	4	-1	-4	4
6 & 6	12	0	0	0
6 & 7	4	1	4	4
	$\Sigma f = 100$		$\Sigma fx = 100$	$\Sigma fx^2 = 180$

$$\text{Mean} = \mu = \frac{\Sigma fx}{\Sigma f} = \frac{100}{100} = 1 \qquad \text{i.e. } \mu_2 - \mu_1$$

$$\text{Variance} = \sigma^2 = \text{mean } x^2 - (\text{mean } x)^2 = \frac{180}{100} - 1^2 = 0.8 \text{ i.e. } \sigma_1^2 + \sigma_2^2$$

So the difference in diameters is distributed with a variance equal to the sum of the variances of the original distributions.

5.8.3.3 EXAMPLE

Your firm, Parry Blouses, is considering producing ladies' blouses and has asked you to consider what proportion of output should be put into each size category.

Market research indicates that women's chest measurements are distributed as follows:—

Chest measurement (inches)	Observed frequency
32–34	60
34–36	400
36–38	680
38–40	660
40–42	180
42–44	20

(a) Calculate the mean.

(b) Calculate the standard deviation.

(c) Assuming that the normal distribution is a good approximation to the distribution of chest measurements and that the blouses are to be manufactured with an allowance of 1″ so that, for example, a size 36″ will fit someone who measures $35\frac{1}{2}$–$36\frac{1}{2}$″, complete the table below.

CHEST (inches)	34	35	36	37	38	39	40	Under 34 Over 40
PROPORTION OF OUTPUT								

ANSWERS:-

CHEST MEASUREMENT (inches)	Mid-point of class (x)	frequency (f)	fx	fx²
32–34	33	60	1,980	65,340
34–36	35	400	14,000	490,000
36–38	37	680	25,160	930,920
38–40	39	660	25,740	1,003,860
40–42	41	180	7,380	302,580
42–44	43	20	860	36,980
		$\Sigma f = 2,000$	$\Sigma fx = 75,120$	$\Sigma fx^2 = 2,829,680$

(a) Mean $= \dfrac{\Sigma fx}{\Sigma f} = \dfrac{75120}{2000} = 37.56''$

(b) Standard deviation $= \sqrt{\dfrac{\Sigma fx^2}{\Sigma f} - \left(\dfrac{\Sigma fx}{\Sigma f}\right)^2} = \sqrt{\dfrac{2829680}{2000} - (37.56)^2}$

$= \sqrt{1414.84 - 1410.7536} = 2.02''$

(c) Assuming a mean of 37.5″ and a standard deviation of 2″, we can calculate the area under the normal curve between the mean and the class limits in the table:

x	Z value	Area under curve
33.5	-2	0.4772
34.5	-1.5	0.4332
35.5	-1	0.3413
36.5	-0.5	0.1915
37.5	0	0.0000
38.5	0.5	0.1915
39.5	1	0.3413
40.5	1.5	0.4332

We can now calculate the proportion in each class as below:—

Chest Measurement (inches)	Class interval (inches)	Proportion in each category		
34	33.5–34.5	0.4772–0.4332	= 0.0440 =	4.4%
35	34.5–35.5	0.4332–0.3413	= 0.0919 =	9.2%
36	35.5–36.5	0.3413–0.1915	= 0.1498 =	15%
37	36.5–37.5	0.1915–0.0000	= 0.1915 =	19.2%
38	37.5–38.5	etc.	=	19.2%
39	38.5–39.5		=	15%
40	39.5–40.5		=	9.2%
	> 40	0.5000–0.4332	= 0.0668 ⎫	
	< 33.5	0.5000–0.4772	= 0.0228 ⎭	= 9%
				100.2%

QUESTIONS — theoretical probability distributions

5.10 (a) A fair die with six sides is thrown three times. Show by means of a tree diagram that the probability of obtaining 0, 1, 2 or 3 sixes from the three throws is given by the binomial probability function:

$$\binom{3}{r}\left(\frac{1}{6}\right)^r\left(\frac{5}{6}\right)^{3-r}$$

where r represents the number of successes.

(b) A department produces a standard product. It is known that 60% of defective products can be satisfactorily reworked.

What is the probability that in a batch of five such defective products at least four can be satisfactorily reworked? *(ICMA)*

5.11 In an acceptance sampling scheme, a random sample of size 100 items is taken from a batch and inspected, and if it contains 3 or fewer defectives the batch is accepted without further inspection, and is said to have passed the sampling scheme. If the sample contains 4 or more defectives then all the remaining items in the batch are inspected and the batch is said to have failed the scheme.

Required:

(a) By using the Poisson distribution to calculate the probability of finding 0, 1, 2 and 3 defectives, determine the proportion of batches containing 2% defective items that will pass the acceptance sampling scheme.

(b) Show that the expected number of defectives found by the scheme in a batch containing 2% defectives that passes the scheme is approximately 1.6. By considering, in addition, those batches that fail the scheme, determine the expected number of defectives found in batches of size 2000 containing 2% defectives. *(ACA)*

5.12 A manufacturer wishes to produce a new line of men's leisure shirts in five sizes, ranging from 'extra small' to 'extra large', i.e. XS, S, M, L and XL. From previous experience it is expected that demand will follow a Normal distribution with a mean chest size of 90cms and a standard deviation of 10cms. For production reasons the manufacturer wishes to produce *equal* numbers of each size, subject to the restriction of catering for only the mean 95% of demand.

You are required to:

(a) Find the upper and lower limits (in centimetres) of each of the five sizes which will meet the manufacturer's requirements.

(16 marks)

(b) Explain *briefly* any advantages and disadvantages of trying to cater for the main 99% of demand, instead of the main 95%.

(4 marks)
(ICMA)

5.13 An assembly produced in large quantities is made up of three different components, A, B and C. The weight of each component is approximately normally distributed with mean and standard deviation as follows:

	Weight (pounds)	
Component	Mean	Standard deviation
A	3.0	0.2
B	2.5	0.2
C	6.0	0.4

Required:

(a) What proportion of assemblies
    (i) exceed 11.8 pounds?
    (ii) are between 11.4 and 11.7 pounds?

(b) Any assembly weighing more than 11.8 pounds is unsatisfactory and is scrapped. Determine the median weight of satisfactory assemblies.   *(ACA)*

5.14 An air charter company has been requested to quote a realistic turn-round time for a contract to handle certain imports and exports of a fragile nature.

The contracts manager has provided the management accountant with the following analysis of turn-round times for similar goods over a given twelve-monthly period.

Turn-round time in hours	Number of frequencies
Less than 2	25
2 and < 4	36
4 and < 6	66
6 and < 8	47
8 and < 10	26
10 and < 12	18
12 and < 14	2

You are required to:

(a) Calculate from the distribution given above:
    (i) the mean;   5·7
    (ii) the standard deviation. 2·9

(b) Advise the contracts manager of the turn-round time to be quoted using:
    (i) the mean plus one standard deviation;
    (ii) the mean plus two standard deviations;
    stating in each case the chance of success in meeting the turn-round time given.

(c)   Explain the merits and the demerits of the standard deviation as a form of measure.   *(ICMA)*

*5.15   A particular type of item is processed first on machine A and then on machine B. The times on each machine vary independently of each other and are normally distributed with a mean of 10.4 hours and standard deviation of 1.2 hours on A and with a mean of 12.6 hours and standard deviation of 1.8 hours on B.

Required:
(a) (i)   How long does it take for an average item to be processed on both A and B?
    (ii) What proportion of jobs take more than 11 hours on A?
    (iii) What proportion of jobs take more than 11 hours on A and less than 13 hours on B?

(b)   The sum of two variables which are each normally distributed is also normally distributed with a variance equal to the sum of the two individual variances. Use this fact to determine the proportion of jobs which take more than a combined time of 25 hours on the two machines.

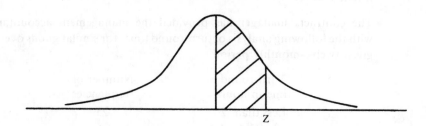

Proportion lying in shaded area of standard normal distribution.

Z	0.0	0.1	0.2	0.3	0.4	0.5	0.6	0.7	0.8	0.9
proportion	0.000	0.040	0.079	0.118	0.155	0.192	0.226	0.258	0.288	0.316
Z	1.0	1.1	1.2	1.3	1.4	1.5	1.6	1.7	1.8	1.9
proportion	0.341	0.364	0.385	0.403	0.419	0.433	0.445	0.455	0.464	0.471
Z	2.0	2.1	2.2	2.3	2.4	2.5	2.6	2.7	2.8	2.9
proportion	0.477	0.482	0.486	0.489	0.492	0.494	0.495	0.496	0.497	0.498

(20 marks)
(ACA)

*5.16 (a) Bus Hire Limited has two coaches which it hires out for local use by the day. The number of demands for a coach on each day is distributed as a Poisson distribution, with a mean of two demands.
  (i) On what proportion of days is neither coach used?
  (ii) On what proportion of days is at least one demand refused?
  (iii) If each coach is used an equal amount, on what proportion of days is **one** particular coach not in use?

(b) Steel rods are manufactured to a specification of 20cm. length and are acceptable only if they are within the limits of 19.9cm. and 20.1cm. If the lengths are normally distributed, with mean 20.02cm and standard deviation 0.05cm, find the percentage of rods which will be rejected as (i) undersize and (ii) oversize.

(ICMA)

APPENDIX 5.1

NORMAL DISTRIBUTION

The table gives the area under the normal curve between the mean and a point z standard deviations above the mean.

z	.00	.01	.02	.03	.04	.05	.06	.07	.08	.09
0.0	.0000	.0040	.0080	.0120	.0160	.0199	.0239	.0279	.0319	.0359
0.1	.0398	.0438	.0478	.0517	.0557	.0596	.0636	.0675	.0714	.0753
0.2	.0793	.0832	.0871	.0910	.0948	.0987	.1026	.1064	.1103	.1141
0.3	.1179	.1217	.1255	.1293	.1331	.1368	.1406	.1443	.1480	.1517
0.4	.1554	.1591	.1628	.1664	.1700	.1736	.1772	.1808	.1844	.1879
0.5	.1915	.1950	.1985	.2019	.2054	.2088	.2123	.2157	.2190	.2224
0.6	.2257	.2291	.2324	.2357	.2389	.2422	.2454	.2486	.2517	.2549
0.7	.2580	.2611	.2642	.2673	.2704	.2734	.2764	.2794	.2823	.2852
0.8	.2881	.2910	.2939	.2967	.2995	.3023	.3051	.3078	.3106	.3133
0.9	.3159	.3186	.3212	.3238	.3264	.3289	.3315	.3340	.3365	.3389
1.0	.3413	.3438	.3461	.3485	.3508	.3531	.3554	.3577	.3599	.3621
1.1	.3643	.3665	.3686	.3708	.3729	.3749	.3770	.3790	.3810	.3830
1.2	.3849	.3869	.3888	.3907	.3925	.3944	.3962	.3980	.3997	.4015
1.3	.4032	.4040	.4066	.4082	.4099	.4115	.4131	.4147	.4162	.4177
1.4	.4192	.4207	.4222	.4236	.4251	.4265	.4279	.4292	.4306	.4319
1.5	.4332	.4345	.4357	.4370	.4382	.4394	.4406	.4418	.4429	.4441
1.6	.4452	.4463	.4474	.4484	.4495	.4505	.4515	.4525	.4535	.4545
1.7	.4554	.4564	.4573	.4582	.4591	.4599	.4608	.4616	.4625	.4633
1.8	.4641	.4649	.4656	.4664	.4671	.4678	.4686	.4693	.4699	.4706
1.9	.4713	.4719	.4726	.4732	.4738	.4744	.4750	.4756	.4761	.4767
2.0	.4772	.4778	.4783	.4788	.4793	.4798	.4803	.4808	.4812	.4817
2.1	.4821	.4826	.4830	.4834	.4838	.4842	.4846	.4580	.4854	.4857
2.2	.4861	.4864	.4868	.4871	.4875	.4878	.4881	.4884	.4887	.4890
2.3	.4893	.4896	.4898	.4901	.4904	.4906	.4909	.4911	.4913	.4916
2.4	.4918	.4920	.4922	.4925	.4927	.4929	.4931	.4932	.4934	.4936
2.5	.4938	.4940	.4941	.4943	.4945	.4946	.4948	.4949	.4951	.4952
2.6	.4953	.4955	.4956	.4957	.4959	.4960	.4961	.4962	.4963	.4964
2.7	.4965	.4966	.4967	.4968	.4969	.4970	.4971	.4972	.4973	.4974
2.8	.4974	.4975	.4976	.4977	.4977	.4978	.4979	.4979	.4980	.4981
2.9	.4981	.4982	.4982	.4983	.4984	.4984	.4985	.4985	.4986	.4986
3.0	.4987	.4987	.4987	.4988	.4988	.4989	.4989	.4989	.4990	.4990

Chapter 6
ESTIMATION

In the example, Parry Blouse Company, at the end of the last chapter, the manufacturer wanted to know the average chest measurement of the adult female population and the standard deviation.

It would, of course, be out of the question to measure the entire female population and so we would have to rely on an estimate. Therefore, we would take a sample and use the sample mean, $\bar{x}$, as an estimate of the population mean, μ. Similarly, we would take the standard deviation of the sample, s, to be an estimate of the population standard deviation, σ.

Now the value of $\bar{x}$, for example, will vary from sample to sample and when we use a sample statistic as an estimate of a population parameter we need to know how large any variation is likely to be. When we express our estimate of a population parameter by a single number it is called a point estimate and when we say that the population parameter lies between two numbers this is called an interval estimate.

6.1 Accuracy, bias, and precision

Let us consider a small scale population; suppose we are interested in the average chest size of just four ladies and that their actual chest measurements are 36″, 37″, 38″, and 39″ so that the population mean chest measurement is 37.5″.

Now suppose we take a sample of two and they turn out to be 36″ and 37″, our sample mean, and estimate of the population mean, would be 36.5″ which is **inaccurate**. The accuracy of a sample estimate is simply the difference between the estimate and the true population value. Of course, we would not usually know the true population value — that is why we are taking a sample — and so we would not normally be able to gauge the accuracy of our estimate. However, we may be able to judge the probable accuracy, or precision, of the estimate as we shall see below.

The particular statistic that we use to estimate a population parameter is called an **estimator;** so we often use a sample mean as an estimator of the population mean. If the expected value of the estimator is equal to the population parameter we say that the estimator is **unbiased.** The expected value of an estimator is the average value of the estimates that we would get from an infinite number of samples.

In the small scale model above, if we took an infinite number of samples of size two, the distribution of the values of the sample means obtained (the sampling distribution of the mean) would have a mean of 37.5″ because each of the four values would, in the long run, occur an equal number of times. Thus, we would say that the sample mean was an unbiased estimator of the population mean.

On the other hand, if because of the method of sampling, or the method of estimation, the expected value of the estimator did not equal the population parameter we would say the estimator was biased. Say, for example, for some reason we never selected the lady with the 36″ chest, the expected value of the estimator (the sample mean) would be 38″ and the estimator would be biased. However, if a particular sample consisted of two ladies measuring 37″ and 38″ then our **estimate** from that sample would be 37.5″ which is accurate even though our **estimator** is biased.

If we consider all the possible samples of size two that we could select from our population, and calculate the sample means, they would be:

Sample	$\bar{x}$
36″ & 37″	36.5
36 & 38	37.0
36 & 39	37.5
37 & 38	37.5
37 & 39	38.0
38 & 39	38.5

So only two out of the six possible samples give an accurate estimate of the population parameter. Fortunately, this is not so worrying as it first appears because if we know how the sample statistic is distributed (in this case the sample mean) we can state the probable accuracy, or precision, of the estimate.

Ideally, we would like our estimates to be clustered around the true value of the population parameter with little variation between the estimates; in other words we would like the standard deviation of the sample statistic to be small (the standard deviation of the distribution of a sample statistic, such as the sample mean, is usually called the standard error). Also, we would want our estimator to be unbiased and so we would always try to use a minimum variance unbiased estimator.

To be able to state the precision of an estimate we need to know more about the distribution of the sample statistic that we are using as our estimator. There are several statistics that we might be interested in but we shall limit our discussion to the sample mean, which is by far the most important, and the proportion which can be very useful. The formulae that we mention below refer to any randomly selected sample provided that the sample is fairly large (more than about 30) and similar formulae can be developed for smaller samples and other statistics.

6.2 Sampling distribution of the mean
Central limit theorem*

If random samples, size n, are taken from a distribution with mean μ and standard deviation σ, the sampling distribution of the sample mean, $\bar{x}$, will be approximately normal with mean μ and standard deviation $\sigma/\sqrt{n}$, and the approximation will improve as n increases.

This is probably the most important result in Statistics and it is certainly most convenient, it means that even if the original population distribution is not normal the sampling distribution of the mean will be normal, or very nearly so, provided the sample is fairly large (about 30). Also, the standard deviation of the sampling distribution of the mean (usually called the standard error of the mean) will be smaller than the standard deviation of the parent population, as illustrated in Diagram 6.1.

DIAGRAM 6.1

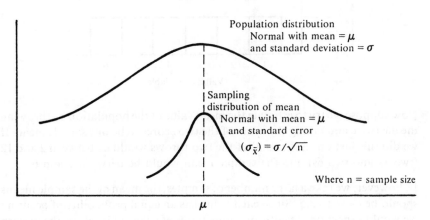

If you think about it, the Central Limit Theorem is not at all unreasonable; obviously some of the sample means will differ from the population mean but if you take a large number of samples the average of the sample means will approach the population mean. So, in our example above concerning chest measurements, we would expect in the long run roughly equal numbers of sample means equal to 36.5", 37", 37.5", 37.5" again, 38", and 38.5" and the mean of these sample means would be 37.5" which is the population mean. Similarly, the standard error will be smaller than the standard deviation of the population because taking a sample mean averages out extreme values. So, in our example above, the range of chest measurements is 36–39" but the range of sample means is 36.5–38.5".

---

*For proof of Central Limit Theorem see, for example, "Introduction to Mathematical Statistics" – P.G. Hoel.

The standard error is equal to $\sigma/\sqrt{n}$ where σ is the standard deviation of the population and n is the sample size; this again accords with common sense — the more variation there is in the population distribution the more one would expect in the sample and the bigger the sample the less one would expect the estimate to deviate from the true population parameter.

To illustrate the fact that the sampling distribution of the mean will be normal even if the original distribution is not normal, consider the following example.

Say we throw a fair die, each number has an equal probability of occuring. The probability distribution is therefore a discrete uniform, or rectangular, distribution with the probability of any of the values occuring being equal to 1/6. The mean, or expected value, of the variable in a long series of trials would be 3.5.

DIAGRAM 6.2

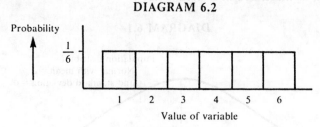

Now suppose we try to estimate the mean value of the population by throwing the die twice and taking the mean of the two scores to be our sample mean. If we did this just once, the total of the two throws would be between 2 and 12 (two 1s and two 6s) and the sample mean would be between 1 and 6.

If, however, we take a large number of samples, the mean of the sample means should be close to 3.5. Since each value has an equal probability of occuring we would expect our results, in a long series of trials, to be along the pattern indicated below:

Sample total	Sample mean	Number of ways of getting sample mean
2	1.0	1
3	1.5	2
4	2.0	3
5	2.5	4
6	3.0	5
7	3.5	6
8	4.0	5
9	4.5	4
10	5.0	3
11	5.5	2
12	6.0	1
		36

A sample total of 4, for example, would be obtained with a 1 on the first throw and a three on the second, or vice versa, or two 2s. So there are three ways of getting a total of 4.

So in a long series of trials we would expect the sample means to be distributed roughly in proportion to the number of ways of getting the particular sample means and the distribution of the sample means would be as in Diagram 6.3.

DIAGRAM 6.3

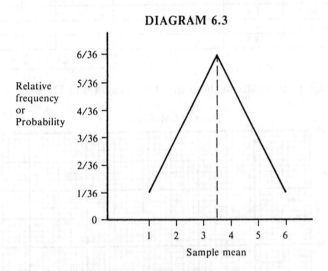

It is not quite a normal distribution yet but it is getting closer. Moreover, the mean of the sampling distribution of the mean is 3.5 which is the same as the population mean and there is less deviation from the mean than in the parent rectangular distribution.

6.2.1 EXPERIMENT
(a) Try a slightly larger sample. Throw a die ten times (still a small sample size) and calculate the sample mean (to one decimal place of course). Repeat the process, let's say, fifty times and enter the sample means in the table, 6.1.

TABLE 6.1

Sample means

(b) Now summarise the results into a grouped frequency distribution using Table 6.2.

TABLE 6.2

Class interval	Mid-point x	'tally marks'	frequency f	fx	fx²
1 — under 2	1.5				
2 — under 3	2.5				
3 — under 4	3.5				
4 — under 5	4.5				
5 — 6	5.5				

$\Sigma f = 50 \quad \Sigma fx = \quad \Sigma fx^2 =$

(c) Now plot your results in the form of a histogram in Diagram 6.4.

DIAGRAM 6.4

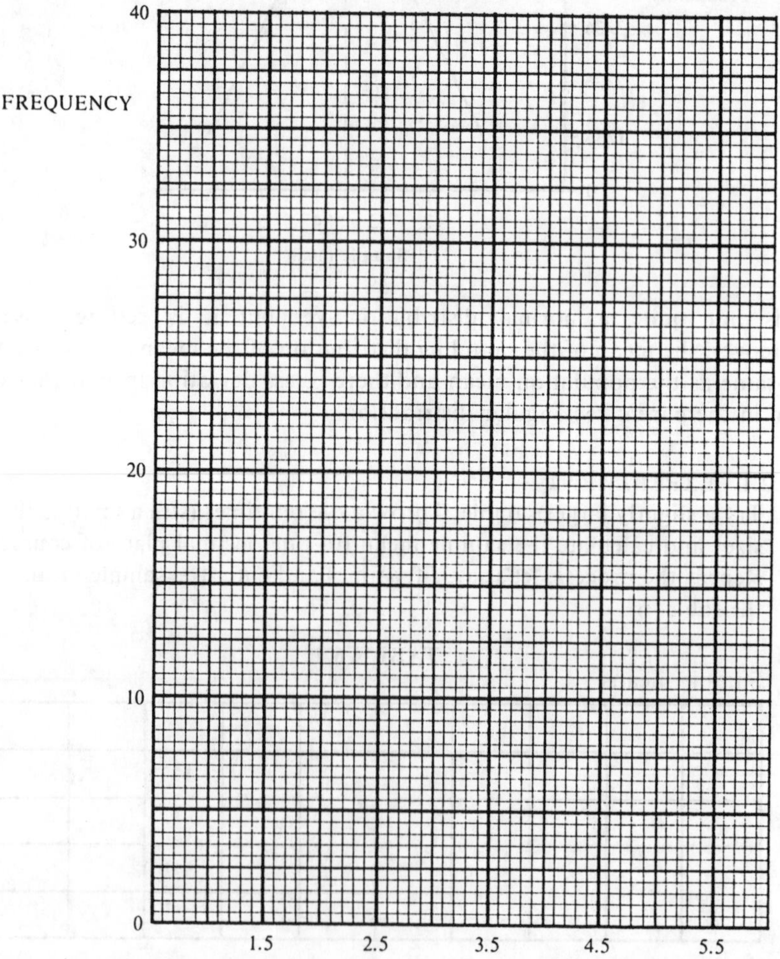

FREQUENCY

(d) Calculate the mean and standard deviation of the distribution of sample means:

Mean, $\bar{x} = \dfrac{\Sigma fx}{\Sigma f} = $ (theoretical value = 3.5)

Standard deviation $= \sqrt{\text{mean } x^2 - (\text{mean } x)^2} = \sqrt{\dfrac{\Sigma fx^2}{\Sigma f} - \left(\dfrac{\Sigma fx}{\Sigma f}\right)^2}$

(theoretical value for standard deviation of the original distribution is 1.708 therefore standard error $\left(\dfrac{\sigma}{\sqrt{n}}\right)$ should be $\doteq \dfrac{1.708}{\sqrt{10}} = .54$).

The results obtained by one student are shown in Appendix 6.1 but try the experiment for yourself.

6.2.3 Estimating the population mean

Armed with the knowledge that the sample means follow a normal distribution, we are able to state the probable accuracy, or precision, of an estimate of the population mean based upon a single sample mean.

DIAGRAM 6.5

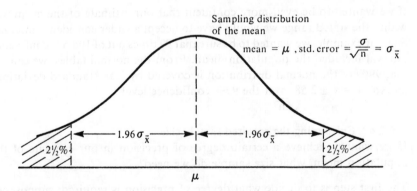

We know that for fairly large samples the sample means follow a normal distribution with a mean, μ, equal to the population mean and a standard deviation, or standard error, equal to $\sigma/\sqrt{n}$ where σ is the standard deviation of the population and n is the sample size.

From the normal tables, we know that 95% of a normal distribution is contained within 1.96 standard deviations (standard errors when talking about a sample statistic) of its mean.

Therefore, we can be 95% certain that any particular sample mean, $\bar{x}$, is within 1.96 standard errors of the population mean μ.

i.e. $\quad \mu = \bar{x} \pm 1.96 \dfrac{\sigma}{\sqrt{n}} \qquad$ at the 95% confidence level

and the extreme values $\bar{x} + 1.96 \dfrac{\sigma}{\sqrt{n}}$ and $\bar{x} - 1.96 \dfrac{\sigma}{\sqrt{n}}$ constitute

the 95% confidence interval for the mean.

There is one problem remaining and that is that we would not usually know the standard deviation of the population. To overcome this problem we use s, the standard deviation, calculated from the sample, as an estimate of σ, the standard deviation of the population. As long as our sample size is reasonably large (>30) this will give a good approximation and our formula becomes

$$\mu = \bar{x} \pm 1.96 \dfrac{s}{\sqrt{n}} \quad \text{at the 95% confidence level.}$$

In other words, 19 times out of 20 we would expect our sample mean to be within 1.96 standard errors of the population mean. How precise the estimate is (how wide the confidence interval is for any particular confidence level) depends upon the variability in the population, which will be reflected in the standard error in the sample, and on the sample size (the bigger the sample size the more precise will be our estimate).

If we wanted to be even more confident that our estimate of the mean was within the stated range we would have to accept a wider confidence interval. Say, for example, we wanted to be sure that 99 times out of 100 our confidence interval included the population mean. From the normal tables, we can see that 99% of the normal distribution is covered by 2.58 standard deviations and so $\mu = \bar{x} \pm 2.58 \dfrac{s}{\sqrt{n}}$ at the 99% confidence level.

6.2.4 Calculating the required sample size

If we want to achieve a certain degree of precision in our estimate of the population mean, what size sample do we need?

The first step is to decide what degree of precision is required; suppose we want to be 95% confident that the population mean falls within the stated confidence interval, we know that 95% of the time the sample mean will be within 1.96 standard deviations of the population mean.

i.e. $\quad \mu = \bar{x} \pm 1.96 \dfrac{\sigma}{\sqrt{n}}.$

The width of the confidence interval depends upon the variability in the data and the size of the sample. If we want the width of the confidence interval to be, for example, $\pm W$ then $\pm W = \pm 1.96 \dfrac{\sigma}{\sqrt{n}}$ or approximately $\pm W = \pm \dfrac{2\sigma}{\sqrt{n}}$

Again, we would not know the value of σ so we would have to do a small survey to get an estimate s. Then $\pm W = \pm \dfrac{2s}{\sqrt{n}}$

Therefore $W^2 = 4s^2/n$

and $n = \dfrac{4s^2}{W^2}$ would be the required sample size at the 95% confidence level.

6.3 Sampling distribution of proportion

A very common problem is that of estimating a population proportion (π) from a simple random sample where P is the proportion in the sample. We might, for example, be interested in what proportion of the population will vote in a certain way at the next election, or what proportion of items in a batch are likely to be defective, etc.

Once again, for a large sample, the sampling proportion will be normally distributed with a mean equal to the true population proportion but, if we took just one sample, we would have a problem in deciding how precise our estimate of the population proportion will be. If we have only one sample estimate of the proportion, how do we calculate the standard error? All we would know is that, say, 50% of the sample intend voting Labour at the next election. We are dealing with a dichotomous variable — people either intend voting Labour or they do not — the variable can only take two values. If you think back, this was the situation that we encountered when we discussed the binomial distribution.

The mean of the binomial distribution $\mu = n \cdot p$
and the standard deviation $\sigma = \sqrt{npq}$ or $\sqrt{np(1-p)}$
where p = probability of a "success" in a single trial, and
n = sample size.

Now, if we think of, π, the proportion of items in a certain category (eg. labour voters) in the population as being equal to the probability of a "success", then the mean will be

$\mu = n\pi$ and the standard deviation will be $\sigma = \sqrt{n\pi(1-\pi)}$.
But the mean and standard deviation will be expressed in terms of a number of items and if we want the mean proportion and standard deviation as a proportion we will have to divide by n so that

$$\mu = \dfrac{1}{n} \times n\pi = \pi \qquad \text{and}$$

$$\sigma = \dfrac{1}{n}\sqrt{n\pi(1-\pi)} = \sqrt{\dfrac{\pi(1-\pi)}{n}}$$

Of course, π is the very thing we are trying to estimate and so we have to use P, the sample proportion, to estimate it and the formulae become

$$\text{population proportion, } \pi = P$$

$$\text{Standard error of proportion, } \sigma_{prop} = \sqrt{\frac{P(1-P)}{n}}$$

where P = sample proportion

N.B. If you are working in percentages P(1-P) becomes P(100-P)

6.3.1 Estimating a proportion

Since the sample proportion follows a normal distribution we can again attach confidence intervals to our estimate of the proportion.

$$\text{e.g.} \quad \pi = P \pm 1.96 \sqrt{\frac{P(1-P)}{n}} \qquad \text{at the 95\% confidence level.}$$

6.3.2 Calculating the required sample size

Assuming again that we want to be 95% sure that the population proportion falls within the stated confidence interval and that ±W is the amount of error in the proportion that we are willing to tolerate then

$$\pm W = \pm 2 \sqrt{\frac{P(1-P)}{n}} \quad \text{approx.} \qquad \text{and}$$

$$n = \frac{4P(1-P)}{W^2} \quad \text{at the 95\% confidence level.}$$

Once again, however, in order to calculate the required sample size we need to have prior knowledge of the population proportion (π) or some estimate from a sample (P). If we do not have such information then it is worth noting that P(100-P) is at its maximum value when P=50% (or $\frac{1}{2}$) and so P=50 can be substituted in the equation to find the maximum sample size given the degree of precision and accuracy required. If the proportion turns out to be very different from 50% then too large a sample will have been taken and so it is much better to do a small sample survey, if other information is not available, to get an estimate of the proportion.

It is certainly not intuitively obvious that you need a larger sample to estimate a proportion of 50% than to estimate a proportion of, say, 10% with the same accuracy and precision. For example, if we wanted to be within 1% of a true population proportion of 50%, at the 95% confidence level, we would need a sample of size $\frac{4.50(100-50)}{1^2}$ = 10,000 compared to one of 3,600 to estimate a proportion of 10% with similar accuracy.

But, if you think about it, a confidence interval of 50% ± 1% in a sample of 10,000 means that the number in the category of interest can lie in the range 5,000 ± 100 whilst a confidence interval of 10% ± 1% in a sample of 3,600 means that the number can lie in the range 360 ± 36. In a sample of 10,000 a proportion of 10% would give a number of 1,000 at confidence limits of ± 100.

QUESTIONS — ESTIMATION

6.1 A sample of 64 TV tubes lasted on average 18,000 hours with a standard deviation of 1200. What are the 95% confidence limits for the average life of the tubes?

6.2 The average IQ of a sample of 36 students from a large college is 110 with a standard deviation of 12. How accurately does this estimate the average IQ of all students? [Use 95% confidence limits]
How many more students must be tested in order to ensure that the estimate is not more than 2 points out with 99% confidence?

*6.3 A mail-order company is analysing a random sample of its computer records of customers. Among the results are the following distributions:

Size of Order	Number of customers	
£	April	September
Less than 1	8	4
1 and less than 5	19	18
5 and less than 10	38	39
10 and less than 15	40	69
15 and less than 20	22	41
20 and less than 30	13	20
30 and over	4	5
Total	144	196

You are required to:
(a) Calculate the arithmetic mean and standard deviation order size for the *April* sample;   *(10 marks)*
(b) Find 95% confidence limits for the overall mean order size for the *April* customers and explain their meaning;   *(6 marks)*
(c) Compare the two distributions, given that the arithmetic mean and standard deviation for the September sample were £13.28 and £7.05 respectively.   *(4 marks)*
                                                  (Total 20 marks)
                                                  (ICMA)

APPENDIX 6.1

Below are the results obtained by a student for the experiment mentioned in section 6.2.1.

(a)
Sample means

3.6	5.3	3.9	4.1	3.6	3.3	3.1	4.1	3.6	3.9
3.3	5.0	2.6	3.6	4.2	3.6	3.1	4.3	4.2	2.6
3.1	3.3	3.9	3.7	3.4	4.5	3.3	4.2	3.4	3.9
2.5	3.2	3.3	2.3	3.1	3.2	2.9	2.9	3.3	3.4
2.7	3.6	2.9	2.9	3.9	4.3	4.5	3.6	3.2	3.3

(b)

Class interval	Mid-point x	'tally marks'	frequency f	fx	fx²
1 – under 2	1.5		0	0	0
2 – under 3	2.5	++++ 1111	9	22.5	56.25
3 – under 4	3.5	++++ ++++ ++++ ++++ ++++ ++++	30	105	367.50
4 – under 5	4.5	++++ 1111	9	40.5	182.25
5 – 6	5.5	11	2	11	60.50
			$\Sigma f=50$	$\Sigma fx=179$	$\Sigma fx^2=666.50$

(c)

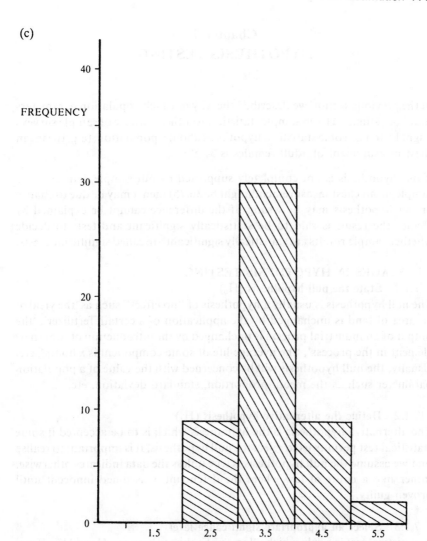

(d)

Mean, $\bar{x} = \dfrac{\Sigma fx}{\Sigma f} = \dfrac{179}{50} = 3.58$ (theoretical value = 3.5)

Standard deviation $= \sqrt{\text{mean } x^2 - (\text{mean } x)^2} = \sqrt{\dfrac{\Sigma fx^2}{\Sigma f} - \left(\dfrac{\Sigma fx}{\Sigma f}\right)^2}$

(theoretical value is 0.54)

$= \sqrt{\dfrac{666.5}{50} - \left(\dfrac{179}{50}\right)^2} = 0.717$

Chapter 7
HYPOTHESIS TESTING

In the previous section we described the way in which population parameters could be estimated from sample statistics. Another purpose of sample surveys might be to test some statistical hypothesis about a population, (e.g. the mean chest measurement of adult females is 37.5").

If our hypothesis is not completely supported by our sample data (e.g. our sample mean chest measurement might be 36.75) then it may be due to chance or our hypothesis may be wrong. If the difference cannot be explained by chance the result is said to be statistically significant and tests to decide whether sample results are statistically significant are called significance tests.

7.1 STAGES IN HYPOTHESIS TESTING
7.1.1 State the null hypothesis (H_0)
The null hypothesis is usually a hypothesis of "no effect" such as 'the yield of an area of land is unchanged by the application of a certain fertilizer', 'the output of an industrial process is unchanged by the introduction of some new element in the process', 'the average life of some component is x hours', etc. Usually, the null hypothesis will be concerned with the value of a population parameter such as the mean, proportion, standard deviation, etc.

7.1.2 Define the alternative hypothesis (H_1)
The alternative hypothesis is the hypothesis which is to be accepted if some statistical test permits us to reject the null hypothesis. It is important to realise that we assume the null hypothesis is true unless the data indicates otherwise, rather like a court of law where the defendant is assumed innocent until proven guilty.

7.1.3 Select an appropriate significance level
A statistical test is a **rule** which allows us to choose between H_0 and H_1. If our test statistic falls within the 'critical region' of the test then this leads to the rejection of H_0 and the probability of this happening by chance is the level of significance.

For example, if a certain variable follows a normal distribution with a mean, μ_0, of 37.5 and standard deviation of 2.0, μ_0 being the current estimate of the true population mean μ, our null hypothesis might be
$$H_0 : \mu = 37.5.$$
Now, we may believe that for some reason the mean value has changed and our alternative hypothesis might be
$$H_1 : \mu \neq 37.5$$

If H_0 is true, we know that the sampling distribution of the mean will be a normal distribution with mean μ_0 and standard error $\sigma_{\bar{x}} = \sigma /\sqrt{n}$ where σ = population standard deviation and n = sample size.

Now if we take a sample, we need to decide what difference between our sample mean, $\bar{x}$, and μ_0 would be large enough to justify rejecting H_0.

If we decide upon a 5% significance level, there is only a 5% probability of getting a sample mean more than 1.96 standard errors away from the true mean. If our sample mean does fall more than 1.96 standard errors from the mean, μ_0, (in the critical region) then we say that the result is significant at the 5% level and we reject the null hypothesis that the true mean equals μ_0. This is illustrated in Diagram 7.1.

DIAGRAM 7.1

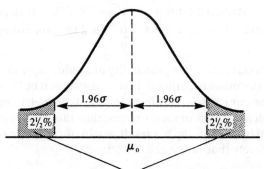

Critical regions of two-tailed test at 5% significance level.

If the sample mean was more than 2.58 standard errors from μ_0 we would say that the result was significant at the 1% level. This would be even more conclusive evidence that the null hypothesis was not true, illustrated in Diagram 7.2.

DIAGRAM 7.2

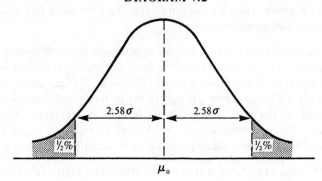

Critical regions of two-tailed test at 1% significance level

So, if we took a sample of size 50, the standard error would be $\sigma/\sqrt{n} = 2/\sqrt{50} = 0.28$ and if our sample mean was more than $1.96 \times 0.28 = 0.55$ away from μ_0 (37.5) we would reject the null hypothesis that the true population mean was 37.5 (at the 5% significance level).

The critical values, the values which must be equalled or exceeded if H_0 is to be rejected, would be $37.5 + 0.55$ and $37.5 - 0.55$. Values greater or less than these would fall in the critical region and lead to the rejection of the null hypothesis.

5% and 1% are commonly used significance levels and one should decide before taking any observations what level of significance is appropriate to reject H_0. However, it is useful to know whether or not the observed result is only just or well inside the critical region. So, say we find a sample mean of 36.75 from our sample of size 50.

$$\bar{x} - \mu_0 = 37.5 - 36.75 = 0.75$$

and our standard error $= \sigma/\sqrt{n} = 2/\sqrt{50} = 0.28$ as before.

This means that our sample mean is $\dfrac{0.75}{0.28} = 2.68$ standard errors below μ_0.

From our Normal tables, the probability of a value more than 2.68 standard errors **below** the mean occuring is $1.000 - 0.9963 = 0.0037$ or 0.37% and we would say that our result is significant at the 0.37% level. In other words, if H_0 is true, a result as extreme or more extreme than this would only occur about 4 times in 1,000 by chance. Such a result would of course be significant at the 5% and 1% levels (but not at the 0.1% level).

7.1.3.1 Types of error and choice of significance level

In testing any null hypothesis, H_0, against any alternative, H_1, there are two possible types of error that may occur:—

Type 1 error — deciding in favour of H_1 when H_0 is true.
Type 2 error — deciding in favour of H_0 when H_1 is true.

The numbering of error types is **not arbitrary,** a type 1 error is always rejecting the null hypothesis when it is true and a type 2 error always refers to accepting an incorrect null hypothesis.

Deciding upon the appropriate level of significance depends upon which is the more serious type of error. If rejecting the null hypothesis when it is true is the more serious type of error then we might choose a 1% significance level so that there is only a 1% chance of wrongly rejecting a true null hypothesis. On the other hand, if the type 2 error is more serious we might choose a 5% significance level so that we are 5 times more likely to reject a true null hypothesis but correspondingly less likely to accept a false null hypothesis.

If, say, the null hypothesis is that a new drug has no harmful side effects, we would be concerned to attach a great deal of importance to the type 2 error because if our null hypothesis is incorrect it could have disastrous results. On the other hand, a type 1 error is also important in such a situation because if the new drug is judged to have harmful side effects when it does not then people who could benefit from using the drug will be prevented from doing so. If we choose a high significance level (a low number like 1% as opposed to 5%) we reduce the probability of a type 1 error but increase the probability of a type 2 error and we have to decide upon the appropriate level according to the cost of each type of wrong decision.

7.1.3.2 One-tailed and two-tailed tests

A test which takes account of departures from the null hypothesis in only one direction is called a "one-sided" or "one-tailed" test. A test in which departures in either direction are important is called a "two-sided" or "two-tailed" test.

We must decide **before** taking any observations which type of test is appropriate. Usually, this will be fairly obvious; if we wish to test whether a coin is biased we would use a two-tailed test because we would be interested in detecting significant differences in the number of heads **or** tails; on the other hand, if we were concerned as to whether a change in production methods had significantly **increased** output, a one-tailed test would be appropriate.

For tests based upon the normal distribution, the significance level of a particular result on a two-tailed test is half that for a one-tailed test, i.e. if a result is just significant at the 5% level on a one-tailed test it is just significant at the 10% level on a two-tailed test.

DIAGRAM 7.3

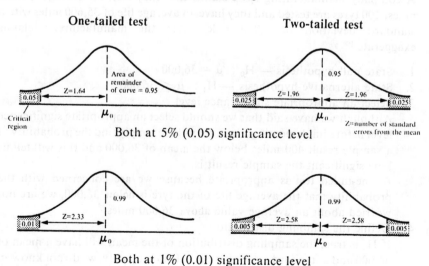

One-tailed test

Area of remainder of curve = 0.95

$Z=1.64$

0.05

μ_0

Critical region

Two-tailed test

0.95

0.025 $Z=1.96$ $Z=1.96$ 0.025

μ_0

Z=number of standard errors from the mean

Both at 5% (0.05) significance level

0.99

$Z=2.33$

0.01

μ_0

0.99

0.005 $Z=2.58$ $Z=2.58$ 0.005

μ_0

Both at 1% (0.01) significance level

7.1.4 Define the sampling distribution

If the null hypothesis is assumed to be true, then our sampling distribution is defined. For example, if H_0 is that the mean of our distribution is 37.5 then the sampling distribution of the mean will follow a normal distribution with a mean of 37.5 if H_0 is true. If we know the population standard deviation, σ, we can find the standard error of the sampling distribution of the mean as $\sigma/\sqrt{n}$ if we do not know σ then we can use our sample standard deviation, s, as an estimate of σ so long as our sample is larger than about 25. If our sample size is less than 25, s is not such a good estimate of σ and we would have to use the t-distribution which is more spread out than the normal distribution.

The significance level that we have decided upon defines the critical region for our test and if our test statistic falls into this region the null hypothesis will be rejected.

7.1.5 Calculate the test statistic and determine its position in the sampling distribution

If our test statistic falls in the critical region the null hypothesis is rejected and the result is said to be significant at the appropriate level.

If the test statistic does not fall in the critical region, it does not mean that H_0 is true; it merely means that there is insufficient evidence to reject it. To use a legal analogy again, it is a case of 'not proven' rather than 'not guilty'.

7.2 WORKED EXAMPLES

1. Testing a population mean

A company manufacturing tyres claims that they last, on average, 36,000 miles. 100 tyres are tested and they have an average life of 35,600 miles with a standard deviation of 1,200 miles. Are the manufacturer's claims exaggerated?

1. State null hypothesis — $H_0 : \mu = 36,000$
2. State alternative hypothesis — $H_1 : \mu < 36,000$
3. Select an appropriate significance level
   Although we have said that we should select an appropriate significance level before implementing a test, let us here simply find the probability of a sample result 400 miles below the mean of 36,000 and this will tell us how significant the sample result is.
   A one-tailed test is appropriate because we are concerned with the probability that the average life of the tyre is **below** 36,000, we are not worried about an average value **above** 36,000 miles.
4. Define the sampling distribution
   If H_0 is true, the sampling distribution of the mean will have a mean of 36,000 and a standard error of $\sigma/\sqrt{n}$. Unfortunately, we do not know σ

but the sample is large enough for us to use the standard deviation as an estimate so the standard error $= \dfrac{s}{\sqrt{n}} = \dfrac{1200}{\sqrt{100}} = 120$ miles.

5. Calculate the test statistic
    We need to know the probability of a sample mean value of 35,600 occuring if the true population mean is 36,000 so we find the Z-value.

$$Z = \frac{\bar{x} - \mu}{\sigma_{\bar{x}}} = \frac{35600 - 36000}{120} = -3.33$$

The probability of a value between 36000 and 35,600 occuring (i.e. the probability of a value up to 3.33 standard errors below the mean) is 0.4988 and so a value of 35600, or less, has a probability of occuring of $0.5 - 0.4988 = 0.0012$ or 0.12%, i.e. $\Pr(\bar{x} \leqslant 35600) = \Pr(Z \geqslant 3.33) = 0.0012$.

So, for a sample of size 100, we would only expect a sample mean of 35,600, or less, to occur 12 times out of 10,000 if the true mean is 36,000. The sample result is therefore significant at the 0.12% level, i.e. it is significant at the 5% and 1% levels but not at the 0.1% level. On this basis, it seems reasonable to reject H_0 and the manufacturer's claims are exaggerated.

2.   Testing a population percentage

The manager of a despatch department maintains that 80% of orders are sent off within four days of receipt of the order. A sample of 100 orders is taken and it is found that only 70% are despatched within four days. Does this prove that the manager is wrong in his assertion?

1. $H_0 : \pi = 80\%$
2. $H_1 : \pi < 80\%$
3. Obviously we are going to use a one-tailed test because we are interested only in the possibility that the level of efficiency is below that specified. Since no significance level is mentioned in the question let us simply calculate the probability that the sample result could be 10% or more below the 80% and this will tell us the significance level of the sample result.
4. If H_0 is true, the sampling proportion will be distributed normally with a mean of 80% and a standard error of $\sigma_{prop} = \sqrt{\dfrac{P(100-P)}{n}} = \sqrt{\dfrac{80 \times 20}{100}} = 4$.

5. The obvious test statistic is the Z-value which will enable us to determine the probability of a sample result 10%, or more, below the mean of 80%.

$$Z = \frac{P - \pi}{\sigma_{prop}} = \frac{70 - 80}{4} = -2.5$$

From our Normal tables, we can ascertain that if the mean is 80% then the probability of getting a sample value between 80% and 70% (i.e. 2.5

standard errors below the mean) is 0.4938.

Therefore, the probability of getting a value of 70%, or less, is $0.5 - 0.4938 = 0.0062$ or 0.62%.

DIAGRAM 7.4

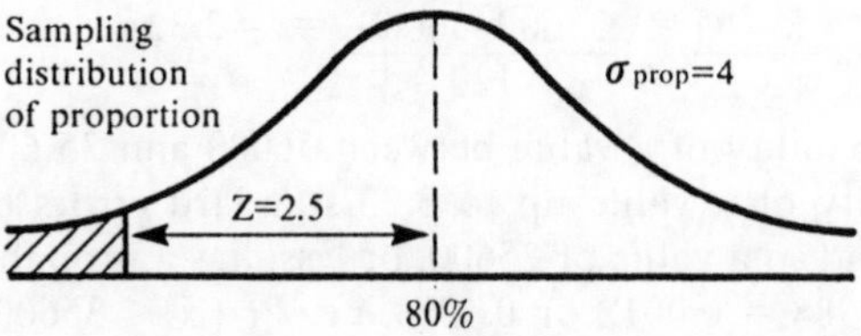

This means that in only about 6 samples of this size out of 1,000 would we expect a value of 70%, or less, to occur and the result is significant at the 1% level.

It would seem reasonable to reject the null hypothesis and accept the alternative that the proportion of orders despatched within four days is, in fact, less than 80%. There is a probability of only 0.0062 of us being wrong in accepting H_1.

7.3   CHI-SQUARED DISTRIBUTION

We said earlier that theoretical distributions, particularly the Normal, can often be used as approximations to "real world" distributions and in the Perry Blouse example we used the normal distribution as an approximation for the distribution of chest sizes.

But how does one know whether a certain theoretical distribution is a good approximation to the actual distribution? Obviously, we need to compare the values that we would expect the variable to take if the theoretical distribution applied with the observed values from a sample; in other words, we would test for "Goodness of Fit". If the theoretical distribution is a good fit with the sample observations then it will be safe to use the theoretical distribution to estimate population parameters, but if there are significant differences between the observed and expected values of the variable we would reject the theoretical distribution.

In such a situation the Chi-squared distribution enables us to distinguish between differences in expected and observed values which are statistically significant and differences which we might reasonably expect to occur as a result of sampling fluctuations.

The Chi-squared distribution is denoted by the square of the Greek letter chi (pronounced "ky"as in sky) and the value of χ^2 is found from the formula:

$$\chi^2 = \sum \frac{(O-E)^2}{E}$$

where O = observed value of variable
E = expected value of variable.

If there were no differences between the observed and expected values then the value of χ^2 would be zero whilst large values of χ^2 suggest that the theoretical distribution is less likely to be a good fit to the actual distribution of data. Of course, a difference of, say, 5 when the expected value is 10 is much more significant than if the expected value is 100 so dividing by the expected value brings the differences into proportion.

EXAMPLE

Suppose we wished to test a die and we threw it 600 times with the following result:

Score	1	2	3	4	5	6
Observed Frequency	104	96	106	100	94	100
Expected Frequency	100	100	100	100	100	100

$$\chi^2 = \sum \frac{(O-E)^2}{E} = \sum \left\{ \frac{4^2}{100} + \frac{4^2}{100} + \frac{6^2}{100} + \frac{0^2}{100} + \frac{6^2}{100} + \frac{0^2}{100} \right\} = \frac{104}{100} = 1.04$$

Do the results prove that the die is fair or not?

If we performed the experiment many times, the values of χ^2 would form a sampling distribution and if the sample corresponds to what we would expect from the theoretical distribution then the sampling distribution would be approximated by the χ^2 distribution. Values of χ^2 are tabulated as for the Normal distribution (with one important difference which we will come to later) and we can simply look up the value of χ^2 which if exceeded will lead us to reject the hypothesis that the die is fair.

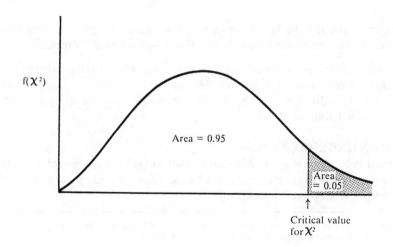

For a 0.05 significance test, the critical value of X^2 turns out to be 11.1 and since our value of 1.04 is less than this we would accept the hypothesis that the die is fair.

7.3.1 Using the X^2 tables

Suppose in the above example we used the same results but reduced the number of categories as below:

SCORE	3 or less	Greater than 3
OBSERVED FREQUENCY	306	294
EXPECTED FREQUENCY	300	300

$$X^2 = \sum \left\{ \frac{6^2}{300} + \frac{6^2}{300} \right\} = \frac{72}{300} = 0.24$$

This shows that, irrespective of the significance of the result, if we have a fewer number of categories the value of X^2 will be smaller and if we have a greater number of categories the value of X^2 will be larger.

The critical values of X^2 depend, therefore, on the number of categories or, in more technical language, the number of **degrees of freedom.**

The general rule is that when you calculate some statistic, such as X^2, the number of degrees of freedom associated with that statistic is reduced by the number of other values which have to be calculated from the sample before the statistic can be calculated.

The number of degrees of freedom upon which X^2 is based is calculated as:

$$df = k - d - 1$$

$$\text{where } k = \text{number of categories}$$
$$d = \text{number of parameters estimated from the sample}$$

In the example, the die has six faces so the number of degrees of freedom associated with the X^2 statistic is 5. i.e. df = 6 – 0 – 1 (see footnote).

Consulting the tables (see Appendix 7.1 — Chi-squared distribution), we see that the critical value of X^2 at the 5% significance level for 5 degrees of freedom is 11.1. In other words, this value would be exceeded, by random chance, only 1 time in 20.

7.4 CONTINGENCY TABLES

The most common use of the X^2 test is in analysing situations where the data can be sub-totalled in two or more directions. Such data may be expressed in the form of a contingency table.

Footnote: One degree of freedom is lost because we have to make the sum of the expected frequencies equal to the total of observed frequencies.

Suppose, for example, a sample of men and women were asked to rate a movie as good, average, or poor and the results were expressed as in the table below:

TABLE 1

	Good	Average	Poor	Row totals
Male	30	15	15	60
Female	10	5	25	40
Col. totals	40	20	40	100

We might wish to know if there is any connection between sex and opinion on the movie.

If we start with the null hypothesis that there is no connection between sex and opinion then we would calculate the expected frequencies for each cell in the table below. In the first cell, for example, how many men would we expect to rate the movie as good? Well, there are 60 men in total and 40% of the sample thought the movie was good so if sex had no effect on opinion we would expect 40% of the men (24) to rate the movie as good.

In general,

$$\text{EXPECTED FREQUENCY FOR ANY CELL} = \text{ROW TOTAL} \times \frac{\text{COLUMN TOTAL}}{\text{OVERALL TOTAL}}$$

TABLE 2

	Good	Average	Poor	Row totals
Male	24	12	24	60
Female	16	8	16	40
Col. totals	40	20	40	100

Calculating X^2 in the normal way using the observed frequencies in Table 1 and the expected frequencies in Table 2 gives the following result.

$$X^2 = \sum \left\{ \frac{6^2}{24} + \frac{3^2}{12} + \frac{9^2}{24} + \frac{6^2}{16} + \frac{3^2}{8} + \frac{9^2}{16} \right\}$$

$$= \frac{24 + 12 + 54 + 36 + 18 + 81}{16} = 13.31$$

In general, if a contingency table has m rows and n columns (excluding the totals) then the number of degrees of freedom for X^2 is given by:

$$df = (m-1)(n-1) \quad \text{(see footnote)}$$

Footnote: $(m-1)(n-1) - k$ if k parameters have to be estimated from the observed frequencies.

In our example, m=2 and n=3 so there are 2 degrees of freedom. The critical value of X^2 at the 5% significance level with 2 df is 5.99 so we would conclude that there are significant differences between male and female opinions on the movie.

7.4.1 Minimum cell frequencies

If the expected frequency for any cell is less than 5 the X^2 test can become unreliable. This problem can be overcome by merging categories so that the minimum expected cell frequency is greater than 5 for all cells

7.4.2 2 × 2 Tables

The value of X^2 becomes less accurate when there are a small number of degrees of freedom. If there is only one degree of freedom, as in a 2 × 2 table, X^2 should be calculated using Yates' correction.

TABLE 3

	Good	Bad	Row totals
Male	a	b	m
Female	c	d	n
Col. totals	r	s	t

To calculate X^2 for the Table 3 the following formula is more accurate than the uncorrected form:

$$X^2 = \frac{\left(ad - bc - \frac{1}{2}\right)^2 t}{mnrs}$$ 　with 1 degree of freedom.

QUESTIONS

7.1 The manufacturer of long-life electric light bulbs claims that the average life of his product is 1,000 hours. A sample of 100 bulbs is found to have an average life of 940 hours with a standard deviation of 200 hours. Is the manufacturer's claim justified on a one-tailed test at the 5% level?

7.2 A TV commercial claims that 60% of consumers prefer Brand X to any of the alternatives. A random sample of 300 consumers shows that only 160 prefer Brand X. Is the claim justified by the sample result on a one-tailed test at the 5% level?

7.3 Support for a candidate at a local election is estimated as 60% of the electorate. An independent random sample shows that out of 500 people 330 intend voting for the candidate. Is there sufficient evidence to suggest that support for the candidate has changed? (Use two-tailed test at the 5% significance level).

7.4 (a) The time for a vehicle to make a particular journey on repeated occasions is found to be approximately normally distributed. On average the journey takes 25 minutes with 68% of journeys taking between 22 and 28 minutes and 95% of journeys taking between 19 and 31 minutes.

Required:
Estimate the standard deviation of journey time and calculate how many journeys out of 60 would take longer than 30 minutes.

(b) The driver is now instructed to follow a different route which is claimed to shorten his average journey time by 5 minutes to a mean of 20 minutes. Once familiar with the route, he finds that his first journey takes 24 minutes and he is not impressed by the claimed improvement.

Required:
(1) Determine the probability that the driver's first journey on a new route having a mean time of 20 minutes, as claimed, would take 24 minutes or longer, and consider, therefore, whether this journey provides any evidence that the reduction is not what it was claimed to be. You may assume that the journey time for the new route is normally distributed, with a standard deviation similar to the old route.
(2) After 20 journeys the mean time on the new route is found to be 21.7 minutes. Determine whether this is consistent with the claim of a 5 minute improvement on the time taken for the original route. *(ACA)*

*7.5 (a) Items produced to a weight specification are rejected if found to be outside the range 2.975 to 3.025 gms. A batch of 500 items is found to have weights which are normally distributed with a mean of 3.005 and a standard deviation of 0.015. How many items are rejected? *(7 marks)*

(b) The standard procedure used by a company for detecting defects in a product has, from experience, been shown to detect 90% of defects present.

Required:
(1) Calculate the standard error of the proportion of defects detected out of 100 examined and find the probability that, out of 100 defects, 15 or more are undetected by the procedure.
(2) An alternative procedure is suggested which during trials detects 368 out of 400 defects. Show that the new procedure does not give a statistically significant improvement in detection rate. *(13 marks)*
(20 marks) (ACA)

QUESTIONS — CHI-SQUARED TEST

7.6 It is believed that applicants for a certain job are equally likely to come from the North, South, East, or West. Test this hypothesis, given that the actual numbers of applicants are 21, 13, 20, and 16 respectively.

7.7 Three types of machine A, B and C are used by a company to produce items which are very prone to a certain type of imperfection. A random sample of 100 items from each machine showed the number of perfect and imperfect items to be as follows:

		Perfect	Imperfect
	A	33	67
MACHINE	B	39	61
	C	48	52

Required:

Use the chi-squared (X^2) list to examine at the 0.05 level of significance whether there is any association between the machine type and proneness to imperfection.

Section of X^2 table

degrees of freedom	1	2	3	4	5	6
$X^2_{0.05}$	3.84	5.99	7.82	9.49	11.07	11.59

(15 marks)

(ACA)

*7.8 A large tutorial school has three lecturers, Smith, Jones and Brown, who prepare different groups of students for the same examination, each group being of the same average ability. Examination results are graded as either distinction, pass or fail, and the results obtained by 100 students are classified below according to lecturer and grade obtained.

	SMITH	JONES	BROWN
DISTINCTION	5	4	8
PASS	13	16	14
FAIL	12	20	8

Required:

(1) Use a suitable test of significance to compare the results obtained by the three lecturers and comment on your findings.

(2) Suppose that, of a large number of students not attending the tutorial school, 11% obtained distinction, 31% passed and 58% failed. Assess whether there is any evidence that a student's performance is improved by attending the tutorial school and state a reservation you might have about your conclusion.

(ACA)

APPENDIX 7.1

THE CHI-SQUARE DISTRIBUTION
with v degrees of freedom
(shaded area = p)

The table gives the value of X^2 which has a probability p of being exceeded.

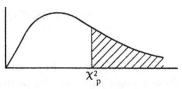

v	$X^2_{.005}$	$X^2_{.01}$	$X^2_{.025}$	$X^2_{.05}$
1	7.88	6.63	5.02	3.84
2	10.6	9.21	7.38	5.99
3	12.8	11.3	9.35	7.81
4	14.9	13.3	11.1	9.49
5	16.7	15.1	12.8	11.1
6	18.5	16.8	14.4	12.6
7	20.3	18.5	16.0	14.1
8	22.0	20.1	17.5	15.5
9	23.6	21.7	19.0	16.9
10	25.2	23.2	20.5	18.3
11	26.8	24.7	21.9	19.7
12	28.3	26.2	23.3	21.0
13	29.8	27.7	24.7	22.4
14	31.3	29.1	26.1	23.7
15	32.8	30.6	27.5	25.0
16	34.3	32.0	28.8	26.3
17	35.7	33.4	30.2	27.6
18	37.2	34.8	31.5	28.9
19	38.6	36.2	32.9	30.1
20	40.0	37.6	34.2	31.4
21	41.4	38.9	35.5	32.7
22	42.8	40.3	36.8	33.9
23	44.2	41.6	38.1	35.2
24	45.6	43.0	39.4	36.4
25	46.9	44.3	40.6	37.7
26	48.3	45.6	41.9	38.9
27	49.6	47.0	43.2	40.1
28	51.0	48.3	44.5	41.3
29	52.3	49.6	45.7	42.6
30	53.7	50.9	47.0	43.8
40	66.8	63.7	59.3	55.8
50	79.5	76.2	71.4	67.5
60	92.0	88.4	83.3	79.1
70	104.2	100.4	95.0	90.5
80	116.3	112.3	106.6	101.9
90	128.3	124.1	118.1	113.1
100	140.2	135.8	129.6	124.3

Chapter 8
REGRESSION AND CORRELATION

So far we have mainly been concerned with the problem of interpreting data about a single variable. Frequently, however, situations arise where there are two or more associated variables which need to be considered together. In such situations, we may wish to know:

(i)   is the evidence strong enough to suggest a relationship between the variables?
(ii) if there is a relationship, how can we best predict one variable from the values of the other variable(s)?
(iii) is the relationship linear? etc. etc.

8.1   Terminology
The technique for finding the equation which fits the data best is called **regression analysis.** When we are concerned with only two variables we refer to **bivariate regression** and when we are concerned with more than two we speak of multivariate or **multiple regression.**

In the case of bivariate regression, we usually refer to the two variables as X and Y and these variables may be related to each other exactly or inexactly.

Y is used to denote the **dependent** variable, also called the response, criterion, or "effect" variable.

X is used to denote the **independent** variable, also called the predictor, controlled, regression, or "cause" variable.

DIAGRAM 8.1

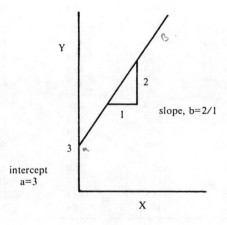

The simplest relationship between the dependent and independent variable is a straight line and the general form for an equation to a straight line is:

$$Y = a + bX \qquad \text{where } a = \text{intercept on the Y axis and}$$
$$b = \text{slope of the line.}$$

For example, the equation $Y = 3 + 2X$ would cut the Y axis at 3 and Y would increase by 2 units for each increase of one unit in X, as in Diagram 8.1.

When we fit a line to data, there may be many different types of equation to consider; a straight line or some sort of curve may provide a line of best fit. As a first step, we would inspect the scatter diagram and, in practice, it might be necessary to try several types of line before choosing the one that fits the data best.

Often, however, we would fit a straight line as a close approximation to a much more complicated curve and the process of fitting a straight line is called **linear regression.** We shall concern ourselves here with linear **bivariate regression** — in other words we shall consider the relationship between only two variables and the fitting of a straight line to pairs of measurements of those variables.

In most cases outside of the physical sciences, and certainly in the business world, the relationship between variables will tend to be inexact (as in Diagram 8.2). Thus, we might more realistically write the equation of the straight line fitted to the data as

$$Y = a + bX + e$$

where e indicates the existence of error,

DIAGRAM 8.2

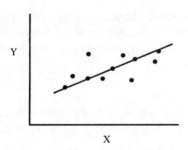

If the relationship between X and Y is approximately linear, the problem is to find values for a and b in the equation $Y = a + bX$ so that the line gives as good a fit as possible to the data. But what criterion do we use to decide which is the line of best fit?

(a) *By eye* —
It is possible to plot a line that goes through as many of the points on a scattergraph as possible and leaves the remaining points approximately evenly distributed either side of the line. However, if several people attempted to plot a line of best fit by this method they would all end up with slightly different lines with different intercepts and slopes.

(b) *High/Low method* —
Another method would be to take the highest and lowest values of X and find the corresponding Y values. The slope, b, could then be estimated as

$$\frac{\text{difference in Y values}}{\text{difference in X values}}$$

The value of the intercept, a, could then be found by using the value for b together with any corresponding values for X and Y in the equation Y = a + bX.

One obvious problem with this method is that the high/low values may not be typical of the data as a whole.

(c) *Three-point method* —
In the three-point method the data is first listed in ascending order of the X values, the mean values, $\bar{x}$ and $\bar{y}$, of X and Y are calculated and the point $(\bar{x}, \bar{y})$ is the first of the three points.

The data is then divided into two parts, one part for values of x greater than $\bar{x}$ and the other part for values of x less than $\bar{x}$, and the means of X and Y are calculated for each part of the data. The two new pairs of means, say $(\bar{x}_1, \bar{y}_1)$ and $(\bar{x}_2, \bar{y}_2)$, provide the other two points and a straight line is plotted through, or as close as possible to, the three points $(\bar{x}, \bar{y})$, $(\bar{x}_1, \bar{y}_1)$, and $(\bar{x}_2, \bar{y}_2)$.

(d) *Method of least squares* —
The three methods mentioned above are really rather primitive and what we need is some method for calculating a unique line which fits the data best according to some mathematically defined criterion. Such a method is that of least squares.

8.2 Method of least squares

What we want to do is find estimates of a and b in the equation Y = a + bX such that the line Y = a + bX provides a good fit to the data.

We have already acknowledged that it is unlikely that the line will provide a perfect fit to the data and so we try to minimise the differences between the values predicted by the equation and the actual values observed.

$$\text{Prediction error} = \text{observed value} - \text{predicted value}$$
$$= Y_i - \hat{Y}_i$$

$$\text{Total Prediction error} = \sum_{i=1}^{i=n}(Y_i - \hat{Y}_i)$$

where n = number of observations
Y_i = observed value
$\hat{Y}_i$ = predicted value

Simply minimising the total prediction error however is not good enough. As can be seen in Diagram 8.3 where TPE = –6 –4 + 10 = 0 the positive and negative errors may cancel out even though the line is obviously not a good fit.

DIAGRAM 8.3

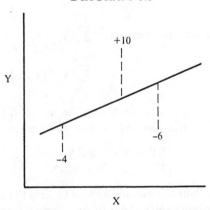

To avoid the positive and negative errors cancelling each other out we could look at the ABSOLUTE ERRORS (i.e. we could ignore the signs). This, again, is not very satisfactory. Consider Diagrams 8.4 and 8.5.

DIAGRAM 8.4   **DIAGRAM 8.5**

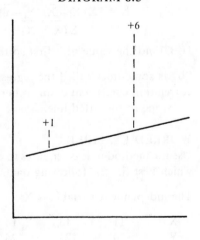

TPE (absolute values)
=2+1+1+2+1+1 = 8

TPE = 1+6 = 7

According to the absolute values of the errors, the line in Diagram 8.5 is a better fit than that in 8.4. This is unsatisfactory because 8.5 contains a large error (admittedly only one) and we would want to avoid large errors. Thus, we may decide that we will give more weight to large errors.

Dealing with absolute values is also computationally difficult and so the criterion that we finally arrive at is to find the **line of best fit which minimises the sum of squares of the errors** thus removing the sign problem and giving extra weight to large errors.

$$\text{Sum of squares of errors } = \sum_{i=1}^{i=n} (Y_i - \hat{Y}_i)^2$$

$$= \sum_{i=1}^{i=n} [Y_i - (a + bX_i)]^2$$

Some not too difficult calculus, involving the partial differentiation of the above equation, shows that the SSE is minimised when

$$\Sigma Y = na + b \Sigma X, \text{ and}$$
$$\Sigma XY = a \Sigma X + b \Sigma X^2$$

These are called the Normal equations and to find the line of best fit, the regression line, we simply solve them to find the values of a and b.

If you don't like simultaneous equations, or even if you do because the normal equations can be quite unwieldy, a and b can be found directly from the following equations:

$$a = \bar{Y} - b\bar{X}$$
$$b = \frac{\Sigma (X_i - \bar{X})(Y_i - \bar{Y})}{\Sigma (X_i - \bar{X})^2} \qquad \text{or} \qquad \frac{\Sigma (XY) - n\bar{X}\bar{Y}}{\Sigma X^2 - n\bar{X}^2}$$

N.B. Find the value of b first so that you can substitute it in $a = \bar{Y} - b\bar{X}$.

"b" is sometimes called the **regression coefficient**. Do not confuse this with correlation coefficient or any other term. The regression coefficient is simply the slope of the fitted line.

WORKED EXAMPLE

Use the method of least squares to determine the equation of the straight line which best fits the following data.

The independent variable is X:

X	11	13	14	17	18	21	26
Y	20	23	25	28	30	34	38

Draw a scatter diagram for the data and plot the least squares regression line on the scatter diagram.

X	Y	X²	XY
11	20	121	220
13	23	169	299
14	25	196	350
17	28	289	476
18	30	324	540
21	34	441	714
26	38	636	988

$$\bar{X} = \frac{\Sigma X}{n} = \frac{120}{7} = 17$$

$$\bar{Y} = \frac{\Sigma Y}{n} = \frac{198}{7} = 28$$

$\Sigma X = 120 \qquad \Sigma Y = 198 \qquad \Sigma X^2 = 2216 \qquad \Sigma XY = 3587$

$$\text{Slope } b = \frac{\Sigma XY - n\bar{X}\bar{Y}}{\Sigma X^2 - n\bar{X}^2} = \frac{3587 - 7 \times 17.14 \times 28.29}{2216 - 7 \times (17.14)^2}$$

$$= 1.208$$

$$\text{Intercept } a = \bar{Y} - b\bar{X} = 28.29 - [1.208 \times 17.14] = 7.58$$

$Y = a + bX = $ our line of best fit.

i.e. $Y = 7.58 + 1.208X$

DIAGRAM 8.6 REGRESSION AND CORRELATION

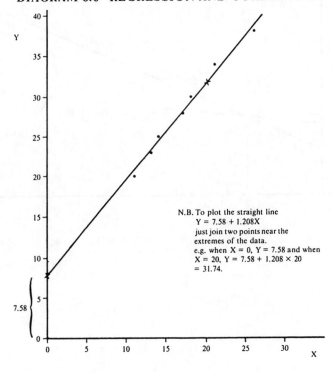

N.B. To plot the straight line
Y = 7.58 + 1.208X
just join two points near the
extremes of the data.
e.g. when X = 0, Y = 7.58 and when
X = 20, Y = 7.58 + 1.208 × 20
= 31.74.

8.3 The Regression Line

The line $Y = a + bX$ obtained by the least squares method is known as the regression line. As described above, it involves minimising the sum of the squares of errors in the estimated Y values for given X values and so is more correctly described as the regression line of Y on X. Of course, we could have measured the errors horizontally rather than vertically and if we minimised these horizontal errors we would obtain the regression line of X on Y.

If you want to predict X for given values of Y, or find the regression line of X on Y, there is no real complication; but rather than change the formulae it is easier to define whatever variable you wish to be the dependent variable as Y, define the independent variable as X, and then proceed as normal.

The two regression lines will usually be different because they minimise the errors in different directions but they will always intersect at the means of X and Y, as in Diagram 8.7.

If the regression line is a perfect fit to the data so that all the data points lie on the regression line the two regression lines will, in fact, coincide and we say that there is perfect correlation between the variables.

DIAGRAM 8.7

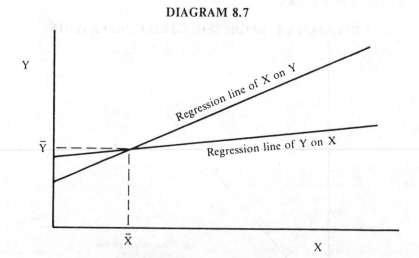

8.4 Interpretation of the regression equation

(a) We can use the regression equation to calculate an estimate of Y for some given value of X. If the regression line has been plotted (since it is a straight line you only have to join up two extreme points) you may simply read off an estimate of Y , $\hat{Y}_i$, for some given value of X, X_i.

(b) Extrapolation must be undertaken with care; if you calculate, or read off, some estimate of Y for a value of X which lies outside the range of the data then the estimate may be suspect because the linear relationship may not hold. In such a situation it is better to collect more data.

(c) The regression line is only a line of best fit, it does not tell you how close a relationship there is between the variables. An examination of the scattergraph will help in deciding how close the fitted line is to the data and it is possible to calculate a correlation coefficient (see later).

(d) The regression coefficient (b), or slope of line, estimates the **average** change in Y associated with a unit change in X. However, the relationship will usually be an inexact one and so one cannot say that a given change in X will produce a certain change in Y in all cases.

(e) The intercept (a) is the average value of Y when X equals zero. In some cases this can be very useful; for example, if we plot a firm's total cost against its output the intercept will be the fixed cost, shown in Diagram 8.8.

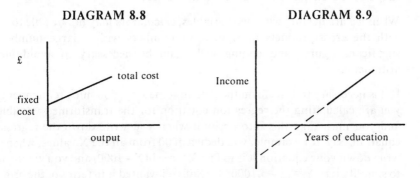

| DIAGRAM 8.8 | DIAGRAM 8.9 |

On other occasions, however, the intercept can produce nonsense results if taken literally. For example, if we plotted years in education and income we might get a regression line such as in Diagram 8.9; extrapolation suggests that someone who has had no education receives a negative income.

(f) The regression equation implies nothing about causality. As we have said, we may choose to find the regression equation of X on Y just as easily as that of Y on X. We do as a rule denote the 'cause' by X and the 'effect' by Y but our choice is dictated by theoretical considerations, commonsense, and previous research — it is nothing to do with estimating values of Y for given values of X.

To quote an example from Economics, there is little doubt that inflation is associated with increases in the money supply but there is disagreement as to whether increases in the money supply cause inflation or whether the authorities simply respond to higher prices by printing more money!

(g)   Although the regression equation implies nothing about causality, and when we are using the regression equation to make predictions we are not concerned with what 'causes' the change in the dependent variable only what enables us to make accurate predictions, prediction and explanation are not divorced from each other. A regression equation that makes useful predictions will usually be based upon causal variables or their surrogates.

8.5   Transformation of data

In sections 4.1.3 and 4.2.4, we mentioned that calculating the mean or standard deviation could be simplified where necessary by coding the data. This was seen to be particularly useful if large numbers or fractions appeared in the original data. As long as we reversed the transformation correctly, we could add or subtract a constant, or multiply or divide by a constant, and the shape of the distribution would be unaffected.

When we are dealing with two variables, calculators may not be able to cope with the cross-products or squares of numbers with a large number of significant figures and coding will again be necessary to avoid messy arithmetic.

If it is necessary to transform the data in some way, you must remember that you are calculating the regression equation for the transformed variable(s) and you must take this into account when you write down the regression equation. Say, for example, you deduct 1000 from all the X values; when you write down your equation it is in fact $Y = a + b(X - 1000)$ and you would need to simplify it to $Y = (a - b.1000) + bX$ if you wanted it in terms of the original variables.

It is a good idea to carry out a rough check on your regression equation to make sure it corresponds approximately with a couple of the data points. To make sure you have carried out the reverse transformation correctly just substitute an X value in your equation and check that it yields a Y value in the region of the corresponding Y value in the original data.

8.6 Fitting a trend line to time series data using least squares

A time series shows how a variable changes over time. We will deal with time series in more detail later but we can fit a trend line to the data using least squares in exactly the same way as already described.

Year	Sales £
1983	40000
1984	50000
1985	60000
1986	70000

Suppose we have the very simple time series on the left and we wish to fit a least squares regression line. We simply call sales the dependent variable and the year the the independent variable.

It will simplify matters if we code the year and sales as shown so that, assuming sales are measured at the mid-point of the year, X=0 is the mid-point of 1980 and Y = sales/1000 i.e. sales are in £000s.

X	Sales £000s Y	X^2	XY
3	40	9	120
4	50	16	200
5	60	25	300
6	70	36	420
18	220	86	1040

$$\bar{X} = \frac{18}{4} = 4.5 \qquad \bar{Y} = \frac{220}{4} = 55$$

$$b = \frac{\Sigma XY - n\bar{X}\bar{Y}}{\Sigma X^2 - n\bar{X}^2} = \frac{1040 - 4.4.5.55}{86 - 4.4.5^2} = 10$$

$$a = \bar{Y} - b\bar{X} = 55 - 10 \times 4.5 = 10$$

Regression equation is Y = a + bX = 10 + 10 X
or, in terms of original variables Sales = 10,000 + 10,000 X   where X = number of years after mid-point of 1980.

Although it is not necessary here, you can reduce calculations further by coding the years so that the mid-point of the series represents X=0 and the other years are deviations from this mid-point. When there are an odd number of years the deviations will be in whole years which is easier, in our example the deviations are in half years because the mid-point of our series is the beginning of 1985.

	X	Y	XY	X^2
1983	− 1.5	40	−60	2.25
1984	− 0.5	50	−25	0.25
	0		0	0
1985	+0.5	60	30	0.25
1986	+1.5	70	105	2.25
		220	50	5

Our calculations are simplified because X is now zero and so our equations for a and b simplify to:

$$b = \frac{\Sigma XY - n\bar{X}\bar{Y}}{\Sigma X^2 - n\bar{X}^2} = \frac{\Sigma XY}{\Sigma X^2} = \frac{50}{5} = 10$$

$$a = \bar{Y} - b\bar{X} = \bar{Y} = \frac{220}{4} = 55$$

Regression equation is Y = 55 + 10 X $\qquad$ where X = +/– number of

or $\quad$ Sales = 55,000 + 10,000 X $\qquad$ years after/before

the start of 1985.

CHECK: What would sales be at mid-point of 1980 on both equations?

$\qquad$ Y = 10,000 + 10,000 X $\quad \rightarrow \quad$ at X = 0 $\qquad$ Y = 10,000

$\qquad$ Y = 55,000 + 10,000 X $\quad \rightarrow \quad$ at X = – 45 $\quad$ Y = 10,000

QED

8.7 Correlation

It is possible to fit a straight line by the method of least squares even if a linear relationship does not exist but the line may not fit the data very well at all. The regression equation itself will not tell us how well the line fits the data and how well the regression equation accounts for changes in the dependent variable.

One way of judging how close a relationship there is between the two variables is to examine the scattergraph; the closer the points are to the regression line the better the line fits the data. More formal measures of the degree of association between the variables are provided by:

$\qquad$ (i) the Coefficient of Determination (R^2), and

$\qquad$ (ii) the Coefficient of Correlation (r).

8.7.1 Coefficient of determination

DIAGRAM 8.10

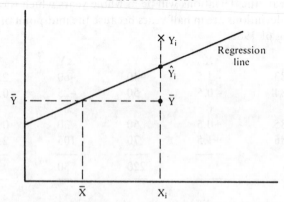

If we are trying to predict the value of Y and we only have values of Y, our best estimate of Y would be the mean value $\bar{Y}$.

If there is a relationship between X and Y, knowing the value of X will help us to predict the value of Y and the extent to which knowing X helps in predicting Y can be used as a measure of the relationship between X and Y.

In Diagram 8.10, the point (X_i, Y_i) is some observed value that does not lie on the regression line. $\hat{Y}_i$ is the value of Y that we would estimate from the regression line as corresponding to the value of the independent variable X_i. $\bar{Y}$ is the mean value of Y.

$$\left.\begin{array}{l} \text{Total deviation of } Y_i \text{ from } \bar{Y} = Y_i - \bar{Y} \\ \text{Explained deviation of } Y_i \text{ from } \bar{Y} = \hat{Y}_i - \bar{Y} \\ \text{Unexplained deviation of } Y_i \text{ from } Y = Y_i - \hat{Y}_i \end{array}\right\} \begin{array}{l} (\text{that part of the deviation} \\ \text{explained by the regression} \\ \text{line}) \end{array}$$

If we take all the observed values and square the deviations then:

Sum of total deviations squared, or total sum of squares, TSS $= \Sigma (Y_i - \bar{Y})^2$

Regression, or explained, sum of squares, RSS $= \Sigma (\hat{Y}_i - \bar{Y})^2$

Error, or unexplained, sum of squares, ESS $= \Sigma (Y_i - \hat{Y}_i)^2$

and TSS = RSS + ESS

Now the purpose of the least squares method is to minimise the sum of squares of the errors (ESS) and the larger the part of the total deviation that is explained by the regression line the less will be the error. So, the greater the RSS is in relation to the TSS the better and the Coefficient of determination is simply the ratio.

$$R^2 = RSS/TSS$$

The coefficient of determination shows what part of the total variation in the dependent variable is accounted for by changes in the independent variable. If $R^2 = 1$ then all the observed points lie on the regression line, the variation in the dependent variable is completely explained by changes in the independent variable and there will be no error in making predictions of the value of the dependent variable from the regression equation. On the other hand, if $R^2 = 0$ a knowledge of the independent variable is no help at all in predicting the value of the dependent variable. So, the closer the coefficient of determination is to one the closer the observed points are to lying on the straight line given by the regression equation.

In the case of linear regression, the coefficient of determination is the square of a more well known measure of association called the coefficient of correlation.

8.7.2 Coefficient of correlation

The most important measure of the degree of association between two variables is the (product moment) correlation coefficient.

DIAGRAM 8.11

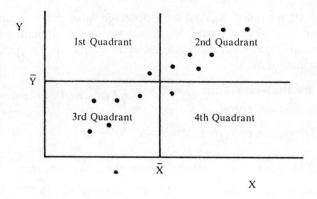

Consider Diagram 8.11. The "centroid" of the data is at $(\bar{X}, \bar{Y})$ and can be used to divide the scattergraph into four quadrants.

Now consider the values of $(X_i - \bar{X})$, $(Y_i - \bar{Y})$, and their product for some point (X_i, Y_i) when that point lies in each of the four quadrants.

	$(X_i - \bar{X})$	$(Y_i - \bar{Y})$	$(X_i - \bar{X})(Y_i - \bar{Y})$
1st Quadrant	NEGATIVE	POSITIVE	NEGATIVE
2nd Quadrant	POSITIVE	POSITIVE	POSITIVE
3rd Quadrant	NEGATIVE	NEGATIVE	POSITIVE
4th Quadrant	POSITIVE	NEGATIVE	NEGATIVE

It can be seen that the product $(X_i - X)(Y_i - Y)$ takes the same sign in diagonally opposite quadrants. Now let us consider four possible sets of data.

The data in Diagram 8.12 indicates that there is a HIGH POSITIVE CORRELATION between X and Y. The correlation is 'high' because the observed points lie close to the regression line and 'positive' because large Y values occur with large X values, i.e. the regression line has a positive slope. When there is a high positive correlation the sum of $(X_i - \bar{X})(Y_i - \bar{Y})$ for all the observations, $\Sigma(X_i - \bar{X})(Y_i - \bar{Y})$, will be large and positive.

The data in Diagram 8.13 shows a low POSITIVE CORRELATION. The regression line still has a positive slope but the observed points are widely

DIAGRAM 8.12   DIAGRAM 8.13

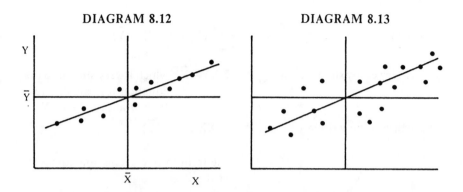

scattered around the regression line. In this case, the value of $\Sigma(X_i - \bar{X})(Y_i - \bar{Y})$ will be positive but small because $(X_i - \bar{X})(Y_i - \bar{Y})$ will take negative values when the data point lies in the 1st or 4th quadrant and this will cancel out some of the positive values when the data points lie in 2nd and 3rd quadrants.

In Diagram 8.14 we have a HIGH NEGATIVE CORRELATION because the points lie close to the regression line but the slope of the line is negative so that high X values are associated with low Y values. The value of $\Sigma(X_i - \bar{X})(Y_i - \bar{Y})$ will be high and negative.

DIAGRAM 8.14   DIAGRAM 8.15

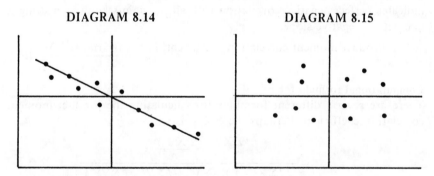

In Diagram 8.15 there is no correlation between the variables. The number of points in each quadrant are roughly equal and so positive and negative values of $(X_i - \bar{X})(Y_i - \bar{Y})$ will tend to cancel each other out so $\Sigma(X_i - \bar{X})(Y_i - \bar{Y})$ will tend towards zero.

From what we have said it would seem that $\sum_{i=1}^{i=n}(X_i - \bar{X})(Y_i - \bar{Y})$ could serve as a measure of the degree of association between the variables. However, there are two problems the first of which is that the more observations that there are the bigger will be the value of $\Sigma(X_i - \bar{X})(Y_i - \bar{Y})$ for i between 1 and n. This is easily overcome by dividing by the number of observations, n, to give a statistic called the covariance of X and Y.

$$\text{Covariance of X and Y} = s_{XY} = \frac{1}{n} \sum_{i=1}^{i=n} (X_i - \bar{X})(Y_i - \bar{Y})$$

This is very easily shown to be $s_{XY} = \dfrac{\Sigma XY - \bar{X}\bar{Y}}{n}$ which is very similar to the equation for calculating the variance of X or Y.

This can also be written $s_{XY} = \dfrac{1}{n}(\Sigma XY - n\bar{X}\bar{Y})$

The term in brackets is sometimes written C_{XY}.

The covariance of X and Y provides a crude measure of the degree of association between the two variables but its value depends upon the variability in the values of X and Y. This problem can be overcome by expressing $(X_i - \bar{X})$ and $(Y_i - \bar{Y})$ in terms of their respective standard deviations s_X and s_Y.

Standardising the covariance in this way gives us the product moment correlation coefficient (r) which, it can be shown, must lie between $+1$ and -1. If $r=+1$ all the points lie on a straight line with a positive slope and we say that the variables are perfectly positively correlated. Similarly, a value of -1 indicates perfect negative correlation with all the points lying on a straight line with a negative slope.

$$\text{Product moment correlation coefficient, } r = \frac{\text{Covariance XY}}{s_X.s_Y}$$

Computational formula for r

There are several different formulae for calculating the product moment correlation coefficient. Perhaps the easiest is

$$r = \frac{\Sigma XY - \dfrac{\Sigma X\ \Sigma Y}{n}}{\sqrt{\left(\Sigma X^2 - \dfrac{(\Sigma X)^2}{n}\right)}\sqrt{\left(\Sigma Y^2 - \dfrac{(\Sigma Y)^2}{n}\right)}} \qquad *$$

If the terms in brackets in the denominator are large it is best to take their square roots before multiplying them, as is indicated in the formula. Alternatively they may be multiplied and then the square root of their product found.

Using the notation mentioned earlier, r is sometimes expressed as $C_{XY}/\sqrt{C_{XX}.C_{YY}}$. Note that using the formula mentioned above*, r can be calculated using the same terms that were used to calculate the regression equation, with the addition of the ΣY^2 term. Coding of the variables has no effect on the calculation.

EXAMPLE

Let us consider the previous example for which we calculated a regression equation

X	11	13	14	17	18	21	26
Y	20	23	25	28	30	34	38

When we plotted the Scattergraph, most of the data points lay very close to our regression line so we would expect a 'High Positive Correlation'.

We have already calculated most of the values that we need, except for the ΣY^2 term but we will write the calculations out in full again.

X	Y	X^2	XY	Y^2
11	20	121	220	400
13	23	169	299	529
14	25	196	350	625
17	28	289	476	784
18	30	324	540	900
21	34	441	714	1156
26	38	636	988	1444
$\Sigma X = 120$	$\Sigma Y = 198$	$\Sigma X^2 = 2216$	$\Sigma XY = 3587$	$\Sigma Y^2 = 5838$

$\bar{X} = 17.14$

$\bar{Y} = 28.29$

$$r = \frac{3587 - \dfrac{120 \times 198}{7}}{\sqrt{\left(2216 - \dfrac{120^2}{7}\right)\left(5838 - \dfrac{198^2}{7}\right)}}$$

$$= \frac{192.7143}{\sqrt{(158.8572)(237.4286)}}$$

$$= \frac{192.7143}{194.20927}$$

$$= \underline{0.99} \text{ confirming the high positive correlation.}$$

8.7.3 Interpretation of the correlation coefficient

There are a number of points that need to be considered when interpreting the correlation coefficient.

1.   We said earlier that the correlation coefficient (r) is the square root of the coefficient of determination (R^2).

$$r^2 = R^2$$

We also pointed out that the coefficient of determination shows what proportion of the total variation in the dependent variable is accounted for by the independent variable.

Now r and R^2 will only be equal when $r=+/-1$ or 0 and we say that there is perfect correlation when $r=+/-1$. This can be a little misleading because you might think that when, for example, $r=0.5$ half of the variation in Y is explained by X. This is not true; when $r=0.5$ the coefficient of determination R^2, and r^2, both equal 0.25 which means that only a quarter of the variation in Y is explained by changes in X.

It is the coefficient of determination that is important when assessing the strength of the relationship between the variables.

2.   Even if there is no correlation between two variables a high correlation may occur in a sample by chance. It is often necessary therefore to perform a significance test to see if the sample correlation coefficient is sufficiently different from zero to indicate a degree of correlation. The line of reasoning is similar to that outlined in the section on hypothesis testing but it is necessary to use the t-distribution rather than the normal distribution*.

3.   If the value of r is low it may mean two things:
(a) The assumption of linearity is wrong but the variables are related in some way.

DIAGRAM 8.16

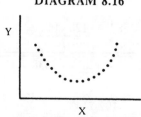

For example, the variables in Diagram 8.16 are clearly related but the value of r would tend towards zero.

Inspection of the scattergraph would reveal some sort of curvilinear relationship and calculation of r is meaningless in such a situation.

(b) There is little correlation between the variables and a knowledge of the independent variable does not help very much in predicting values of the dependent variable.

Although we are usually happier when we find a high correlation because it means we can predict accurately from the regression equation, a low correlation may still be revealing and will at least suggest that other avenues may provide more fruitful lines of enquiry.

---

*See, for example, 'Statistics for technology' — Chatfield for details.

4. A high correlation does not imply causality. We said earlier that the direction of causality (whether changes in X cause changes in Y or vice versa) is a matter for theory and commonsense. Similarly, we need to be aware that a close relationship between two variables may be the result of some third variable. For example, there is no doubt a high correlation between the number of TV sets owned and the number of motor cars owned but there is no causality involved; changes in these variables are, one supposes, caused by changes in some third variable, the level of incomes.

8.7.4 Spearman's rank order correlation coefficient (r_s)

Often a variable can only be measured at the ordinal-level of measurement which means that they can only be placed in rank-order according to some criterion. So, for example, we can categorise people according to their social class; we can rank firms as small, medium, or large size; we can grade examination scripts as A, B, C, D, E, or F etc. This tells us, for example, that a grade A student is better than a grade B student but it does not tell us how much better — the difference between the categories is not clearly defined.

It is possible to calculate a correlation coefficient between two variables based upon the rank orders of the variables. Spearman's rank order correlation coefficient is the most often quoted measure and, although we can always calculate the product moment correlation coefficient, r_s will give a quick approximation to r and can have advantages in some situations.

DIAGRAM 8.17

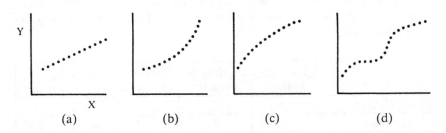

(a)   (b)   (c)   (d)

For example, in all of the above situations r_s would be equal to one but only in the case of (a) would r be equal to one.

To calculate r_s, if there are n pairs of observations each series should be ranked from 1 to n. These rankings correspond to the variables X and Y and each variable should be ranked in a similar way; for example, if we were ranking people according to height and weight and we decided to rank the tallest as 1 then the heaviest should also be ranked 1 so that a positive correlation indicates that tall people tend to be heavier. A product moment correlation coefficient can be calculated from the X and Y values (ranks) as illustrated previously but the rank order correlation coefficient can be calculated more quickly from the following formula:

$$r_s = 1 - \frac{6\,\Sigma\,d^2}{n(n^2 - 1)}$$
where d = difference in rankings
n = number of paired observations.

As with r, r_s can take values between +1 and –1 with +1 indicating perfect positive correlation and –1 indicating perfect negative correlation.

Tied variables
If the variable takes the same value a number of times, each observation should be assigned a rank equal to the average of the ranks which would span the ranks if the values had been slightly different.

Example:
Measurement	0.1	0.5	0.6	0.6	0.7	0.9
Rank	1	2	3.5	3.5	5	6

Answers for r and r_s will often be close but information is lost when ranks are used in place of the original data. You should always use all the information available and so it is better to calculate r where possible as it is more accurate. In situations where measurement is difficult or incomplete, however, ranking can be the answer. Even if only ranks are available, r may still be calculated but as we have said r_s can be very useful if a non-linear relationship is involved.

Example: A group of males and a group of females were each asked to rank the following 'sex symbols' in order of "attractiveness". Do the results below indicate a correlation between male and female perceptions of "attractiveness"?

	Ranking according to Males	Females	differences in ranks d	d^2
Joan Collins	5	6	–1	1
Madonna	1.5	3	–1.5	2.25
Samantha Fox	3.5	7	–3.5	12.25
Selina Scott	6	5	1	1
Nastassja Kinski	1.5	1	0.5	0.25
Victoria Principal	3.5	2	1.5	2.25
Anneka Rice	7	4	3	9
				28

$$r_s = 1 - \frac{6 \times 28}{7(7^2 - 1)} = +0.5$$

Obviously, the experiment was more a bit of fun than a serious academic exercise; the question posed was badly worded and the sample small and unrepresentative. But taking the results at face value they suggest that there is a positive correlation between male and female views of "attractiveness" but it is not a very strong correlation.

WORKED EXAMPLES
Example 1:
Manufacturing industry is a major user of coal and the Index of Industrial Production is an indicator of the level of industrial output. One would expect a fairly high level of correlation between industrial output and coal consumption.

From the data below you are required to:
(a) Calculate the correlation coefficient between coal consumption and industrial production.
(b) Calculate the linear regression equation to estimate coal consumption from industrial production.
(c) According to your regression equation what would be the level of coal consumption if the Index of Industrial Production increased to 105?
(d) What would be the main problem in using your regression equation to predict the demand for coal?

N.B. You may find it helpful to code the data so that
$$Y = \text{coal consumption} - 130 = y - 130$$
$$X = \text{Index of industrial production} - 90 = x - 90$$

Please express your answers to (b) and (c) in terms of the original variables x and y.

Year	Weekly average coal consumption by industry (thousand tonnes) y	Index of Industrial Production (1980=100) (Manufacturing only) x	X	Y	XY	X²	Y²
1979	178	109.4	19.4	48	931.2	376.36	2304
1980	151	100.0	10.0	21	210.0	100.0	441
1981	134	93.6	3.6	4	14.4	12.96	16
1982	137	93.7	3.7	7	25.9	13.69	49
1983	138	95.0	5.0	8	40.0	25.0	64
			41.7	88	1221.5	528.01	2874

Working: $\bar{X}=8.34$ $\bar{Y}=17.6$

For the regression equation $Y = a + bX$

$$b = \frac{\Sigma XY - n\bar{X}\bar{Y}}{\Sigma X^2 - n\bar{X}^2} = \frac{1221.5 - 5 \times 17.6 \times 8.34}{528.01 - 5 \times (8.34)^2} = 2.705291$$

$$a = 17.6 - 2.705291 \times 8.34 = -4.9621266$$

$$\therefore \ Y = -4.9621266 + 2.705291 \ X$$

In terms of the original variables

$$y - 130 = -4.9621266 + 2.705291 \ (x - 90)$$

which simplifies to $\quad y = -118 + 2.7 \ x$

$$r = \frac{1221.5 - \dfrac{41.7 \times 88}{5}}{\sqrt{\left[528.01 - \dfrac{(41.7)^2}{5}\right]\left[2874 - \dfrac{(88)^2}{5}\right]}} = 0.998$$

Answers:
(a) $r = 0.998$
(b) Regression equation is $y = -118 + 2.7x$ where y is coal consumption in thousand tonnes and x is the Index of Industrial Production.
(c) Level of coal consumption would be 165.6 thousand tonnes.
(d) The main problem in using the regression equation would be the level of coal consumption is predicted from the level of industrial production which means that you need to know the level of production before you can predict the demand for coal. If the level of industrial production is itself difficult to estimate then forecasts of the demand for coal will be correspondingly difficult to arrive at.

Example 2

Year	Units of sales	Total costs £
1976	2000	8204
77	4000	13578
78	6000	16175
79	8000	26679
80	11000	33051
81	12000	39615
82	13000	47807
83	14000	50500

The table above shows the sales in units for a firm between 1976 and 1983, and the corresponding level of costs.

Obviously, the more sales and output the firm produces, the higher will be its level of costs.

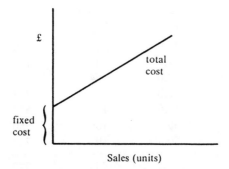

You are required to fit the least squares regression line to the data and hence estimate
1.   TOTAL FIXED COST, and
2.   VARIABLE COST per UNIT (Marginal cost)

However, the costs will have been increased by inflation as well as by the firm's higher output and so before you fit the regression line you must calculate what the total costs would have been at constant prices (please convert all the costs to 1983 price levels). You will need to consult your extract from the Monthly Digest of Statistics to do this.

ANSWER:

Units of Sales	Total Costs* at 1983 prices
2000	17,500
4000	25,000
6000	27,500
8000	40,000
11000	42,000
12000	45,000
13000	50,000
14000	50,500

*For example, the 1976 figure is adjusted to 1983 prices by multiplying by the ratio of the 1983 RPI to the 1976 RPI, i.e. $8204 \times \dfrac{335.1}{157.1} \simeq 17,500$. Sales are clearly the independent variable while total cost depends upon sales. To simplify calculations, code X = Sales/1000 and Y = Cost/1000

X	Y	X²	XY
2	17.5	4	35
4	25.0	16	100
6	27.5	36	165
8	40.0	64	320
11	42.0	121	462
12	45.0	144	540
13	50.0	169	650
14	50.5	196	707
70	297.5	750	2979

$$\bar{X} = \frac{70}{8} = 8.75 \qquad \bar{Y} = \frac{297.5}{8} = 37.1875$$

$$b = \frac{\Sigma XY - n\bar{X}\bar{Y}}{\Sigma X^2 - n\bar{X}^2} = \frac{2979 - 8 \times 8.75 \times 37.1875}{750 - 8 \times 8.75^2} = 2.7336364$$

$$a = \bar{Y} - b\bar{X} = 37.1875 - 2.73 \times 8.75 = 13.268182$$

Regression equation is $Y = 13.268 + 2.734\ X$
or in terms of original variables

$$\text{Total Cost} = 13,268 + 2.734\ X \text{ units of sales}$$

Therefore, Total Fixed Cost = £13268
and Marginal Cost = £2.734 per unit of sales.

QUESTIONS

8.1 An accountant has derived the following data on production costs (£Y) and units of output for the last twelve months:

Y:	150	63	65	165	126	120	91	60	100	90	90	120
X:	30	3	6	34	27	21	15	12	20	13	10	16

$\Sigma X = 207, \Sigma Y = 1,240, \Sigma X^2 = 4,565, \Sigma Y^2 = 140,676, \Sigma XY = 24,686$

You are required:

(a) to plot a scatter diagram of Y against X; *(4 marks)*

(b) to find the least squares regression of production costs on output, and plot the line on the diagram; *(10 marks)*

(c) without performing any further calculations, to *estimate* the approximate value of the correlation coefficient between X and Y; *(2 marks)*

(d) to predict production costs for next month if it is planned to produce 20 units of output, and discuss the likely reliability of this prediction. *(4 marks)*
(Total 20 marks)
(ICMA)

8.2 (a) The least squares line of regression of y upon x is often used in order to predict the value of y given the value of x.
Explain with the aid of a diagram, what is meant by the term 'least squares'.

(b) The following data refer to the time taken to perform a particular operation and its cost.
Determine the least squares regression line of cost upon time taken, and illustrate graphically how well your line fits the data. Indicate on your graph the maximum error that would have been made if the regression line had been used to estimate the cost of these operations.

time (mins)	cost (£)
4	7
4	4
5	7
6	9
7	10
8	14
10	18
12	18

(ACA)

8.3 A book publisher has produced seven comparable books with the following costs:

Quantity produced (000):	1 3 4 5 7 9 13
	Sum of squares = 350
Manufacturing costs (£000):	5 6.2 6.5 7 8 9 10.8
	Sum of squares = 416.33
Sum of cross products, $\sum XY = 362$	

[*Source: Data based on RSS News and Notes, September 1983*]

You are required:
(a) to draw an appropriate scatter diagram on squared paper;
(4 marks)

(b) to derive the least squares regression of manufacturing costs on quantity produced and interpret your results; *(10 marks)*

(c) the company planning a production run of 10,000 copies of an eighth book, to use the results of your regression analysis to estimate the manufacturing costs for this eighth book;

(2 marks)

(d) the publisher receiving £2 per book, to state at what point he will break-even on this eighth book. *(4 marks)*

(ICMA)

*8.4 (a) Measurements on two variables are found to yield a correlation coefficient of 0.35. Give two reasons why it cannot necessarily be inferred that the two variables are causally related. *(6 marks)*

(b) The following table gives the mean daily temperature and the amount of electricity consumed on 8 consecutive Mondays during a year.

Temperature (°F)	37	32	35	40	40	44	42	48
Electricity Consumption (Megawatt hours)	3.7	3.8	3.7	3.6	3.7	3.4	3.4	3.3

Required:

Code the data about the assumed means of 40 and 3.5 so that x = temperature -40; y = electricity consumption -3.5, and use the formula below, or some alternative you prefer, to calculate the coefficient of correlation between temperature and electricity consumption. Comment on your result.

$$r = \left(\Sigma xy - \frac{\Sigma x \Sigma y}{n} \right) \bigg/ \sqrt{\left(\Sigma x^2 - \frac{(\Sigma x)^2}{n} \right) \left(\Sigma y^2 - \frac{(\Sigma y)^2}{n} \right)}$$

(14 marks)

(ACA)

8.5 (a) Explain the purpose of calculating a correlation coefficient and give the possible range of values it may take *(4 marks)*

(b) Suppose that it is found, using some statistical test, that a calculated correlation coefficient of +0.6 between two variables is not significantly different from zero. What does this mean?

(4 marks)

(c) The following table gives the monthly output, x, and labour cost, y, of a factory.

Monthly output (tons × 10³)	Labour cost (£ × 10³)
66	50
74	53
78	59
70	52
81	64
90	85
87	77
85	68

Required:
Calculate the correlation coefficient using

$$r = \frac{n\,\Sigma xy - \Sigma x\,\Sigma y}{\sqrt{[n\,\Sigma x^2 - (\Sigma x)^2]\,[n\,\Sigma y^2 - (\Sigma y)^2]}}, \quad \text{or}$$

some alternative formula that you prefer, and comment on your result. How would your answer be affected if output were measured in tonnes, instead of tons, where 1 ton = 1.016 tonne? *(12 marks)*
(ACA)

8.6 Ten petrol stations, A–J, which are situated in areas of similar traffic density are ranked firstly according to quality of service, secondly according to the size of the forecourt and thirdly according to the price of the petrol sold. Rank 1 indicates best service, largest forecourt and lowest price. The results, including the average weekly petrol sales, are given below.

Station	Quality of service	Forecourt size	Petrol Price	Sales (hundreds of gallons)
A	3	8	2	47
B	7	4	9	20
C	4	10	8	23
D	8	2	1	36
E	2	1	4	36
F	5	3	5	31
G	10	9	7	33
H	9	6	10	28
I	1	4	3	42
J	6	7	6	24

Required:

(1) Carry out calculations to decide whether price of petrol or quality of service is likely to be the more important factor in determining the volume of petrol sales, or whether neither appears to be important.

(2) Is there any evidence to suggest that those stations with large forecourts give better service?

(3) For what reason do you think that the above analysis has been confined to stations having similar traffic density?

You are given Spearman's rank correlation coefficient

$$R = 1 - \frac{6\,\Sigma d^2}{n(n^2 - 1)}$$

(20 marks)
(ACA)

8.7 The time taken to produce batches of an item is found to be related to the number of items in the batch. Records show the production times for 6 batches to be as follows:

Batch size	Production time (hours)
50	4.0
90	5.8
150	6.8
220	7.6
280	7.6
350	8.6

Two alternatives are suggested for estimating the production time, t, from the batch size, r.

(i) $t = 3.5 + r/50$

(ii) $t = 2 + \sqrt{r}/8$

Required:

(1) For each of the two relationships find the values of t corresponding to $r = 72, 128, 200$ and 288.

(2) Use the values obtained in part (1) to construct a graph illustrating the two alternative relationships. From observing your graph state which best represents the data given in the table.

(3) Find the best fitting curve of the form $t = a + b\sqrt{r}$ using least squares regression of t on $\sqrt{r}$.

(You may assume the following, or any other, formula for the regression coefficient, b.)

$$b = \frac{\Sigma xy - n\bar{x}\bar{y}}{\Sigma x^2 - n\bar{x}^2}$$

(20 marks)
(ACA)

*8.8 A national consumer protection society investigated seven brands of paint to determine their quality relative to price. The society's conclusions were ranked as follows:

Brand	Price per litre £	Quality ranking
T	1.92	2
U	1.58	6
V	1.35	7
W	1.60	4
X	2.05	3
Y	1.39	5
Z	1.77	1

Using Spearman's rank correlation coefficient, determine whether the consumer generally gets value for money. *(ICMA)*

Chapter 9
TIME SERIES ANALYSIS

A time series is a set of observations of the value of some variable taken at regular intervals of time. The daily average temperature, the monthly retail price index, the annual balance of payments figures, are all examples of time series.

The analysis of time series data has two main purposes:

(a) **Forecasting**

The most widespread use of time series is to produce forecasts of the value of some variable in the future. So, one will often hear someone say something like "On current trends the level of unemployment will be 5m by 1990". Great care has to be taken when making statements of this type; the further one projects current trends into the future (extrapolation) the more likely it is that some extraneous factor will have a significant effect on the variable in question.

(b) **Control purposes**

Another reason for analysing time series data is that it may be desirable to identify changes in trends so that corrective action can be taken. So, for example, if a firm's sales were falling the firm would obviously wish to identify the reason and, if possible, take corrective action. The trouble is that it is not always obvious that a firm's sales are tending to fall because the trend can be masked by other components in the time series and it is the statistician's job to clarify the situation. A familiar example of trends being masked by other components in a time series is the publication of the monthly unemployment figures; until the introduction of the Youth Training Scheme the unemployment figures were always swollen in the summer months by school-leavers, the figures are worsened in the early winter as construction workers are laid off due to bad weather and are improved in spring and summer as people get seasonal jobs. Government statisticians therefore estimate the underlying trend in the unemployment figures and they are more worthy of attention than the raw figures.

9.1 Elements of time series data

The hypothetical sales data illustrated in Diagram 9.1 exhibits the components which might be encountered in time series data, viz:

(a) **TREND**

The trend is the general movement over a long period of time. It increases or decreases due to factors which tend to change only slowly over time, such as the size of the population, changes in technology, etc. In the diagram the trend is shown by the dotted straight line.

DIAGRAM 9.1

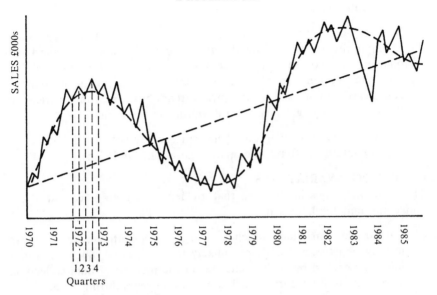

The trend may be difficult to detect if the data is not extensive enough for the cyclical movements to be detected. For example, if we considered only the data between 1973 and 1976 we would assume that the trend was downwards; it is only when we examine the full range of data that it becomes obvious that the downward trend is really part of a long-term cyclical variation. Obviously, extrapolation of a trend is suspect when sufficient data is not available to detect such cyclical variation.

(b) REGULAR VARIATIONS
These are oscillations about the trend which occur, more or less, regularly. Such oscillations may be divided into:

(i) Cyclical variations
Cyclical variations occur at regular intervals but over a fairly long period of time. In the diagram the length of the cycle, the time between each peak or each trough, is about ten years and the dotted curved line shows the long-run trend plus the cyclical variation. These cyclical movements are usually associated with the trade cycle which is a phenomenon familiar to most students of Economics.

(ii) Seasonal variations
Seasonal variations occur over a much shorter period of time and will often have a period of variation related to the calendar year. Increased sales during the Christmas period, changes in demand for electricity at certain times of the day or year, increased demand for public transport at

certain times of the day or week, are all short-term fluctuations that we might call 'seasonal'.

In the diagram, the seasonal nature of the data is quite obvious, sales falling in the second and fourth quarters and rising in the third and first quarters. Of course, the diagram is simplified and exaggerated to illustrate the point; in practice the seasonal decline in the 4th quarter could easily be masked by an upward trend, or the seasonal increase in the 1st quarter might disguise a downturn in the trend.

The solid line in the diagram, then, represents the observed data points which contain the trend, the regular variations, and also:

(c) RANDOM VARIATIONS

These are variations in the data that are left after taking account of the above and may be divided into

(i) **Catastrophic variations** which are large infrequent changes that can usually be explained and are unlikely to be repeated. Such variations might be caused by strikes, changes in the method of data collection, wars, etc. In our diagram, such a variation occurs during 1983.

(ii) **Random variations** — these are small, numerous variations, essentially without pattern, which occur due to random influences. For the sake of clarity, we have not included such variation in our diagram but it would obviously be present in all 'real-world' data.

The task of the statistician is to disentangle these various influences in time series data so that the general trend can be seen, the effect of seasonal (or cyclical) variations can be estimated, and forecasts of future values of the variable made. Each analysis of time series data is probably unique but the main elements would probably be as below.

9.2 Analysis of time series data

1. PLOT THE DATA

The first step is to make a preliminary examination of the data. Simply plotting the data on a time-graph (a historigram not a histogram) may help in identifying any patterns of variability in the data.

2. FIT A TREND LINE TO THE DATA

In section 8.6 we described how we could fit a straight line to time series data by the method of least squares and long-range forecasting is mainly concerned with fitting straight lines or curves to identify the long-term trend in the data.

When we are dealing with a shorter time span we will again be concerned with fitting a trend line to the data but we will want to incorporate the cyclical element as well as the underlying trend into the trend line so that seasonal variation can be estimated.

Deciding what type of line should be fitted to the data can be difficult (in both the long and short-term case), clearly a straight line would not be appropriate for the data in our diagram, and so the method of moving averages is often used to provide an estimate of the trend line. As we shall see, the effect of the moving average is to smooth out the variation in the time series so that we can estimate the seasonal variation in the data (or the cyclical variation when dealing with annual data).

3. ESTIMATE THE SEASONAL VARIATION

Once we have derived the trend line, the deviations between the trend figures and the original series can be used to estimate any seasonal pattern in the data.

4. ESTIMATE THE RESIDUAL VARIATION

We have said that the observed data is composed of various elements.

Observed values = Trend + seasonal variation + residual variation

The residual variations are simply the differences between the observed values and our estimates of the trend and seasonal variations. If we calculate these residuals then we can see how large they are as a proportion of the observed values and if they are only small then we can be confident that forecasts based upon our analysis will be reasonably accurate.

5. DESEASONALISE THE TIME SERIES

When we have an estimate of the seasonal effects in a time series we can deseasonalise the data so that we are left with the trend and residual variation.

If we assume that seasonal variation continues unchanged, we can seasonally adjust future observations so that we can see what is happening to the trend.

6. FORECASTING

By projecting the trend line into the future and adjusting for the appropriate seasonal variation, we can forecast the value of the variable in the future.

It is important to realise that all forecasts will be wrong, what the statistician is trying to do is minimise the forecasting errors. The further ahead one tries to forecast, of course, the more one is likely to be wrong and a good rule of thumb is to never try to forecast more than half as far ahead as the period for which there is past data available.

9.3 **Method of moving averages**

To illustrate the technique of moving averages let us try to analyse the following time series data:

		Units of sales			
Year	Quarter	1	2	3	4
1983		410	320	340	460
1984		420	325	345	470
1985		435	329	349	475
1986		440	335		

9.3.1 Plot the data

The plot of the data (see graph — Diagram 9.2) shows that sales peak during the 4th quarter of each year and then fall away, reaching their lowest level in the 2nd quarter, before increasing again in the 3rd quarter. Each succeeding peak and trough is at a higher level indicating a rising trend.

9.3.2 Moving average estimate of trend

The method of moving averages is simply to calculate the arithmetic mean for a series of measurements covering the seasonal variations (or cyclical variations when dealing with annual data). This average is then used as an estimate of the trend at the centre of the series of measurements to which it refers.

In this example we take a 4-point average of the quarterly data. Each estimate of the trend (Moving Quarterly Average — MQA) covers a full year and so the effect of seasonal fluctuations is removed. Because, in this case, there are an even number of points the MQA is centred between two observations; this does not matter from the point of view of plotting the trend line but when we calculate the seasonal factors we need to compare the actual observations with the trend estimate and so the MQA has to be re-centred to coincide with the observed values.

The Moving Annual Total (MAT) was mentioned in connection with Z charts. The MAT at the mid-point of 1983 = 410+320+340+460=1530. The MAT centred between the 3rd and 4th quarters of 1983 = 320+340+460+420= 1540 and so on with the sales figure that is dropped being replaced by the sales figure for the corresponding quarter of the following year.

The Moving Quarterly Average is simply the MAT divided by 4.

The re-centred trend estimate is the average of the two MQAs that estimate the trend either side of the point; for example, the recentred trend estimate at the 3rd quarter of 1983 is $\frac{1}{2}(382.5+385) = 383.75$.

The principle for calculating the moving average with monthly data is exactly the same except that the MAT consists of 12 monthly figures and the Monthly Moving Average is calculated by dividing by 12. If it is possible to use a 13-point average of four-weekly data it has the advantage of not requiring re-centring and of being based on **exactly** equally-spaced measurements.

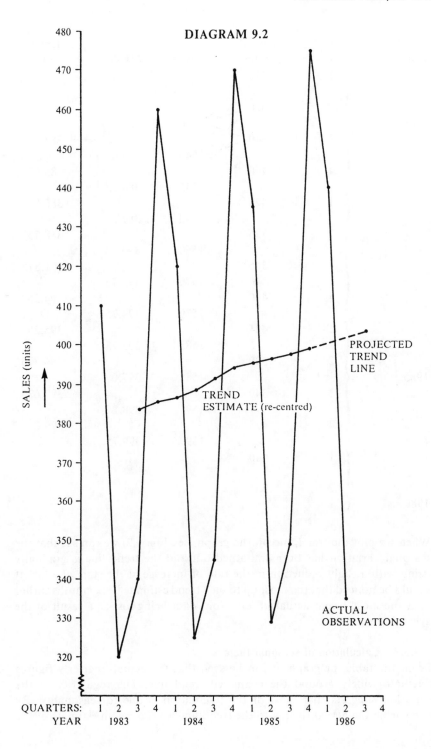

DIAGRAM 9.2

Year	Quarter	Actual Sales	MAT	MQA	Recentred trend estimate
1983	1	410			
	2	320			
			1530	382.5	
	3	340			383.75
			1540	385.0	
	4	460			385.625
			1545	386.25	
1984	1	420			386.875
			1550	387.5	
	2	325			388.75
			1560	390.0	
	3	345			391.875
			1575	393.75	
	4	470			394.25
			1579	394.75	
1985	1	435			395.25
			1583	395.75	
	2	329			396.375
			1588	397.0	
	3	349			397.625
			1593	398.25	
	4	475			399.0
			1599	399.75	
1986	1	440			
	2	335			

When we plot the trend line on the graph (see Fig. 9.2) we can see that the seasonal variation has been smoothed out and the trend line is gradually rising with a slight reduction in the rate of increase at the start of 1985. It should be noticed that the most up to date trend estimate is six months earlier than the most recent actual observation, data being lost as a result of the averaging process.

9.3.3 Calculation of seasonal factors

From the table, or graph, it can be seen that the actual quarterly figures fluctuate widely around the estimated trend line. The regularity of the variation suggests that most of the fluctuation is due to seasonality. By comparing the actual figures to the trend line we can get an estimate of the seasonal factor for each quarter. There are two methods of dealing with seasonal factors:

Multiplicative model: Observed figure = trend figure $\times$ seasonal factor

so that, seasonal factor $= \dfrac{\text{observed figure}}{\text{trend figure}}$ (Ratio)

Additive model: Observed figure = trend figure + seasonal factor

so that, seasonal factor = observed figure – trend figure (Deviation)

The multiplicative method tends to be used more frequently because it tends to be more realistic. Both methods are illustrated below.

Year	Quarter	Actual Sales	Trend estimate	Seasonal factors Ratio	Seasonal factors Deviation
1983	1	410			
	2	320			
	3	340	383.75	0.886	–43.75
	4	460	385.625	1.193	74.375
1984	1	420	386.875	1.086	33.125
	2	325	388.75	0.836	–63.75
	3	345	391.875	0.880	–46.875
	4	470	394.25	1.192	75.75
1985	1	435	395.25	1.101	39.75
	2	329	396.375	0.830	–67.375
	3	349	397.625	0.878	–48.625
	4	475	399.000	1.190	76.00
1986	1	440			
	2	335			

The seasonal factors are reasonably constant indicating that most of the variation is the result of seasonality. Of course, some of the variation is due to random influences and the seasonal effects will be slightly different between years.

To get a more representative measure of the seasonal effects we can take the average of 2 or 3 years' estimates of the seasonal factors:

Average Seasonal Factors

Quarter	Ratio	Deviation
1	1.093 [3]	36.4375
2	0.833	–65.5625
3	0.881 [1]	–46.417 [2]
4	1.192	75.375
	3.999	–0.127

$$^{(1)} \quad \frac{0.886 + 0.880 + 0.878}{3} = 0.881$$

$$^{(2)} \quad \frac{-(43.75 + 46.875 + 48.625)}{3} = -46.417$$

$$^{(3)} \quad \frac{1.086 + 1.101}{2} = 1.0935$$

The seasonal factors indicate that in the 3rd quarter, for example, sales are on average 88% of the underlying trend level or 46 units below the trend figure.

Strictly speaking, the sum of the seasonal factors should be 4.000 and zero for the ratios and deviations respectively. This is because the seasonal effects must balance out around the average otherwise the sum of the trend figures and the deviations (or the trend figures multiplied by the relevant seasonal factors) will not be the same as the annual total obtained by adding up the four quarterly trend figures. We can correct the rounding errors in the seasonal factors by multiplying each of the ratios by 4.000/3.999 and adding 0.127/4 to each of the deviations or by making some other 'ad hoc' adjustment.

In this example, the ratio for the first quarter was 1.0935 and so we can legitimately call it 1.094 to make the ratios total to 4.000 (note that if we had monthly data the ratios would have to sum to 12). In the case of the deviations, the original series was in whole numbers and we are claiming more accuracy than is warranted when quoting the seasonal deviations to two decimal places. When we add 0.127/4 to each of the seasonal deviations and round to whole numbers the deviations do sum to zero as below.

Average Seasonal Factors (corrected)

Quarter	Ratio	Deviation
1	1.094	36
2	0.833	−65
3	0.881	−46
4	1.192	75
	4.000	0.000

9.3.4 Examine the residuals

As we said earlier, the observed data is composed of various elements, viz:

Observed value = Trend + seasonal variation + residual variation

The residual variation is thus the difference between the observed values and the values "predicted" by the trend line and seasonal factors.

Using the corrected seasonal factors above, let us calculate the residual variation.

Year	Quarter	Actual sales	Trend estimate	Average seasonal factor (ratio)	Seasonally adjusted trend figure	Residual variation [i.e. Actual sales – seasonally adjusted trend figure]	Residual variation as % of actual sales
1983	3	340	383.75	0.881	338.1	1.9	0.56
	4	460	385.625	1.192	459.7	0.3	0.06
1984	1	420	386.875	1.094	423.2	–3.2	0.76
	2	325	388.75	0.833	323.8	1.2	0.37
	3	345	391.875	0.881	345.2	–0.2	0.06
	4	470	394.25	1.192	469.9	0.1	0.02
1985	1	435	395.25	1.094	432.4	2.6	0.59
	2	329	396.375	0.833	330.2	–1.2	0.36
	3	349	397.625	0.881	350.3	–1.3	0.37
	4	475	399.000	1.192	475.6	–0.6	0.13

We can see that in this case the residual variation is very small, never approaching even 1% of the observed value.

We could therefore be confident that any forecasts based upon the analysis would, other things being equal, be reasonably accurate.

9.3.5 Seasonal Adjustments
Estimates of the seasonal factors can be useful when interpreting subsequent figures in the time series. If, for example, the level of unemployment was 3.3m last month and this month it is 3.29m can we infer that the underlying trend is coming down?

If we know the seasonal variation we can deseasonalise, or seasonally adjust, the data. To remove the seasonal element from an actual figure we simply apply the seasonal factor in reverse, i.e. we divide the actual figure by the seasonal ratio or deduct a positive deviation.

For example, if the sales figure for the 3rd quarter of 1986 turned out to be 350, is this an increase or decrease on the previous quarter?

			Seasonal factor	Seasonally adjusted figure
1986	2nd Qtr	335	÷ 0.833	402
	3rd Qtr	350	÷ 0.881	397

This result shows that the underlying trend has turned downwards.

9.3.6 Forecasting
To produce a forecast we have to project the trend line into the future. Unless we fit some kind of curve to the trend we have to assume that the trend can be approximated by a straight line. Even if the trend is a curve, a straight line

approximation will be reasonably accurate as long as we do not try to predict too far ahead. Of course, many factors may change in the long-run and so that is another reason why we should not try to forecast too far ahead.

We can make our forecast by continuing the trend line on our time graph and reading off the relevant sales forecast. Alternatively, and probably more accurately, we can average out the last few increments in the trend line to estimate the slope of the trend line. It is best to take only 2 or 3 increments because if we go too far back we may dampen the current trend.

The MQA extends slightly further than the recentred trend so we will look at the MQA. The last three increments are 1.25, 1.25, and 1.5 (average=1.33). If we wish to forecast the sales figure for the 3rd Quarter of 1986 we can project the MQA forward at the average rate of 1.33 per Quarter and recentre as shown below.

	Qtr	MQA	MQA increment	
1985	1			
		395.75		
	2		1.25	
		397.00		
	3		1.25	
		398.25		
	4		1.50	
		399.75		
1986	1		1.33	
		401.08		
	2		1.33	
		402.41		Estimated
	3		1.33	
		403.74		
	4			

The recentred trend estimate $= \dfrac{402.41 + 403.74}{2} = 403.075$ for the 3rd Qtr. of 1986.

Alternatively, we could say that the least MQA is centred between the 4th Qtr of 1985 and the 1st Qtr of 1986. We want the estimate at the 3rd Qtr of 1986 which is $2\frac{1}{2}$ quarters ahead. Our estimate of the trend would be the MQA centred between the 4th Qtr of 1985 and the 1st Qtr of 1986 plus $2\frac{1}{2}$ increments

i.e. $399.75 + 2\frac{1}{2} \times 1.33 = 403.075$

Adjusting for seasonality our forecast would be $403.075 \times 0.881 = \underline{\underline{355}}$.

In conclusion, we must again point out that all forecasts will be wrong! No matter how sophisticated the forecasting model, nobody can foretell the future. All that we can do is examine the patterns revealed in the past data and project them into the future. Even if we try to forecast for only a short period ahead any major change in factors outside our model may completely invalidate our forecasts.

Sales forecasting, in particular, is fraught with difficulties even in the short-run. Have any major customers appeared or disappeared? How is the level of demand behaving nationally? Can the firm increase its market share? Do competitors have any surprises up their sleeve? Have supply figures failed to match demand in the past? etc. Needless to say, dealing with non-numerical information is especially difficult.

Having added these caveats, the patterns of the past do repeat themselves and time series analysis is an important tool in removing some of the uncertainties facing organisations when planning for the future.

9.4   Exponential Smoothing

If you look again at Fig. 9.2 you will see that the most recent trend estimate is 6 months behind the most recent observation. This is because data is lost as a result of the averaging process.

The trend estimate is simply an average over a period chosen to cover the seasonal variation. In our example, each trend estimate included each of the four quarters of a year. This averaging process means that equal weight is given to all the data available over the previous year and if there is a change in the trend then there is a lag before this is reflected in the trend estimates.

It can be argued that the best estimate of the future is the present and so we should give more weight to the most recent data so that changes are quickly reflected in the trend estimates. A method which adopts this approach is **exponential smoothing,** so called because the weights form a negative exponential distribution, reducing by a constant proportion, with the greatest weight being attached to the most recent observation.

The calculation of a trend estimate using exponential smoothing is very simple and is performed using the formula:—

$$E_t = \alpha X_t + (1 - \alpha) E_{t-1}$$

where X_t = Observed value for time period t;
E_t = Estimated value for time period t;
E_{t-1} = Estimated value for time period (t–1); and
α = a smoothing constant

Computationally, the formula is best re-arranged as:—

$$E_t = E_{t-1} + \alpha (X_t - E_{t-1})$$

i.e. Latest estimate = last estimate + α (latest observation – last estimate).

The smoothing constant can take any value between 0 and 1. A high value will give more weight to recent observations but this may not be desirable if one wishes to average out random variations. In practice, a range of values would be tried on the data to find which gave the best results.

As with simple moving averages, the latest trend estimate calculated by exponential smoothing is centred on a time period behind the observed values. The 'lag' can be shown to be $\frac{1-\alpha}{\alpha}$ time periods.

So, if we choose a smoothing constant of $\alpha = 0.2$ then our latest trend estimate is $\frac{1-0.2}{0.2} = 4$ time points behind the latest observed value.

To illustrate the method, let us use the deseasonalised figures from our example and a value of $\alpha = 0.2$.

Year	Quarter	Actual sales	Average seasonal factor (ratio)	Seasonally adjusted sales figures X_t	E_{t-1}	(X_t-E_{t-1})	$\alpha(X_t-E_{t-1})$	E_t
1983	1	410	1.094	374.8	370 ①	4.8	0.96	370.96
	2	320	0.833	384.1	370.96	13.14	2.628	373.588
	3	340	0.881	385.9	373.588	12.312	2.462	376.050
	4	460	1.192	385.9	376.050	9.850	1.970	378.020
1984	1	420	1.094	383.9	378.020	5.88	1.176	379.196
	2	325	0.833	390.2	379.196	11.004	2.201	381.397
	3	345	0.881	391.6	381.397	10.203	2.041	383.438
	4	470	1.192	394.3	383.438	10.862	2.172	385.610
1985	1	435	1.094	397.6	385.610	11.99	2.398	388.008
	2	329	0.833	395.0	388.008	6.992	1.398	389.406
	3	349	0.881	396.1	389.406	6.694	1.339	390.745
	4	475	1.192	398.5	390.745	7.755	1.551	392.296
1986	1	440	1.094	402.2	392.296	9.904	1.981	394.277
	2	335	0.833	402.2	394.277	7.923	1.585	395.862

① The initial value of the last estimate can be any reasonable value because its effect on the trend estimate quickly disappears in the up-dating process.

Our latest trend estimate is 395.862 but this is centred 4 periods back — the 2nd Quarter of 1985.

If we wished to produce a forecast for the 3rd Quarter of 1986 we would need to project the trend 5 time periods forward. There are more sophisticated methods but let us simply average out the last three increments in the trend.

The average increment is therefore $\frac{1}{3}(1.551 + 1.981 + 1.585) = 1.706$.

Our trend estimate for the 3rd Quarter of 1986 would therefore be 395.862 + 5 × 1.706 = 404.392.

Adjusting for seasonality, our forecast would be 404.392 × 0.881 = 356. (The simple moving average gave a forecast of 355).

Notice that we had to deseasonalise the data before using the smoothing constant. If this is not done the trend estimate will also exhibit seasonal variation but it will probably be "out of phase" with the actual seasonal variation. This is not a major problem so long as the seasonal effects are reasonably constant and/or are regularly updated. More sophisticated models incorporate seasonal terms into the forecasting equation.

QUESTIONS — TIME SERIES ANALYSIS

9.1   The following information has been supplied by the sales department. Sales in units.

Quarter:	1	2	3	4
Year				
1973	100	125	127	102
1974	104	128	130	107
1975	110	131	133	107
1976	109	132		

You are required to:
(a)   calculate a four quarterly moving average of the above series;
(b)   calculate the sales corrected for seasonal movements;
(c)   plot the actual sales and the sales corrected for seasonal movements on a single graph; and
(d)   comment on your findings.   *(ICMA)*

9.2   The sales of an item which show a marked seasonal variation are given below for the last three years.

			Sales (thousands)			
	Jan/Feb	Mar/Apr	May/Jun	Jul/Aug	Sept/Oct	Nov/Dec
1973			10.3	12.8	20.3	32.4
1974	6.8	9.0	10.9	14.4	23.1	35.4
1975	7.0	9.5	11.6	15.3	24.5	37.4
1976	7.3	9.9				

Required:
(1)   Use the method of moving averages to find the trend.

(2)   Assuming that the general rate of increase of sales occurring over the period observed is maintained, estimate graphically the trend values for each of the remaining two-month periods of 1976.

(3) Determine the seasonal effect for the period July/August and estimate the sales that will occur in the period July/August 1976.

(20 marks)
(ACA)

9.3 The daily output of your company over a four week period is shown in the following table.

Number of units of output

	Monday	Tuesday	Wednesday	Thursday	Friday
Week 1	187	203	208	207	217
Week 2	207	208	210	206	212
Week 3	202	210	212	205	214
Week 4	208	215	217	217	213

Required:

(a) Using the additive time series model establish the five-period moving average trend of output. *(5 marks)*

(b) Display on a graph the actual data together with the trend figures. *(5 marks)*

(c) Establish the daily deviations from the trend and use these to determine the average daily variations. *(5 marks)*

(d) Forecast the daily output for the first two days of Week 5 to the nearest unit of production. *(3 marks)*

(e) Comment upon the accuracy of the forecast that you have made. *(2 marks)*

(Total 20 marks)
(ACA)

*9.4   Index numbers of retail sales in Great Britain (1978 = 100)

	1980	1981	1982	1983
Q1	—	131	141	153
Q2	124	134	145	—
Q3	129	139	151	—
Q4	155	168	184	—

(Source: Monthly Digest of Statistics, August 1983)

You are required:

(a) to plot these data and an appropriate moving average on the same graph; *(12 marks)*

(b) assuming an additive model, to find the mean seasonal variations for each quarter and predict retail sales for the *fourth* quarter of 1983. *(8 marks)*
(ICMA)

9.5 The sales of an item with a marked seasonal pattern are given below for each quarter of the last three years:

		Quarter		
	1	2	3	4
1975	325	382	350	363
1976	393	452	430	421
1977	471	530	500	510

Required:
(1) Use the method of moving averages to find the trend.
(2) The company is considering using the following simple rule in future for detecting whether the trend of sales is rising or falling:

If the sales in the 2nd quarter are s_2 and the sales in the 4th quarter are s_4, then sales are falling if the difference, $s_2 - s_4$, is greater than some quantity d.
Carry out any necessary calculations to explain which of the following values is most suitable for d.
$$-100, -70, -40, -10, 0, 10, 40, 70, 100.$$

(20 marks)
(ACA)

9.6 Your company, Manco plc., is currently analyzing the hours worked by its employees both manual and non-manual in the production department. The average hours worked in a week by a sample of forty employees are shown in the following table:

46.2	45.0	45.1	45.6	45.8	46.0	45.0	43.5
39.1	39.2	39.1	39.2	39.4	39.6	39.4	38.8
44.3	43.4	43.4	43.8	44.0	44.2	43.4	42.0
43.0	42.3	42.3	42.7	42.8	43.0	42.3	41.2
39.9	39.5	39.6	39.8	39.9	39.9	39.8	39.6

Required:
(a) Group the figures into a frequency distribution in four groups.
(4 marks)
(b) Calculate the mean of the distribution. *(4 marks)*
(c) Calculate the standard deviation of the distribution. *(4 marks)*
(d) Interpret the results that you obtain in parts (b) and (c) in the context of the average hours worked by the employees of Manco plc. *(2 marks)*

(e) One of the employees worked 44.2, 45.4, 46.2, 46.0, and 45.7 hours in a five week period. Smooth the data by using the formula
$$S_t = S_{t-1} + 0.1(A_t - S_{t-1}).$$
Where S_t is the new smoothed value
S_{t-1} is the previous smoothed value
A_t is the actual value
and $S_0 = 40$ *(4 marks)*

(f) Explain what purpose such a smoothing process as in part (e) serves. *(2 marks)*
(Total 20 marks)
(ACA)

9.7 The following is extracted from the Monthly Digest of Statistics:

Chemicals

	Fertiliser Production (thousands of tons)
1974	
April	37.7
May	32.3
June	39.3
July	42.0
August	38.0
September	41.2
October	36.0
November	28.5
December	35.3
1975	
January	32.9
February	38.4
March	36.9
April	35.3
May	34.1
June	31.9
July	39.5

(Source: Department of Industry)

You are required to:
(a) round the production figures to the nearest whole thousand tons;
(b) calculate a five-month moving average of the rounded series;
(c) plot actual and moving average figures on a graph;
(d) state the error due to rounding on each moving average.
(ICMA)

*9.8 The quarterly electricity account for your company is tabulated as follows:

Electricity Account (£)
Quarter

Year	1	2	3	4
1982		662	712	790
1983	686	718	821	846
1984	743	782	827	876
1985	805	842	876	

Required:

(a) Assuming the additive model, establish the centred trend values for the data using a method moving averages. *(6 marks)*

(b) (i) Plot the original data and the trend values together on a properly labelled graph. *(4 marks)*

(ii) Draw the trend line on the graph. *(2 marks)*

(c) If the seasonal variations are –56 for quarter 1, –39 for quarter 2, 45 for quarter 3 and 51 for quarter 4 deseasonalise the original data. *(4 marks)*

(d) By extending the trend line establish forecasts for the electricity account values for quarter 4, 1985 and quarter 1, 1986. *(4 marks)*

(20 marks)
(ACA)

*9.9 (a) The last eight quarterly figures for the cost of temporary secretarial staff is as follows:

Cost of temporary secretarial staff in £
Quarter

Year	I	II	III	IV
1984				2,700
1985	2,800	2,709	2,574	2,790
1986	2,910	2,721	2,640	

Required:

(i) Forecast the cost of temporary secretarial staff for the fourth quarter of 1986, using exponential smoothing with a smoothing constant of 0.4.

Using the method of exponential smoothing, the appropriate formula is;

New forecast = Old forecast + 0.4 (Actual cost – Old forecast). *(5 marks)*

(ii) What is the purpose of exponential smoothing in this case? *(3 marks)*

(b) Your company manufactures three products B209, K257 and LB3. It has been decided for the information of the shareholders to produce a sales price index for use in the annual report and accounts. It is your task to construct and explain this index number from the following data:

Annual Sales Data
(at 31 March)

| | 1982 | | 1986 | |
	Sales Price £	Sales Quantity (thousands of items)	Sales Price £	Sales Quantity (thousands of items)
B209	1.67	953	2.57	692
K257	3.23	295	4.28	398
LB3	3.81	175	4.68	202

Required:

(i) Calculate the base weighted sales price index for the year ended 31 March 1986 based on the year ended 31 March 1982.

(4 marks)

(ii) Calculate the current weighted sales price index for the year ended 31 March 1986 based on the year ended 31 March 1982.

(4 marks)

(iii) You chose to publish the base weighted sales price index number. Describe to a non-enlightened shareholder how this index has been set up and its purpose. *(4 marks)*

(Total 20 marks)

(ACA)

Chapter 10
BASIC CONCEPTS IN MATHEMATICS

Although we have already employed some quite complicated formulae the explanations of these formulae have avoided all but the most simple mathematics.

The purpose of this chapter is to introduce some fairly basic concepts in mathematics which can be useful in a business, and wider, context. Some of the topics also provide a foundation for more advanced quantitative and analytical techniques.

10.1 The concept of a function
When the value of one variable is determined by the value of another variable we say that there is a functional relationship between the two variables. The two variables are often separated into a dependent variable (usually denoted by the letter 'y') and an independent variable (usually denoted by 'x') and we say that "y is a function of x".

Mathematically, this can be written:—
$$y = f(x)$$
This **does not mean** that y equals f times x, it means that the value of y depends upon the value assigned to x.

Usually, we will want to know the specific form of the functional relationship so that the value of y can be found for a specific value of x. For example, when we used the method of least squares to fit a line to the data in the worked example in Section 8.2 we found the equation to the regression line to be
$$Y = 7.58 + 1.208X$$

This was not a perfect mathematical relationship, but we later found that there was a high correlation between X and Y and so we could use the equation to deduce values of Y for given values of X with some confidence.

The set of values which x may take (i.e. those values of x for which y is defined) is called the **DOMAIN** of the function and the set of values which y takes is called the **RANGE** of the function. In the case of our regression equation we would need to be careful when 'extrapolating'; we would accept a domain wider than that for which we have values of X and Y but not too wide.

Sometimes, a mathematical relationship may be stated more precisely. For example,
$$y = + \sqrt{(2-x)(x-1)}$$
$$1 \leqslant x \leqslant 2$$

means that y is the positive square root of the product of (2–x) and (x–1) for values of x between 1 and 2. As a matter of interest, the range of this function is all numbers between 0 and $\frac{1}{2}$ inclusive.

10.2 Graphs of functions

It is often useful to present a functional relationship in the form of a graph. We have already dealt with the graphs of functions in Section 3.4.6.5 and you might like to refer back at this point.

Sometimes we may wish to simply sketch the graph of a function rather than laboriously preparing a schedule of the corresponding values of x and y before plotting them on graph paper.

Sketching graphs will become easier when you have had a little practice and studied a little more mathematics. At this point, the following rules may be helpful:—

(i) Examine the equation to discover if it is a straight line. If the equation contains x and/or y to the power one only then it is a straight line. So the following equations would all be straight lines:—

$$y = 10 + 3x$$
$$y = 5$$
$$x = 3$$
$$\frac{x}{7} + \frac{y}{2} = 35$$
$$5x - 7y = 319 \quad \text{etc.}$$

If the equation is a straight line then it is a simple matter to sketch it. Usually it will be advisable to calculate the values of y when x=0 and when x = some other value in the domain of x.

For example, if we wished to sketch the function y=10 + 3x, as in Diagram 10.1, we could note immediately that if x=0 then y=10 and we could calculate another value for y when x equals say 5 to be y = 10 + 3 × 5 = 25.

DIAGRAM 10.1

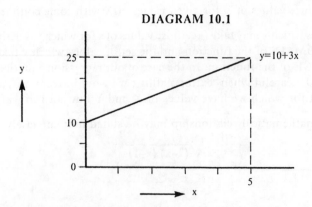

(ii) If the equation contains terms with higher, or lower, powers than one we get curves and these are more difficult to sketch; there are, however, some tricks of the trade which may help:—

(a) Find out at what value(s) of x the function is zero.

(b) Put x=0 into the equation to find the value(s) of the function at that point.

(c) Consider the behaviour of the function when x is very large or very small, i.e. $x \rightarrow \pm \infty$.

(d) Calculate the values of x and y when y is at a maximum or minimum value. This involves "differentiation" which we will deal with at a later stage.

(e) Calculate any key values for x and y which have not already emerged.

As an example, suppose that we wanted to sketch the graph of the function
$$y = f(x) = x^2 - 2x - 8$$

Following the rules laid out above:

(a) If the function is zero
$$y = 0 = x^2 - 2x - 8$$
So at what values of x does y = 0?

This is not obvious until we realise that we can "factorise" the function to give
$$x^2 - 2x - 8 = (x - 4)(x + 2)$$
So that when f(x)=0 x=4 or –2 since either (x–4) or (x+2) must equal zero.

We will deal with "factorisation" in detail later.

(b) If x = 0 what is the value of the function?
$$y = x^2 - 2x - 8 = 0^2 - 2 \times 0 - 8 = -8$$

(c) What happens when x is very large or very small?

If $x = +\infty$, $x^2 - 2x - 8$ will be very large and positive because x^2 will be very large and positive and will dominate the value of the expression.

Similarly, if $x = -\infty$, x^2 will again be large and positive (a minus times a minus gives a plus) and so the function will be large and positive.

(d) What is the max/min value of y?
$$y = x^2 - 2x - 8$$
$$\therefore \quad \frac{dy}{dx} = 2x - 2 = 0 \text{ at max or min}$$
$$\therefore \quad 2x = 2 \text{ at max or min}$$
$$\therefore \quad x = 1 \text{ at max or min}$$

We will explain this later, suffice to say for the moment that $x = 1$ is at the minimum value of y and that value of y is given by substituting $x = 1$ in the equation to give $y = 1 - 2 - 8 = -9$

(e) In this case it is unnecessary to calculate any further values and we can sketch the graph as in Diagram 10.2.

DIAGRAM 10.2

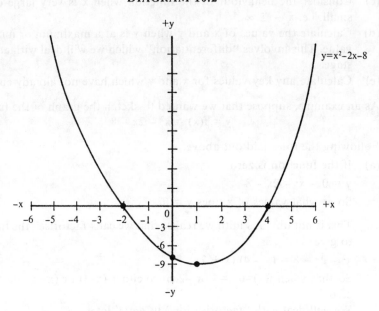

$y=x^2-2x-8$

10.3 Simultaneous linear equations

Two equations are "simultaneous" if there exist values for x and y (the variables) which satisfy both equations. Consider, for example, the two equations

$$y = 3x \quad \text{and} \quad y = 2x + 1$$

DIAGRAM 10.3

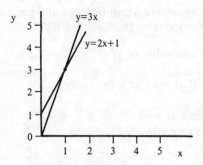

The graph in Diagram 10.3 illustrates that the values y=3, x=1 satisfy both equations and provide a solution to the simultaneous equations.

A set of simultaneous linear equations may not always possess a unique solution; it is possible that there is no solution or more than one solution. Graphically, we could illustrate these possibilities as below

DIAGRAM 10.4   **DIAGRAM 10.5**

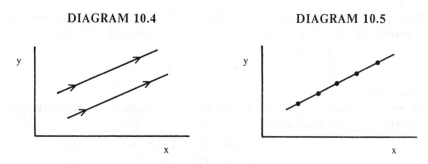

If the equations are represented, as in Diagram 10.4, by parallel (and distinct) lines then there is no solution and the equations are said to be **inconsistent**.

$$\text{e.g. } 2x + 3y = 1 \quad \text{and} \quad 6x + 9y = 2$$

If the equations, as in Diagram 10.5, are represented by co-incident lines then there are infinitely many solutions and one of the equations is **redundant,** i.e. a multiple of the other.

$$\text{e.g. } 2x + 3y = 1 \quad \text{and} \quad 6x + 9y = 3$$

10.3.1   Solving simultaneous linear equations

Rather than graphing the two lines to find the point of intersection, it is usually quicker, and more accurate, to solve simultaneous equations algebraically.

The procedure which is usually best adopted is:—

(a) Multiply one, or both, equations so that the coefficient of one of the variables (the number in front of the x or y) is the same in both equations.

Unless there is an easier way, you can always achieve this by multiplying each equation by the coefficient of the chosen variable in the other equation.

(b) Add, or subtract, the two equations (after the necessary multiplication) so that one of the variables disappears from the resultant equation and solve for the remaining variable.

(c) Substitute the value of the variable which is now known in one of the equations to solve for the other variable.

(d) Check that the values of the variables do, in fact, satisfy both equations.

EXAMPLE:
Solve the simultaneous equations

$$5x - 3y = 34 \qquad ①$$
$$3x - 4y = 16 \qquad ②$$

SOLUTION:
Stage ⓐ
Multiply equation ① by 4 (the coefficient of y in equation ② and multiply equation ② by 3 (the coefficient of y in equation ①) to give

$$① \times 4 \qquad 20 \quad - 12y = 136 \qquad ③$$
$$② \times 3 \qquad 9x - 12y = \;\; 48 \qquad ④$$

Stage ⓑ
Since the sign in front of 12y is negative in both equations we need to subtract equation ④ from equation ③

$$20x - 12y = 136 \qquad\qquad ③$$
$$9x - 12y = \;\; 48 \qquad\qquad ④$$

$$③ - ④ \qquad 11x \qquad = \;\; 88$$

$$\therefore \; x = 8$$

Stage ⓒ
If we now substitute x=8 in, say, equation ① we can find y.

$$5x - 3y = 34 \qquad ①$$
$$\therefore \;\; 40 - 3y = 34$$
$$-3y = 34-40$$
$$-3y = -6$$
$$y = +2$$

Stage ⓓ
Check that y=2, x=8 satisfies both equations.

$$① \qquad 5\times8 - 3\times2 = 34$$
$$② \qquad 3\times8 - 4\times2 = 16$$

Answer: y=2, x=8.

Alternatively, you can use one of the equations to express one of the variables in terms of the other variable (plus constant terms), substitute this expression in the other equation, and solve directly.

So, in the above example, from equation ①

$$x = \left[\frac{34+3y}{5} \right]$$

and substituting for x in equation ②

$$3 \left[\frac{34 + 3y}{5} \right] - 4y = 16$$

which contains only one unknown and so can be solved as follows:

$$\frac{102 + 9y}{5} - 4y = 16$$

$$\frac{102 + 9y - 20y}{5} = \frac{80}{5}$$

$$102 + 9y - 20y = 80$$
$$9y - 20y = 80 - 102$$
$$-11y = -22$$
$$y = 2$$

then substitute y=2 in equation ① or ② to give x=8 as before.

Two things to remember:
1. If you do something to one side of an equation you must do the same to the other side.
2. If a term is moved from one side of an equation to the other, the sign in front of it is altered.

10.3.2 Simultaneous linear equations in three unknowns

If we have three variables we need three simultaneous equations to find a solution (assuming one exists). As we shall see later, the theory of determinants provides a systematic method of elimination of unknowns between simultaneous linear equations but, in practice, it is usually simpler to solve by elementary algebra. The procedure is:—
(a) Eliminate one of the unknowns in two pairs of equations and then
(b) solve the two simultaneous equations obtained as already described.

EXAMPLE:
Solve the following simultaneous equations

$$6x + 4y - 2z = 5 \qquad ①$$
$$3x - 2y + 4z = 10 \qquad ②$$
$$5x - 2y + 6z = -13 \qquad ③$$

SOLUTION:

①
②× 2

$$6x + 4y - 2z = 5$$
$$6x - 4y + 8z = -20$$

Adding $12x \qquad + 6z = -15 \qquad$ ④

③ - ② $2x \qquad + 2z = -3 \qquad$ ⑤

Equations ④ and ⑤ can now be solved in the normal way

⑤× 3 $6x + 6z = -9$

④ $12x + 6z = -15$

Subtracting $-6x = +6$

$x = -1$
$y = 2\frac{1}{2}$
$z = -\frac{1}{2}$

10.3.3 Simultaneous Linear and Quadratic Equations

A quadratic equation is one which contains the square of one of the variables. Examples of quadratic equations would be

$$y = x^2$$
$$y = x^2 + 2x$$
$$y = x^2 + 2x - 3$$
$$y = 5x^2 - 2x - 3$$
etc.

Suppose we had to solve the following simultaneous equations:—

$$y = 10 + 3x + x^2 \qquad \text{(quadratic)}$$
$$y = 22 + 2x \qquad \text{(linear)}$$

We could, of course, draw a graph.

DIAGRAM 10.6

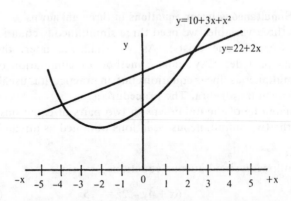

If we constructed the graph, as in Diagram 10.6, we could simply read off the values of x which satisfy both equations.

i.e. x=−4 and x=+4

and the corresponding values for y

i.e. y=+14 and y=+28

Again, we might be able to find the solution more quickly, and sometimes more accurately, by algebraic methods.

The procedure is to simply replace one of the unknowns in the quadratic equation. Replacing for y gives

$$22 + 2x = 10 + 3x + x^2 \qquad \text{which simplifies to give}$$
$$x^2 + x - 12 = 0$$

We now have a quadratic equation in the single variable x and we need to find the values or "roots" of x which satisfy the equation. For the moment, let us again factorise the equation.

$$x^2 + x - 12 = 0 \qquad \text{to give}$$
$$(x+4)(x-3) = 0$$
$$\therefore \ x = -4 \text{ or } 3$$

These values can be substituted in one of the original equations to find the corresponding values for y as above.

What is required then is some method for solving quadratic equations. There are, in fact, two methods:—
1. Formula method;
2. factorisation.

10.3.4 General formula for the roots of a quadratic equation

Any quadratic equation can be expressed in the form
$$ax^2 + bx + c = 0$$
and the values or "roots" of x which satisfy this equation are

$$x = \frac{-b \pm \sqrt{b^2 - 4ac}}{2a}$$

N.B. You must learn this formula.

Proof:

If $\quad ax^2 + bx + c = 0$

Then $\quad x^2 + \dfrac{bx}{a} + \dfrac{c}{a} = 0 \qquad$ (dividing by a)

$x^2 + \dfrac{bx}{a} \qquad = -\dfrac{c}{a} \qquad$ (re-arranging)

$x^2 + \dfrac{bx}{a} + \dfrac{b^2}{4a^2} = -\dfrac{c}{a} + \dfrac{b^2}{4a^2} \qquad$ (adding $\dfrac{b^2}{4a^2}$ to both sides in order to complete square on LHS)

$\left(x + \dfrac{b}{2a} \right)^2 = \dfrac{b^2}{4a^2} - \dfrac{c}{a} \qquad$ (factorising LHS)

$\left(x + \dfrac{b}{2a} \right)^2 = \dfrac{b^2 - 4ac}{4a^2} \qquad$ (re-arranging RHS)

$$x + \frac{b}{2a} = \pm \sqrt{\frac{b^2 - 4ac}{4a^2}} \quad \text{(taking square root of RHS)}$$

$$x + \frac{b}{2a} \qquad \frac{\pm \sqrt{b^2 - 4ac}}{2a}$$

$$\therefore \quad x = \frac{-b \pm \sqrt{b^2 - 4ac}}{2a}$$

Q.E.D.

EXAMPLE 1

Solve the simultaneous equations

$$y = 2x^2 + 6x - 6 \qquad \text{①}$$
$$y + 12 = 14x \qquad \text{②}$$

SOLUTION:

$$y = 14x - 12 \qquad \text{(from 2)}$$
$$14x - 12 = 2x^2 + 6x - 6 \qquad \text{(substituting in 1)}$$
$$\therefore \ 2x^2 - 8x + 6 = 0$$

which is in the form $ax^2 + bx + c = 0$

$$a = 2, \ b = -8, \ c = 6$$

$$\text{roots of } x = \frac{-b \pm \sqrt{b^2 - 4ac}}{2a} = \frac{8 \pm \sqrt{64 - 48}}{4}$$

$$x = 3 \text{ or } 1$$
$$y = 30 \text{ or } 2$$

EXAMPLE 2

If $y = x^2 - x - 15$

what are the values of x when $y = 5$?

SOLUTION:

When $y = 5$, $\quad x^2 - x - 15 = 5$

and $\quad x^2 - x - 20 = 0$

$$a = 1, \quad b = -1, \quad c = -20$$

$$\text{roots of } x = \frac{1 \pm \sqrt{1 + 80}}{2} = \frac{1 \pm \sqrt{81}}{2} = \frac{10}{2} \quad \text{or} \quad \frac{-8}{2}$$

$$= 5 \text{ or } -4$$

10.3.5 FACTORISATION

The above mentioned formula will always enable you to find the roots of a quadratic equation but you may be able to find the roots more quickly through factorisation. Also, some examination questions do require you to factorise quadratic equations — you could "cheat" by using the formula and then form the factors from the roots but you could lose time by doing this.

In the case of quadratic equations, factorisation involves breaking down the expression into two parts, each containing x, which when multiplied together give the expression.

In Example 2 above, the equation

$$x^2 - x - 20 = 0$$

could be factorised to give

$$(x - 5)(x + 4) = 0$$

and since one of the factors must be zero

$$x = 5 \text{ and } x = -4 \text{ are the roots.}$$

More generally, if we let α and β be the roots then any quadratic can be written

$$(x - \alpha)(x - \beta) = 0 \qquad \text{and when we expand}$$
$$x^2 - (\alpha + \beta)x + \alpha\beta = 0$$

If we compare this to the general form which we used earlier

i.e. $$ax^2 + bx + c = 0$$

or $$x^2 + \frac{b}{a}x + \frac{c}{a} = 0 \qquad \text{(dividing by a)}$$

We can see that

the sum of the roots, $\alpha + \beta = \dfrac{-b}{a}$ and

the product of the roots, $\alpha\beta = \dfrac{c}{a}$

So to factorise any quadratic you need only find two numbers which when added together give $\dfrac{-b}{a}$ and when multiplied give $\dfrac{c}{a}$

In the above example, $x^2 - x - 20 = 0$,
$a = 1$, $b = -1$, and $c = -20$.

Therefore $\alpha + \beta = \dfrac{-b}{a} = 1$

and $\alpha\beta = \dfrac{c}{a} = -20$

So, we need two numbers; the sum of which is $+1$ and the product of which is -20. The required numbers are $+5$ and -4. Therefore, $(x-\alpha)(x-\beta) = (x-5)(x+4) = 0$ and $x=5$ or -4.

248 Basic Concepts in Mathematics

The above description of the process is perhaps making the problem too complicated. Usually, and especially if the coefficient of x^2 is not one, it is best to proceed through trial and error.

If we write the quadratic in the form

$$(x + j)(x + k) = 0 \qquad \text{(j, and k being the roots}$$
$$\text{or} \qquad x^2 + (j + k)x + jk = 0 \qquad \text{multiplied by } -1)$$

Then, using the example $x^2 - x - 20 = 0$ again, the product of j and k has to be -20. The possibilities are thus

$$-1 \text{ and } +20$$
$$+1 \text{ and } -20$$
$$-2 \text{ and } +10$$
$$+2 \text{ and } -10$$
$$-4 \text{ and } +5 \qquad \text{or}$$
$$+4 \text{ and } -5.$$

The sum of j and k has to be -1 and so $+4$ and -5 are the required numbers.

$$\therefore \quad x^2 - x - 20 = (x - 5)(x + 4) = 0$$
$$\text{and either } (x - 5) = 0 \text{ or } (x + 4) = 0$$
$$\therefore \quad x = 5 \text{ or } -4$$

It is advisable to check that the factors do expand to form the required expression.

$$\text{Check:} \quad (x - 5)(x + 4) = x(x + 4) - 5(x + 4)$$
$$= x^2 + 4x - 5x - 20$$
$$= x^2 - x - 20.$$

A more complicated example

Suppose the coefficient of x^2 is not equal to one, for example $6x^2 + x - 12 = 0$.

Now the factors may be
$$(6x + j)(x + k) \qquad \text{or}$$
$$(2x + j)(3x + k)$$

The product of j and k has to be -12 and the possibilities are

$$-1 \text{ and } +12$$
$$+1 \text{ and } -12$$
$$-2 \text{ and } +6$$
$$+2 \text{ and } -6$$
$$-3 \text{ and } +4 \qquad \text{or}$$
$$+3 \text{ and } -4$$

Each of these pairs of values has to be substituted in the two possible combinations of factors until the expansion of the factors yields $6x^2 + x - 12$. It eventually emerges that the required values of j and k are $+3$ and -4 respectively so that $6x^2 + x - 12 = (2x + 3)(3x - 4) = 0$ and the required roots are $x = \dfrac{-3}{2}$ and $\dfrac{+4}{3}$

10.4 ARITHMETIC and GEOMETRIC PROGRESSIONS

A progression is a sequence or series of values in which there is a common difference between each successive term (Arithmetic) or a common ratio between each successive term (Geometric).

For example,

1,2,3,4,5,6,7,8,9,10	is a sequence with a common difference of 1 and so is an arithmetic progression.
1+2+3+4+5+6+7+8+9+10	is similarly an arithmetic series or progression.
1+2+4+8+16+32	is a geometric progression with each successive term being equal to the previous term multiplied by 2.

Arithmetic progressions

An arithmetic progression is one in which there is a common difference between each successive term in the progression.

For example: 2,4,6,8,10,12,14   in which the common difference is 2, or
10,20,30,40,50,60   in which the common difference is 10.

The general form of such progressions may be expressed algebraically as

$$a + [a + d] + [a + 2d] + [a + 3d] + - - - - - + [a + (n-1)d]$$

where a = 1st term in progression
d = the common difference
n = number of terms in the progression.
Note that the nth term in the series is $[a + (n-1)d]$

The sum of an arithmetic progression may be found by adding the first and last term, the second and second from last term, and so on.

Let the sum of the n terms in the progression be S_n.

Then, $S_n = a + [a+d] + [a+2d] + - - - - + [a+(n-2)d] + [a+(n-1)d]$

or, if we write the progression in reverse order

$$S_n = [a+(n-1)d] + [a+(n-2)d] + - - - - - - - - - - - + [a + d] + a.$$

Adding,

$$2S_n = [2a+(n-1)d] + [2a+(n-1)d] + - - - - - - - + [2a+(n-1)d] + [2a+(n-1)d]$$

$$= n [2a+(n-1)d] \text{ since there are n terms.}$$

$$S_n = \frac{n}{2} [2a+(n-1)d]$$

An alternative notation would be

$$\sum_{r=1}^{r=n} [a+(n-1)d] = \frac{n}{2} [2a+(n-1)d]$$

where $[a+(r-1)d]$ is the general term and r takes values from 1 to n.

EXAMPLE:
Find the tenth term and the sum of the first ten terms in the arithmetic progression   5,8,11,14, etc.

(a)   The nth term $= a + (n-1)d$
where $a = $ 1st term $= 5$ and
$d = $ difference $= 3$

10th term $= 5 + (10-1)3 = 32.$

(b) $S_n = \dfrac{n}{2}[2a + (n-1)d]$

$S_{10} = \dfrac{10}{2}[2.5 + (10-1)3] = 185$

Geometric progressions
A Geometric progression is one in which there is a common ratio between each successive term in the progression.

For example:
2,4,8,16,32,64 in which each successive term equals the previous term $\times 2$
or
2,10,50,250,1250 in which the common ratio is 5.

The general form of such a progression can be expressed algebraically as
$$a + ar + ar^2 + ar^3 + - - - - - + ar^{n-1}$$
where $a = $ 1st term in the progression;
$r = $ common ratio;
$n = $ number of terms in the progression.

Note that the nth term in the series is ar^{n-1}

The sum of a geometric progression can be found from the difference between the progression and some other progression which is a multiple of the progression. If we again let S_n equal the sum of the n terms in the above progression:

$S_n = a + ar + ar^2 + ar^3 + - - - - + ar^{n-2} + ar^{n-1}$ ①

Then, $rS_n = \quad ar + ar^2 + ar^3 + - - - - - - - - - + ar^{n-1} + ar^n$ ②

(multiplying both sides by r)

Subtracting equation ② from ① gives

$S_n - rS_n = a - ar^n$ since all the intermediate terms cancel
$S_n(1 - r) = a(1 - r^n)$
$S_n = \dfrac{a(1 - r^n)}{(1 - r)}$ or $\dfrac{a(r^n - 1)}{r - 1}$

In the alternative notation

$$\sum_{x=1}^{n} ar^{x-1} = \frac{a(1 - r^n)}{(1 - r)}$$

Summations of geometric progressions are of great importance in compound interest calculations and discounted cash flow as we shall see in the chapter on financial arithmetic.

Sum to infinity
If n is very large and r is greater than one then r^n will be very large and $\frac{(r^n - 1)}{(1 - r)}$ will be very large

So, $\sum_{x=1}^{n} ar^{x-1}$ will tend towards infinity as n tends towards infinity.

However, if r is less than one the "sum to infinity" of the geometric series is finite. As n increases r^n decreases for $r < 1$ and tends towards zero as n tends towards infinity.

Therefore, $\frac{a(1 - r^n)}{1 - r}$ will become $\frac{a(1 - 0)}{1 - r} = \frac{a}{1 - r}$

as $n \Rightarrow \infty$

$$\sum_{x=1}^{n} ar^{x-1} = \frac{a}{1 - r} \qquad \begin{array}{l} n \Rightarrow \infty \\ r < 1 \end{array}$$

or $S = \frac{a}{1 - r}$ where S denotes the "sum to infinity" and $r < 1$.

Identifying the general term in a series
Identifying the general term in a series is not always as straightforward as in the examples considered so far. The differences between the original terms in a series are known as first order differences, the differences between the first order differences are known as second order differences, and so on. The level of difference at which the differences are equal indicates the order of the general term.

For example; if we had the progression

	2	4	6	8	10	12
1st order differences		2	2	2	2	2

The fact that the first order differences are equal indicates an arithmetic progression in which the general term is [a + (n - 1) d] where a=d=2.

But consider a more complicated series such as

$$2 + 6 + 12 + 20 + 30 + 42$$

1st order differences   4   6   8   10   12

2nd order differences   2   2   2   2

This indicates that the general term is a second order expression (or quadratic) of the form

$$Kr^2 + Lr + M \quad \text{where K, L, and M are constants.}$$

If r=1 $K + L + M = 2$ (the first term)   ①

If r=2 $4K + 2L + M = 6$ (the second term)   ②

If r=3 $9K + 3L + M = 12$ (the third term)   ③

We now have three simultaneous equations in three unknowns which we can solve quite easily as follows:

$$3K + L = 4 \qquad ② - ①$$
$$5K + L = 6 \qquad ③ - ②$$

$$
\begin{aligned}
2K &= 2 \\
\therefore K &= 1 \\
\therefore L &= 1 \\
\therefore M &= 0
\end{aligned}
$$

The general term is therefore $r^2 + r$ or $r(r+1)$ and we can now see that the series is in fact

$$1.2 + 2.3 + 3.4 + 4.5 + 5.6 + 6.7$$

The summation of such series involves the "method of differences" which is beyond the scope of this book.

QUESTIONS

10.1   The marketing department estimates that if the selling price of the new product A1 is set at £40 per unit then the sales will be 400 units per week, while, if the selling price is set at £20 per unit, the sales will be 800 units per week. Assume that the graph of this function is linear.

The production department estimates that the variable costs will be £7.50 per unit and that the fixed costs will be £10,000 per week.

Required:

(a)   Derive the cost, sales revenue, and profit equations.

(b)   Graph the three equations derived in (a).

(c)   From the graph estimate the maximum profit that can be obtained, stating the number of sales units and the selling price necessary to achieve this profit.   *(ICMA)*

10.2 (a) Draw a graph of the equation:
$$2x^2 - 8x - y = -4$$
(b) Use the appropriate formula to calculate the value of x where:
$$2x^2 - 8x + 4 = 0$$
(c) On the graph produced in answer to (a) draw the equation:
$$14 - 18x = 2y$$
(d) Solve (showing clearly your workings) the two equations given in (a) and (c) above.
(e) Indicate on the graph your solutions to (b) and (d) above.

(ICMA)

10.3 (a) Solve the following:
$$2x - 4y + z = 7$$
$$x + 3y - 2z = 11$$
$$3x - y - 3z = 4$$

(b) The difference between two positive numbers is 5 and the sum of their squares is 193. Find the two numbers.

(c) A rectangle has a perimeter of 114 metres and an area of 800 square metres. Find the dimensions.

(ICMA)

10.4 (a) Solve: $\dfrac{1}{x} + \dfrac{1}{y} + \dfrac{1}{z} = 5$

$$\frac{4}{x} + \frac{2}{y} + \frac{3}{z} = 9$$

$$\frac{3}{x} - \frac{3}{y} - \frac{3}{z} = -3$$

(b) If $x:y:z = 3:-4:4$ and $2x - 2y - 3xy = 8$ find the value of x, y, and z.

(c) Simplify:

$$\frac{\left(a + \dfrac{1}{b}\right)^x \cdot \left(a - \dfrac{1}{b}\right)^y}{\left(b + \dfrac{1}{a}\right)^x \cdot \left(b - \dfrac{1}{a}\right)^y}$$

(ICMA)

*10.5 (a) Solve the following set of equations:
$$p + q + 2r = 6$$
$$p - q + r = 2$$
$$2p + q \quad = 3$$

(b) One solution of the equation $2x^3 - 5x^2 - 81x + 126 = 0$ is $x = 1\frac{1}{2}$.

By rearranging the equation into the form:

$(x - 1\frac{1}{2})(Ax^2 + Bx + C) = 0$

obtain all the solutions of the equation:

$2x^3 - 5x^2 - 81x + 126 = 0$.

(c) Using the graphical method solve the following simultaneous equations:

$2x - 3y = 9$

$4x - y = 8$ *(ICMA)*

*10.6 A production department has determined that the cost per unit follows the equation:

$$\frac{£2,000 + 2x}{x}$$

and the profit or loss per unit follows the equation:

$$\frac{£0.5x - 2,000}{x}$$

where x represents the number of units produced. The production capacity of the department is 10,000 units.

You are required to:

(a) draw a graph of the two equations;

(b) identify on the graph, and also to calculate the level of production, when:
   (i) neither a profit nor a loss is made;
   (ii) a profit of £0.10 per unit is required;

(c) state, if the selling price were to be increased by 20% the level of production, when:
   (i) neither a profit nor a loss is made;
   (ii) a profit of £0.10 per unit is required. *(ICMA)*

10.7 A manufacturer of fertilisers competes in a market in which price is **not** constant and his revenue function is **not** linear.

The manufacturer finds that his weekly production costs are £1,300 when producing 20 tonnes per week, and £1,700 when producing 30 tonnes per week. He finds that he can sell 20 tonnes per week at a price of £80 per tonne but has to reduce the price to £70 per tonne in order to well 30 tonnes per week.

The manufacturer knows that the cost and price functions are **linear**.

All production is sold.

C = production costs   R = weekly revenue
Q = quantity sold   P = price per tonne

(i) Show that the weekly production costs, as a function of the quantity sold, are given by the equation C = 500 + 40Q.
(ii) Find the price per tonne, P, as a function of the quantity sold.
(iii) Find the weekly revenue, R, as a function of the quantity sold.
(iv) At the break-even point, find the quantity sold, the price, and the weekly revenue.

(N.B. The break-even point is here defined as the smallest quantity sold at which total revenue equals total costs.) *(ICMA)*

10.8 (a) Calculate the tenth term and the sum of the first nine terms of the geometric progression 4, –6, 9, . . .

(b) Solve: $\dfrac{1}{x} - \dfrac{1}{x+3} = \dfrac{1}{x+2} - \dfrac{1}{x+5}$

(c) If x:y:z = 4:–3:8
and x – 4y – z = 48
find x, y, z.   *(ICMA)*

10.9 (a) A company manufactures a single product. Each unit is sold for £15.

The operating costs are:

                                        £
Fixed, per week 800
Prime, per unit produced 5

The weekly maintenance cost M is given by:
$$M = 0.009x^2$$
where x is the weekly production in units.

You are required to:
(i) calculate the range of possible production in whole units, when no units are left unfinished at the end of the week, to provide a weekly profit of at least £200;
(ii) illustrate your answer to (i) above by drawing a graph of the profit equation.

(b) Over a six-year period an investment depreciated in value from £32,000 to £23,500. If a reducing balance method of depreciation was used, determine the rate per annum to one decimal place.
(ICMA)

Chapter 11
THE METHOD OF CALCULUS

Calculus is, in the main, concerned with examining the relationships between variables. In particular, differential calculus is concerned with the changes in one variable associated with changes in another variable and integral calculus is concerned with the summation of these differentials (the area under a curve). Both differentiation and integration can be very useful in the solution of business problems.

11.1 The gradient of a curve

The gradient, or slope, of a straight line is "the difference in the y values divided by the difference in the corresponding x values".

For example, consider the straight line y=2x+2, plotted in Diagram 11.1.

DIAGRAM 11.1

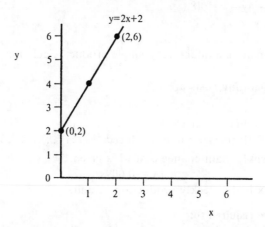

Taking the two ends of the plotted line, the co-ordinates are (x=0, y=2) and (x=2, y=6)

$$\text{Slope} = \frac{\text{difference in y values}}{\text{difference in x values}} = \frac{6-2}{2-0} = \frac{+4}{+2} = +2$$

Of course, this should come as no surprise because y=2x+2 is a straight line of the form y=ax+b where a = slope and b = point of intersection on y-axis.

The gradient of a curve is different at different points as is illustrated in Diagram 11.2, by drawing tangents to the curve at three points A, B, and C.

DIAGRAM 11.2

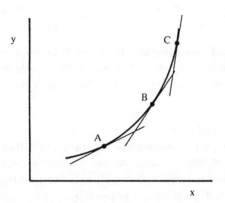

Where it is possible to draw a unique non-vertical tangent the slope of that tangent is the slope of the curve at the point in question. When this is possible we say that the function is "differentiable" at the point in question. The gradient, or slope, of the curve could thus be found by plotting the curve, drawing the tangent at the relevant point and measuring the gradient of the tangent. This method would be both time-consuming and inaccurate so we need some other method.

11.1.1 Chord Approximation Method

Say we wanted to calculate the gradient of the curve $y=x^2$ at the point (a,a^2), in Diagram 11.3.

DIAGRAM 11.3

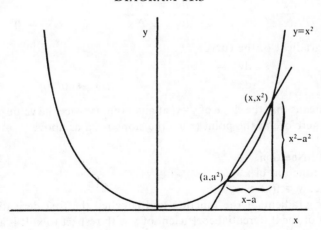

The chord between the points (a,a^2) and (x,x^2) would have a gradient

$$= \frac{\text{difference in y-values}}{\text{difference in x-values}} = \frac{x^2 - a^2}{x - a} = \frac{(x-a)(x+a)}{(x-a)} = x + a$$

As the two points get closer together the chord becomes a tangent and x tends towards a. The gradient therefore tends towards x+a=2a as x → a and so the gradient of y=x² at the point (a,a^2) equals 2a. This is the method of "differentiation".

11.2 DIFFERENTIATION

As described above, differentiation is a method of finding the gradient of a function by finding the change in the y-value at some point for an infinitesimally small increase in the x-value. Let us find the gradient of y=x² again but using a slightly different approach.

Suppose that Δx represents a small increase in the value of x and Δy represents the corresponding change in y.

Then, $y + \Delta y = (x + \Delta x)^2$

∴ $y + \Delta y = x^2 + 2\Delta x.x + (\Delta x)^2$ ①

But $y = x^2$ ②

Therefore, $\Delta y = 2\Delta x.x + (\Delta x)^2$ (② − ①)

and $\frac{\Delta y}{\Delta x} = 2x + \Delta x$ (dividing by Δx)

Now $\frac{\Delta y}{\Delta x}$ represents the change in y for a small change in x; when the increase in x tends towards zero $\frac{\Delta y}{\Delta x}$ will represent the gradient of the curve which we denote by the symbols

$$\frac{dy}{dx} \qquad \text{i.e.} \qquad \frac{dy}{dx} = \frac{\Delta y}{\Delta x} \qquad \Delta x \to 0$$

So, the gradient of the curve

$$\frac{dy}{dx} = 2x \qquad \Delta x \to 0$$

Which means that the slope of y=x² at any point is twice the value of x at that point. Therefore at the point (a,a^2) the slope is 2a as above.

11.2.1 Notation

If y is a function of x

i.e. $y = f(x)$

$\frac{dy}{dx}$ is the gradient of the function and is called the first derivative of the function or the differential coefficient of y with respect to x. It is also sometimes written f'(x) or Dy or D(f(x)). The process of finding $\frac{dy}{dx}$ is called "differentiating y with respect to x".

11.2.2 Successive differentiation

if $y = f(x)$

then $\frac{dy}{dx}$ or $f'(x)$ is the gradient of the function and will itself be a function. The gradient of $f'(x)$ is denoted by $\frac{d^2y}{dx^2}$ or $f''(x)$ or D^2y or $D^2(f(x))$ and is called the second derivative or the second differential coefficient of y with respect to x.

Similarly, the third derivative is denoted by $\frac{d^3y}{dx^3}$ etc.

11.2.3 General formula for differentiation

Differentiation would be a tedious business if we had to use first principles, such as described above, each time we wanted to find the derivative of a function.

Fortunately, differentiation can be carried out quite easily using the following general formula:

$$\text{If} \quad y = x^n$$

$$\frac{dy}{dx} = nx^{n-1}$$

EXAMPLES:

$$\text{If} \quad y = x^2 \quad , \quad \frac{dy}{dx} = 2.x^{2-1} = 2x$$

$$\text{If} \quad y = x^3 \quad , \quad \frac{dy}{dx} = 3.x^{3-1} = 3x^2$$

$$\text{If} \quad y = x^6 \quad , \quad \frac{dy}{dx} = 6.x^{6-1} = 6x^5$$

11.2.4 Differentiation of a constant

$$\text{If } y = k \qquad \text{where k is some constant}$$

$$\frac{dy}{dx} = 0$$

EXAMPLE:

$$\text{If } y = 10 \ , \quad \frac{dy}{dx} = 0$$

This is obvious if one considers that $x^0 = 1$ and $y = 10$ can therefore be written

$$y = 10.x^0 , \quad \frac{dy}{dx} = 0.\,10.\,x^{0-1} = 0$$

11.2.5 Differentiation of more complex functions

Say $\quad y = f(x) = \alpha\, g(x) + \beta\, h(x)$

where α and β are constants and $g(x)$ and $h(x)$ are functions of x.

$$\frac{dy}{dx} \text{ or } f'(x) = \alpha\, g'(x) + \beta\, h'(x)$$

Put more simply, each term in the function has to be differentiated and constants which are coefficients of a term including x are unchanged by differentiation.

i.e. $\quad$ If $\quad y = kx^n$, $\qquad \dfrac{dy}{dx} = n.\, kx^{n-1}$

EXAMPLES:

(i) $\quad$ If $\quad y = 3x^2$, $\quad \dfrac{dy}{dx} = 2.3x^{2-1} = 6x$

(ii) $\quad$ If $\quad y = 3x^2 + 7x^3$, $\quad \dfrac{dy}{dx} = 2.3x^{2-1} + 3.7x^{3-2} = 6x + 21x^2$

(iii) If $\quad y = 3x^2 + 7x^3 + 20$, $\quad \dfrac{dy}{dx} = 6x + 21x^2 + 0 = 6x + 21x^2$

(iv) If $\quad y = 2x^5 + 5x^3 + \dfrac{7}{x} + 36$

$\dfrac{dy}{dx} = 5.2x^{5-1} + 3.5x^{3-1} - 1.7x^{-1-1} + 0 = 10x^4 + 15x^2 - \dfrac{7}{x^2}$

$$\left(\text{N.B. } \frac{7}{x} = 7x^{-1} \right)$$

(v) $\quad$ If $\quad y = 10\sqrt{x} \qquad$ i.e. $y = 10$ times the square root of x

$y = 10x^{\frac{1}{2}}$

$\dfrac{dy}{dx} = \dfrac{1}{2}.\, 10.\, x^{\frac{1}{2}-1} = 5x^{-\frac{1}{2}} = \dfrac{5}{x^{\frac{1}{2}}} = \dfrac{5}{\sqrt{x}}$

QUESTIONS

11.1 $\quad$ Differentiate the following functions:—

(a) $\quad y = 2x + 2$

(b) $\quad y = x^2 + 2$

(c) $\quad y = x^3 + 2x$

(d) $\quad y = \dfrac{1}{x^2}$

(e) $\quad y = 12x^2 + 5x - 9$

(f) $\quad y = 3x^3 + 3x - 3$

(g) $\quad y = \dfrac{5}{x} + 2x$

(h) $\quad y = \dfrac{5}{x^3} + \dfrac{4}{x^2} + \dfrac{2}{x}$

(i) $\quad S = ut + \frac{1}{2}at^2$

$\qquad$ where u and a are constants.

11.2 $\quad$ Find the second derivatives of the above functions.

11.3 MAXIMA and MINIMA

An important reason for being interested in differentiation is that it enables us to calculate maximum and minimum values of functions. In a business context, we might be interested in the level of sales which maximises revenue or profit, or the level of output at which costs are minimised, the level of stock which minimises holding costs, and so on. If functional relationships exist then differentiation may enable us to find the maximum or minimum value of the functions.

Of course, not all functions have maximum, or minimum, values; $y=x$, for example, has no maximum or minimum value. It is also possible for a function to attain its greatest value at many different points. For example, the function in Diagram 11.5 has a greatest value of $+1$ which is attained at $x=0$ and many other values of x.

DIAGRAM 11.5

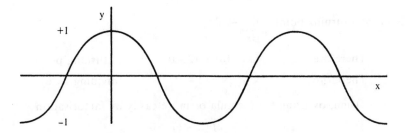

A function is said to have a maximum value at a point if the value of the function is greater at that point than at other points "sufficiently" close to that point (a minimum value is defined similarly). Consider, for example, the function $y=2x^3 - 3x^2$ in Diagram 11.6.

DIAGRAM 11.6

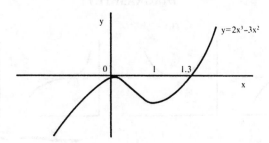

This function has a maximum value of zero when x equals zero and a minimum value of -1 when x equals $+1$.

It is obvious, however, that the function has a greatest value higher than zero and a least value lower than –1. So maximum and minimum values are only the greatest and least values of the function within the domain which is of interest.

In order to find a maximum or minimum value (turning point) of a function we take advantage of the fact that at such a turning point the tangent will be horizontal (i.e. the slope, or gradient, of the tangent will be zero) and so $\frac{dy}{dx} = 0$.

For example, suppose we wished to find any maximum or minimum values for the curve

$$y = 2x^3 - 9x^2 + 12x + 4$$

We calculate the gradient

$$\frac{dy}{dx} = 6x^2 - 18x + 12$$

Now, at a turning point $\quad \frac{dy}{dx} = 0$

Therefore,	$6x^2 - 18x + 12 = 0$	at turning point
Therefore,	$x^2 - 3x + 2 = 0$	(dividing by 6)

Then, by using the formula or more easily by factorisation

$$(x - 2)(x - 1) = 0$$

Therefore, at max. or min. $\quad x = 1$ or 2.

The problem is that we don't know if these points give maximum or minimum values of the function, and there is also the possibility that they are points of inflexion — as Diagram 11.7 illustrates, a "stationary point" at which $\frac{dy}{dx} = 0$ may be a maximum, minimum, or point of inflexion.

DIAGRAM 11.7

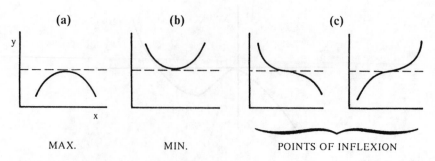

(a)	(b)	(c)
MAX.	MIN.	POINTS OF INFLEXION

To decide what is happening at a stationary point, there are two basic methods:

(1) **Examine the sign of $\frac{dy}{dx}$** on both sides of the stationary point. This method will always work but can be rather tedious. It uses the fact that at, for example, a maximum value the tangent will be changing from a positive to a negative slope.

If the stationary point is at x=a then the behaviour of the function and the derivative will be as follows:

	MAX.			MIN.			POINTS OF INFLEXION					
Value of x	x<a	x=a	x>a	x<a	x=a	x>a	x<a	x=a	x>a	x<a	x=a	x>a
Value of $\frac{dy}{dx}$	+	0	−	−	0	+	−	0	−	+	0	+
Value of y *	↗	→	↘	↘	→	↗	↘	→	↘	↗	→	↗

*N.B. Arrows indicate direction of curve.

In the above example, if I wanted to know whether x=1 gives a min, max, or point of inflexion I could examine $\frac{dy}{dx}$ at just below x=1 and just above. How much above or below? Well, I know there is another stationary point at x=2 so I don't want to be near that region of the function. $x = 1 \pm \frac{1}{5}$ should be satisfactory.

$$\frac{dy}{dx} = (x-2)(x-1)$$

$$\text{When } x = \frac{4}{5} \quad \frac{dy}{dx} = \left(\frac{4}{5}-2\right)\left(\frac{4}{5}-1\right) = \frac{+6}{5}$$

$$\text{When } x = \frac{6}{5} \quad \frac{dy}{dx} = \left(\frac{6}{5}-2\right)\left(\frac{6}{5}-1\right) = \frac{-4}{5}$$

The tangent changes from a positive to a negative slope on either side of the stationary point which means that x=1 gives a MAXIMUM value for the function.

(2) **Examine the second derivative**
A far easier method of deciding on the nature of a stationary point is to examine $\frac{d^2y}{dx^2}$.

At a maximum, $\frac{dy}{dx}$ will change from positive to negative.

In other words, $\frac{dy}{dx}$ will be falling and so the derivative of the gradient function will be negative, i.e. $\frac{d^2y}{dx^2} < 0$.

Similarly, at a minimum $\frac{d^2y}{dx^2} > 0$.

Unfortunately this test fails if $\frac{d^2y}{dx^2} = 0$. You might think that $\frac{d^2y}{dx^2} = 0$ would imply a point of inflexion. In fact you would be right, at a point of inflexion both $\frac{dy}{dx}$ and $\frac{d^2y}{dx^2}$ do equal zero but this can also happen at a maximum or minimum. For example, consider $y = x^4$

$$\frac{dy}{dx} = 4x^3 = 0 \text{ at max or min}$$

$$x = 0 \text{ is thus a max or min}$$

$$\frac{d^2y}{dx^2} = 12x^2 = 0 \text{ at } x = 0 \qquad \text{and the test fails,}$$

and the test fails, $x=0$ is in fact at the minimum value of $y=x^4$.

It will be unusual, especially in an examination, for $\frac{d^2y}{dx^2}$ to be zero at a max. or min. value and so it is recommended that you use this second method. If you do encounter a problem where $\frac{dy}{dx}$ and $\frac{d^2y}{dx^2}$ both equal zero resort to the first method.

To summarise:

$$\text{At both Max. and Min.} \qquad \frac{dy}{dx} = 0$$

$$\text{At Max.} \qquad \frac{d^2y}{dx^2} < 0$$

$$\text{At Min.} \qquad \frac{d^2y}{dx^2} > 0$$

If $\frac{dy}{dx}$ and $\frac{d^2y}{dx^2}$ both equal zero, y may be at max. or min. or neither.

EXAMPLE:
Find the maximum and minimum values of
$$y = 2x^3 - 9x^2 + 12x + 4$$

$\frac{dy}{dx} = 6x^2 - 18x + 12 = 6(x-2)(x-1) = 0$ at max. or min.

$\therefore$ At max. or min. $x = 1$ or 2

$\frac{d^2y}{dx^2} = 12x - 18 = -6$ when $x = 1$ (Max.)

$\qquad\qquad = +6$ when $x = 2$ (Min.)

$y = 9$ when $x = 1$ is max. value and
$y = 8$ when $x = 2$ is min. value.

11.3.1 Some business applications

The calculation of maximum or minimum values has many applications in a business context. The examples quoted below may be rather simplified versions of real-life problems but they do indicate the way in which mathematical tools can help in the solution of business problems.

1. Economic Order Quantity

Inventory control is a science in itself and one upon which many textbooks have been written. If a firm holds excessively high levels of stocks it incurs additional costs such as warehousing costs, insurance, deterioration of stocks, cost of capital tied up in stocks. This last cost is an example of the economist's "opportunity cost", the cost of holding stock is the loss of revenue through not being able to use the capital tied up in stock for some other purpose.

On the other hand, if a firm holds too low a level of stock it runs the danger of running out of stock. In the case of raw material stocks this may mean lost production, in the case of finished goods it may mean lost sales and customer goodwill.

Another problem associated with holding low levels of stock is that orders will have to be placed more frequently than if higher levels of stock were held and so procurement costs will increase.

The simplest inventory control model is the E.O.Q. or "saw-tooth" model based upon the following assumptions:
(a)   Lead time (delay between order being placed and delivery) is zero.
(b)   Demand is constant.

These assumptions mean that the stock level falls at a constant rate and when the last unit of stock is used the stock level is immediately restored by the order and delivery of, say, Q units. This gives rise to the typical "saw-tooth" model in Diagram 11.8.

DIAGRAM 11.8

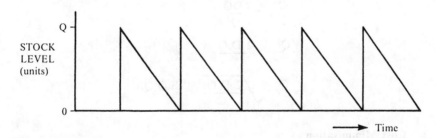

Now, suppose
        C = Cost of carrying a unit of stock for one year.
        O = Cost of placing an order for stock.
        D = Annual Demand (units).

From the diagram we see that the level of stock falls from Q to zero at a steady rate. The average level of stock held over a period of time is therefore $\frac{Q}{2}$.

$$\text{Cost of holding stock for one year} = \frac{Q}{2} \times C = \frac{QC}{2}$$

If D units are required over the year and Q units are ordered each time then the firm will need to place $\frac{D}{Q}$ orders per annum.

$$\text{Total ordering cost for one year} = \frac{D}{Q} \times O = \frac{DO}{Q}$$

The total inventory cost (holding and ordering) per annum, T, can now be expressed by the following function:

$$T = \frac{QC}{2} + \frac{DO}{Q}$$

What is now required is to find the order size, Q, which minimises the total inventory cost (the Economic Order Quantity). This is quite a simple matter.

$$T = \frac{QC}{2} + \frac{DO}{Q} = \frac{C}{2} \cdot Q + DO \cdot Q^{-1} \qquad \left[\begin{array}{l} \text{D, O, and C} \\ \text{are constants} \end{array} \right]$$

$$\frac{dT}{dQ} = \frac{C}{2} - DO \cdot Q^{-2} = \frac{C}{2} - \frac{D.O}{Q^2}$$

$$\text{At min. value} \quad \frac{dT}{dQ} = 0$$

$$\text{Therefore} \quad \frac{C}{2} - \frac{DO}{Q^2} = 0$$

$$\frac{C}{2} = \frac{DO}{Q^2}$$

$$Q^2 = \frac{2\,D.O.}{C}$$

$$Q = \sqrt{\frac{2\,D.O.}{C}} = \text{E.O.Q.}$$

2. Cost Minimisation

The E.O.Q. model is concerned with finding the size of order which minimises total inventory cost. A more general, and frequently examined, problem is to find the level of output which minimises some cost function.

Within a given range of output, a firm will usually be faced with some fixed costs which do not change with output and some variable costs which rise with output. Economists refer to the resultant average cost curve as U-shaped, as shown in Diagram 11.9.

DIAGRAM 11.9

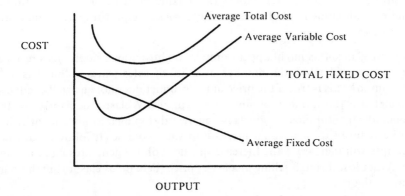

If the average cost curve can be described by an algebraic function then the level of output at which the cost per unit of output is minimised can be found by differentiation.

Suppose, for example, the total production cost for a level of output x was given by the following function:

$$\text{TOTAL COST} = 50{,}000 + 20x^2 + 50x$$

The average cost, or cost per unit, can be found by dividing the total cost by the output, so

$$\text{Average cost (y)} = \frac{50{,}000}{x} + 20x + 50$$

Now to find the level of output at which the cost per unit is minimised we differentiate with respect to x.

$$\frac{dy}{dx} = -\frac{50{,}000}{x^2} + 20 = 0 \text{ at max. or min.}$$

$$\therefore \quad \text{At max. or min.} \quad -\frac{50{,}000}{x^2} = -20$$

$$\therefore \quad x^2 = 2{,}500$$
$$\therefore \quad x = 50 \qquad \text{(We reject the negative value of the square root as we cannot have negative output)}$$

To check if 50 units is a min. rather than max. we calculate the second derivative

$$\frac{d^2y}{dx^2} = \frac{100{,}000}{x^3} > 0 \text{ at } x = 50$$

Therefore the lowest cost per unit occurs when output is 50 units.

3. Revenue Maximisation

A problem which requires finding the maximum value of some function is that of finding the level of sales at which sales receipts (or total revenue) are maximised.

At first glance this might appear quite straightforward; surely sales receipts are maximised when the number of units of sales (sales volume) is at a maximum? This is true if the price of the product does not have to be reduced to increase the number of units sold (perfectly elastic demand) but the demand curve for most products is downward sloping meaning that price has to be reduced to achieve an increase in sales volume. It follows that sales receipts will increase if the increase in sales volume generates more income than that lost through selling at a lower price (demand is elastic) but this may not be the case.

Consider the demand schedule below:

Price (£/unit)	Quantity demanded (units)
6	200
5	400
4	600
3	800
2	1000
1	1200

The equation which describes this demand schedule is $q = 200 (7 - p)$
where q = quantity demanded (units)
and p = price/unit

The total revenue at any level of demand is the number of units sold multiplied by the price per unit.

$$\therefore \quad \text{Revenue}, \quad R = q.p = 200 (7 - p).p.$$
$$\therefore \qquad\qquad R = 1400p - 200p^2$$

To find the price at which total revenue is maximised we differentiate in the normal way:

$$\frac{dR}{dp} = 1400 - 400p = 0 \text{ at max. or min.}$$

$$400p = 1400 \qquad \text{at max. or min. which is easily}$$
$$p = 3.5 \qquad \text{shown to be a maximum.}$$

Therefore, total revenue is maximised at a price of £3.5 per unit.

4. Profit Maximisation

There is, of course, little point in maximising total revenue if this requires a level of output at which costs are very high and profits consequently low. A more practical question, therefore, is at what level of output is profit maximised?

In the above example, the level of demand, q, was given by the expression $q = 200(7-p)$. This can be rearranged to give

$$p = 7 - \frac{q}{200}$$

and, accordingly, Total revenue, $R = 7q - \frac{q^2}{200}$

Suppose also that Total Cost, $C = 200 + q + \frac{q^2}{400}$

At what level of output is profit maximised?

For the sake of simplicity we will assume that all output is sold. Now profit (π) is simply the difference between revenue and cost:

$$\pi = R - C = 7q - \frac{q^2}{200} - 200 - q - \frac{q^2}{400}$$

$$\pi = 6q - 200 - \frac{3q^2}{400}$$

$$\frac{d(\pi)}{dq} = 6 - \frac{6q}{400} = 0 \quad \text{at max. or min.}$$

$$\therefore \quad q = 400 \quad \text{at max.}$$

So profit is maximised at a level of output of 400 units.

An alternative approach for those familiar, from studies of Economics, with the concept of the margin would be to calculate Marginal Cost and Marginal Revenue.

If Marginal Revenue (the increase in revenue from the sale of an extra unit, i.e. $\frac{dR}{dq}$) is greater than Marginal Cost (the increase in cost from the production of an extra unit, i.e. $\frac{dC}{dq}$) then profits can be increased by increasing production and sales. Profits are maximised when

$$MR = MC$$

or $$\frac{dR}{dq} = \frac{dC}{dq}$$

$$R = 7q - \frac{q^2}{200}$$

$$\therefore \quad \frac{dR}{dq} = 7 - \frac{q}{100}$$

$$C = 200 + q + \frac{q^2}{400}$$

$$\therefore \quad \frac{dC}{dq} = 1 + \frac{q}{200}$$

At profit maximising output $MC = MR$ i.e. $\dfrac{dC}{dq} = \dfrac{dR}{dq}$

i.e. $\qquad 1 + \dfrac{q}{200} = 7 - \dfrac{q}{100}$

$$\frac{3q}{200} = 6$$

$$q = 400 \qquad \text{as above.}$$

11.4 INTEGRATION

Integration is the reverse process to differentiation.

For example,   if $\qquad y = 3x^2$

$$\frac{dy}{dx} = 6x \qquad\qquad \text{(differentation)}$$

if $\qquad \dfrac{dy}{dx} = 6x$

$$y = 3x^2 \qquad\qquad \text{(integration)}$$

But suppose, $\qquad y = 3x^2 + 12 \quad : \dfrac{dy}{dx} = 6x$

or $\qquad y = 3x^2 + 500 \quad : \dfrac{dy}{dx} = 6x$

or $\qquad y = 3x^2 + 0.5 \quad : \dfrac{dy}{dx} = 6x$

Each of the above functions has a first derivative of $6x$. Therefore, to be more precise:

If $\qquad \dfrac{dy}{dx} = 6x$

$$y = 3x^2 + C \qquad \text{where C is some constant.}$$

As we shall see later this constant will usually disappear in our calculations or be easily identified.

11.4.1 Notation

If we have some function of x, say f(x), which when differentiated gives some other function, say g(x), then as we already know we may write

$$\frac{d[f(x)]}{dx} = g(x)$$

or $\quad f'(x) = g(x)$ (differentiation)

It is convenient to have a notation for the reverse process of integration and so we write

$$\int g(x).dx = f(x) \quad \text{and } f(x) \text{ is referred to}$$

as the "indefinite integral" of g(x) with respect to x.

In the above example, $\int 6x.dx = 3x^2 + C$.

11.4.2 General Formula for integration

From the above it is probably obvious that the general formula for integration is:

$$\int x.^n dx = \frac{x^{n+1}}{n+1} + C$$

where C is the constant
of integration
$n \neq -1$

*

As with differentiation, if a function consists of more than one term in x each term is integrated separately.

i.e. $\int [f(x) + g(x) + h(x)]\, dx = \int f(x)dx + \int g(x)dx + \int h(x)dx$

Again, as in differentiation, constants which are coefficients of terms including x are unchanged by integration.

i.e. $\int \alpha f(x)dx = \alpha \int f(x)dx.$

Finally, a term containing x and constants to some power may be integrated as follows:

$$\int (ax+b)^n dx = \frac{(ax+b)^{n+1}}{a(n+1)} + C$$

where a and b
are constants.

---

*There is one situation in which this formula fails and that is when n=-1. It can be shown that $\int \frac{1}{x}dx = \log_e x$ is the missing result in the general formula but you may ignore this complication.

EXAMPLES:

(i) $\int x^4 dx = \dfrac{x^5}{5} + C$

(ii) $\int \dfrac{1}{x^4} dx = -\dfrac{x^{-3}}{3} + C = -\dfrac{1}{3x^3} + C$

(iii) $\int 3x^2 = \dfrac{3x^3}{3} + C = x^3 + C$

(iv) $\int (3x^2 + 7x^3) dx = x^3 + \dfrac{7x^4}{4} + C$

(v) $\int (3x^2 + 7x^3 + 20) dx = x^3 + \dfrac{7x^4}{4} + 20x + C$

(vi) $\int 10\sqrt{x}.dx = \int 10x^{\frac{1}{2}} dx = \dfrac{10x^{\frac{3}{2}}}{\frac{3}{2}} + C = \dfrac{20x^{\frac{3}{2}}}{3} + C$

(vii) $\int (3x-9)^{10} dx = \dfrac{(3x-9)^{11}}{3 \times 11} + C = \dfrac{(3x-9)^{11}}{33} + C$

N.B. Integration is a fairly "messy" process so it is a good idea to differentiate your answer to make sure you have not made a slip in the integration.

Note also that the constant of integration will usually take different values and has to be treated with care when dealing with indefinite integrals.

QUESTIONS

11.3   Integrate the following functions with respect to x.

    (i) x

    (ii) $4x^3$

    (iii) $(7x + 1)^{\frac{1}{2}}$

    (iv) $5x^2 + 3x + 10$

    (v) $\dfrac{x^2 - 3x + 2}{8}$

    (vi) $\dfrac{1}{x^2} + 2x^2 + 7$

    (vii) $10 + 12x - x^2$

    (viii) $6x + 20$

    (ix) $\dfrac{5x - 7x^3 + 8}{3x^4}$

    (x) $\dfrac{x}{\sqrt{1-x}}$ [This is very tricky. Try to divide the expression into two terms each with a denominator of $\sqrt{1-x}$]

11.4   The Marginal Cost of a firm's output (i.e. the increase in total cost when output increases by one unit) is given by the following function:

$$\text{Marginal cost} = £[50 + (q - 2)^2]$$
$$\text{where } q = \text{output in units.}$$

If fixed cost is £10,000, derive an expression for the total cost at any level of output.

11.4.3 Definite Integrals

The symbol $\int_a^b f(x)dx$ is used to represent the value of $\int f(x)dx$ when $x=b$ minus the value when $x=a$.

Such an expression is called a definite integral because the arbitrary constant automatically disappears in the subtraction.

EXAMPLES:

$$\int_0^2 2x.dx \quad = \quad [x^2 + C]_0^2$$
$$= [4 + C] - [0 + C]$$
$$= 4 + C - C$$
$$= 4.$$

The integral $\int_a^b f(x)dx$ is actually the area between the graph $y=f(x)$, the x-axis, and the values $x=a$, $x=b$.

What we are really doing is taking an infinitely large number of strips with width dx and height given by the function $f(x)$ and adding up the areas of these strips to obtain the area under the curve.

In the above example we would not have to resort to integration to find the area. The area required is the same as the area of a right-angled triangle with base equal to 2 and height equal to 4 (Diagram 11.10).

DIAGRAM 11.10

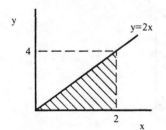

Area of right-angled
triangle $\quad = \dfrac{1}{2}$ base + height

$\quad = \dfrac{1}{2} \times 4 \times 2 = 4$

as above.

Similarly,
$$\int_4^7 5.dx = [5x + C]_4^7$$
$$= [35 + C] - [20 + C] = 15$$

Again, this is a very simple problem; the required area is that of the rectangle (Diagram 11.11) with height of 5 and base of 3, i.e. Area $= 5 \times 3 = 15$ as above.

DIAGRAM 11.11

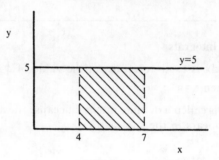

Suppose, however, that we wanted to find the area under the curve $y=x^2$ between $x=0$ and $x=1$.

There is no easy geometric solution to this problem; one way of finding an approximate answer would be to divide up the interval $x=0$ to $x=1$ into a number of subintervals, as shown in Diagram 11.12.

Obviously the area of the upper rectangles will overestimate the area under the curve and the lower rectangles (shaded) will underestimate it but at least we will have boundaries on the area.

DIAGRAM 11.12

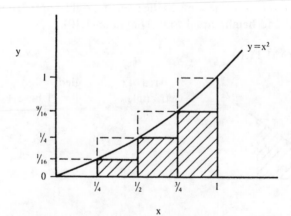

$$\text{Sum of upper rectangles} = \frac{1}{4} \times \frac{1}{16} + \frac{1}{4} \times \frac{1}{4} + \frac{1}{4} \times \frac{9}{16} + \frac{1}{4} \times 1 = \frac{15}{32}$$

$$\text{Sum of lower rectangles} = \frac{1}{4} \times 0 + \frac{1}{4} \times \frac{1}{16} + \frac{1}{4} \times \frac{1}{4} + \frac{1}{4} \times \frac{9}{16} = \frac{7}{32}$$

So, the required area is greater than $\frac{7}{32}$ and less than $\frac{15}{32}$ and as an approximation we could take $\frac{1}{2}\left(\frac{7}{32} + \frac{15}{32}\right) = \frac{11}{32}$ as the area.

This approximation could be improved by taking smaller subintervals, and there are better methods for estimating the area under a curve, but if we can integrate the function we can find the area precisely. In the above example, the required area is given by

$$\text{Area} = \int_0^1 x^2.dx = \left[\frac{x^3}{3} + C\right]_0^1 = \left(\frac{1}{3} + C\right) - \left(0 + C\right)$$

$$= \frac{1}{3}$$

More generally, $\int_a^b f(x)dx$ will always give the value of the area between the curve $f(x)$, the x-axis, and the values x=a to x=b.

EXAMPLE:

Suppose the Marginal Revenue (the increase in revenue from the sale of one unit) of a product is given by the expression $\left(7 - \frac{q}{100}\right)$ where q = number of units sold.

How much would be earned from the sale of 400 units?

The total revenue will equal the sum of all the marginal revenues from 0 to 400 units.

$$\frac{dR}{dq} = 7 - \frac{q}{100}$$

$$\text{Total Revenue, R} = \int_0^{400} \left(7 - \frac{q}{100}\right) dq$$

$$= \left[7q - \frac{q^2}{200} + C\right]_0^{400}$$

Since no revenue will be earned when no units are sold C is zero and disappears anyway in the subtraction.

$$\text{Total Revenue} = 7 \times 400 - \frac{400 \times 400}{200} = £2{,}000$$

If you refer back to 11.3.1 "Revenue maximisation" you will see that this answer is consistent with the demand schedule.

QUESTIONS

11.5 The weekly revenue £R of a small company is given by

$R = 14 + 81x - \dfrac{x^3}{12}$, where x is the number of units produced.

Required:
(i) Determine the number of units that maximise the revenue.

(6 marks)

(ii) Determine the maximum revenue. *(2 marks)*

(iii) Determine the price per unit that will maximise the revenue.

(2 marks)

(Total 10 marks) (ACA)

11.6 An accountant has estimated that the weekly costs of production, C, for a product are given by the equation:

$$C = 100 + 23x + \tfrac{1}{2}x^2,$$

where x is the number of tonnes produced. The weekly revenue equation, R, is given by

$$R = 100x - x^2 \ (x < 100)$$

You are required to:
(a) find the production level(s) at which profit is maximised;

(5 marks)

(b) find any break-even point(s); *(5 marks)*

(c) find the point at which revenue would be maximised; *(3 marks)*

(d) sketch a graph which describes approximately the cost/revenue situation; *(4 marks)*

(e) recommend a level of x which it would be rational to produce and justify your answer. *(3 marks)*

(Total 20 marks)
(ICMA)

*11.7 (a) The total cost function is given by $C = x^2 + 16x + 39$, where x units is the quantity produced and £C the total cost.

Required:
(i) Write down the expression for the average cost per unit.

(2 marks)

(ii) Sketch the average cost function against x, for values of x between x = 0 and x = 8. *(6 marks)*

(b) The demand function is given by $p = x^2 - 24x + 117$, where x units is the quantity demanded and £p the price per unit.

Required:

(i) Write down an expression for the total revenue for x units of production. *(3 marks)*

(ii) Using the methods of differential calculus establish the number of units of production and the price at which total revenue will be maximised. *(6 marks)*

(iii) If elasticity of demand is defined as (p/x) (1/dp/dx) determine the elasticity of demand for the quantity which maximizes the total revenue. *(3 marks)*

(Total 20 marks) (ACA)

11.8 Your company manufactures large scale items. It has been shown that the marginal (or variable) cost, which is the gradient of the total cost curve, is (92–2x) £thousands, where x is the number of units of output per annum. The fixed costs are £800,000 per annum. It has also been shown that the marginal revenue, which is the gradient of the total revenue curve, is (112–2x) £thousands.

Required:

(a) Establish by integration the equation of the total cost curve. *(4 marks)*

(b) Establish by integration the equation of the total revenue curve. *(4 marks)*

(c) Establish the break-even situation for your company. *(2 marks)*

(d) Determine the number of units of output that would:
   (i) maximise the total revenue, and
   (ii) maximise the total costs, together with the maximum total revenue and total costs. *(6 marks)*

(e) Assuming that your company cannot manufacture more than 60 units of output per annum, what interpretation can be put on the results you obtain in (d)? (a sketch of the total revenue and cost curve will be helpful.) *(4 marks)*

(Total 20 marks) (ACA)

11.9 *(a) The quantity of a commodity demanded or supplied is represented by q tonnes and £p represents its price. The demand equation is $2p - q = 15$ and the supply equation is $-p + 3q = 5$.

Required:

(i) Express these equations in matrix form. *(2 marks)*

(ii) Using matrix methods establish the values of p and q which satisfy the demand and supply equations simultaneously. *(6 marks)*

Do not attempt part (a) until you have studied CHAPTER 14.

(b) Another demand equation is given by $q = 2p^3 - 21p^2 + 36p + 9$.

Required:

Using the method of differential calculus establish the maximum demand and its corresponding price.   *(8 marks)*

(c) Elasticity of demand is given by the expression

$$\left(\frac{dq}{dp}\right)\frac{p}{q}$$

Required:

If the demand function is given by $q = \dfrac{90}{p^3}$, show that the elasticity of demand is constant.   *(4 marks)*

(Total 20 marks)

(ACCA)

11.10 A company making a single product has manufacturing and distribution divisions. Stocks of finished goods are not held, all production being to order.

The average net revenue per unit, allowing for quantity discounts, is £100 – £0.01Q where Q is the quantity sold.

The average variable costs per unit for the two divisions are:

Manufacturing = £10 + £0.015Q
Distribution   = £2 + £0.001Q

The fixed costs per annum are:

Manufacturing: £40,000
Distribution: £20,000

You are required to calculate:
(a) the optimum annual production quantity to maximise the profit of the company;
(b) the profit of the company at the level of activity in (a) above;
(c) the annual production quantity to maximise the manufacturing division's profit, if it has been instructed to transfer the product to the distribution division at £73 per unit;
(d) the profit of the company, showing the results of the two divisions, at the level of activity in (c) above.   *(ICMA)*

(Quantitative Techniques paper)

*11.11 The production processes at Southern Chemicals Limited can be represented by the following diagram. The initial process converts raw material into equal quantities of the two joint products M and N. Both of these require separate finishing processes before they can be sold.

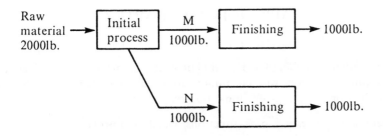

The expected variable costs are:　£
Raw material . . . . 65 per 2,000 lb.
Operating costs:
　Initial process . . . . 15 per 2,000 lb.
　　　　　　　　　　　　 of raw material
　Finishing M . . . . 10 per 1,000 lb.
　Finishing N . . . . 20 per 1,000 lb.
The expected selling prices in £'s are:

1

$$P_m = 300 - \frac{1}{10} \, Q_m$$

$$P_n = 250 - \frac{1}{5} \, Q_n$$

where P_m and P_n are the sales prices per 1,000lb. that will be obtained when the quantities (1,000's) Q_m and Q_n are sold.

There are no costs associated with the disposal of unfinished intermediate products and no process losses. No stocks for M or N are held in either the intermediate or finished state.

You are required to:
(a) formulate the equations relating contribution, revenue and costs for M, N and the company;

(b) calculate the quantity of raw materials used and the price and quantity sold of M and N at the level of activity that will maximise contribution for the company.　　　　　*(ICMA)*

(Quantitative Techniques paper)

APPENDIX TO CHAPTER 11

The contents of Chapter 11 will hopefully enable you to deal with any functions that you will encounter up to at least the foundation level examinations of the professional bodies.

There are, however, some functions which require other techniques of differentiation and integration. For the naturally curious, and those studying at a higher level, some of these techniques are outlined in this appendix.

We assume throughout that u and v are functions of x.

General Methods of Differentiation

(1) PRODUCT RULE

$$\frac{d(uv)}{dx} = v\frac{du}{dx} + u\frac{dv}{dx}$$

e.g. $\frac{d[(x^2+1)(2x+3)]}{dx} = (x^2+1)\frac{d(2x+3)}{dx} + (2x+3)\frac{d(x^2+1)}{dx}$

$$= (x^2+1)2 + (2x+3)2x$$
$$= 6x^2 + 6x + 2$$

N.B. If you are confronted by more than two factors multiply until two factors remain.

i.e. $\frac{d(u.v.w)}{dx} = \frac{d((uv)w)}{dx} = uv\frac{dw}{dx} + w\frac{d(uv)}{dx}$

(2) QUOTIENT RULE

$$\frac{d\left(\frac{u}{v}\right)}{dx} = \frac{v\frac{du}{dx} - u\frac{dv}{dx}}{v^2}$$

eg. $\frac{d\left(\frac{x^2+1}{3x+2}\right)}{dx} = \frac{(3x+2)\frac{d(x^2+1)}{dx} - (x^2+1)\frac{d(3x+2)}{dx}}{(3x+2)^2}$

$$= \frac{3x^2 + 4x - 3}{(3x+2)^2}$$

(3) CHAIN RULE (Function of a Function)

$$\frac{dy}{dx} = \frac{dy}{du} \times \frac{du}{dx}$$

This rule enables us to introduce a new variable in order to differentiate functions which cannot be differentiated by the normal rules. Success depends upon deciding a suitable substitution.

$$\text{eg.} \quad y = \sqrt{1 + x}$$

$$\text{Let} \quad u = 1 + x$$

$$\frac{du}{dx} = 1$$

$$y = u^{\frac{1}{2}}$$

$$\frac{dy}{du} = \frac{1}{2} u^{-\frac{1}{2}}$$

$$\frac{dy}{dx} = \frac{dy}{du} \times \frac{du}{dx} = \frac{1 u^{-\frac{1}{2}}}{2} \times 1 = \frac{1}{2 u^{\frac{1}{2}}}$$

$$= \frac{1}{2 \sqrt{1+x}}$$

(4) INVERSE FUNCTION

A corollary of the chain rule is that

$$\frac{dx}{dy} = \frac{1}{\left(\frac{dy}{dx}\right)}$$

N.B. This does not hold if $\frac{dy}{dx} = 0$

Consequently, the derivative $\frac{dy}{dx}$ may be found from the inverse of $\frac{dx}{dy}$ where x can be more easily expressed as a function of y than vice versa.

$$\text{eg.} \quad y^2 = x + 2$$
$$x = y^2 - 2$$
$$\frac{dx}{dy} = 2y$$
$$\frac{dy}{dx} = \frac{1}{2y} = \frac{1}{2 \sqrt{x + 2}}$$

Check this result for yourself, using the chain rule.

(5) IMPLICIT FUNCTIONS

Sometimes it is difficult to express x or y as functions of each other. A further corollary of the chain rule is that each term in such a function may be differentiated with respect to one of the variables.

$$\text{Example:} \quad \text{Find} \quad \frac{dy}{dx} \quad \text{if} \quad x^2 + 3xy + y^2 = 4$$

Differentiating each term by rule with respect to x:

$$\frac{d(x^2)}{dx} + \frac{3\ d(xy)}{dx} + \frac{d(y^2)}{dx} = \frac{d(4)}{dx}$$

$$2x + 3\left\{y + \frac{x\,dy}{\cdot\ \ dx}\right\} + 2y\ \frac{dy}{dx} = 0$$

$$2x + 3y + \frac{dy}{dx}\ (3x+2y) = 0$$

$$\frac{dy}{dx} = -\ \frac{2x+3y}{3x+2y}$$

General Methods of Integration

Apart from the straightforward functions already discussed, integration is largely a tentative process — a matter of "inspired guesswork".

There are, however, two general methods for determining complicated integrals:

(1) Change of variable

This method is based upon the chain rule and its success depends upon being able to make a substitution which reduces the integration to a familiar form.

The only type of integration we have mentioned is of the form $\int x^n dx$. There are others which involve logarithms and trigonometic functions but they are beyond the scope of this book and are unlikely to be useful in practice or to be examined.

EXAMPLE: $\int x \sqrt{x^2+1}\ .dx$

Let $\quad z = \int x \sqrt{x^2+1}\ dx$

Then $\quad \frac{dz}{dx} = x \sqrt{x^2+1}$

The substitution to make in this case is $\quad u = x^2+1$

Then $\quad \frac{du}{dx} = 2x$

From the chain rule: $\quad \frac{dz}{du} = \frac{dz}{dx}\ .\ \frac{dx}{du}$

$$= x \sqrt{x^2+1}\ \times\ \frac{1}{2x}$$

$$= \frac{\sqrt{x^2+1}}{2}$$

$$= \frac{u^{1/2}}{2}$$

Integrating both sides with respect to u.

$$z = \int \frac{u^{1/2}}{2} du$$

which is of the form $\int x^n dx$ with which we are familiar

$$= \frac{1}{3} u^{1/2} + C$$

$$= \frac{(x^2+1)^{3/2}}{3} + C$$

Definite Integrals: If we wished to evaluate $\int_0^2 x \sqrt{x^2+1}$

The answer would be

$$\left[\frac{(x^2+1)^{1/2}}{3} + C \right]_0^2$$

or

$$\left[\frac{1}{3} u^{1/2} + C \right]_1^5$$

since $u=x^2+1$
when $x=2$ $u=5$
when $x=0$ $u=1$

Both of which give $\frac{1}{3}(5^{1/2}-1)$

(2) Integration by parts

This technique is derived from the product rule which is

$$\frac{d(uv)}{dx} = u\frac{dv}{dx} + v\frac{du}{dx}$$

where u and v are functions of x.

Integrating both sides with respect to x

$$uv = \int u\, dv + \int v\, du$$

N.B. if $u = f(x)$

$$\frac{du}{dx} = f'(x)$$

and $du = f'(x)dx$

so du is the differential of u, which is a function of x, by dx.

Rearranging the above expression

$$\int u\, dv = uv - \int v\, du$$

which means that the method depends upon being able to find $\int v.du$ rather than $\int udv$.

An example will make the method clear, suppose we wanted to find $\int x^3(x^2+1)dx$.

In fact we could simply multiply out and integrate in the normal way

i.e. $\int x^3(x^2+1)dx = \int (x^5+x^3)dx = \dfrac{x^6}{6} + \dfrac{x^4}{4} + C$

Integration by parts provides another method because $\int x^3(x^2+1)dx$ can be rearranged as

$$\int (x^2+1)x^3 dx = \int (x^2+1) d\left(\dfrac{x^4}{4}\right)$$

so that $u = (x^2+1)$ and $v = \dfrac{x^4}{4}$

Now $\int u\,dv = uv - \int v\,du$

$$\therefore \int (x^2+1) \, d\left(\dfrac{x^4}{4}\right) dx = (x^2+1)\dfrac{x^4}{4} - \int \dfrac{x^4}{4} \, d(x^2+1)$$

$$= \dfrac{x^6}{4} + \dfrac{x^4}{4} - \int \dfrac{x^4}{4} .2x \, dx$$

$$= \dfrac{x^6}{4} + \dfrac{x^4}{4} - \int \dfrac{x^5}{2} . dx$$

$$= \dfrac{x^6}{4} + \dfrac{x^4}{4} - \dfrac{x^6}{12} + C$$

$$= \dfrac{x^6}{6} + \dfrac{x^4}{4} + C \qquad \text{as before.}$$

That was rather like using a sledgehammer to crack a nut because the integration could be performed quite easily by first multiplying the factors together as shown. Nevertheless we have demonstrated the validity of the method and integration by parts can be useful in solving difficult integration problems.

EXAMPLE:

$$\int \dfrac{x}{(x+1)^3} \, dx = \int x. (x+1)^{-3} dx = - \int x. \, d\left(\dfrac{(x+1)^{-2}}{2}\right)$$

$$\int u \, dv = uv - \int v \, du$$

$$- \int x. \, d\left(\dfrac{(x+1)^{-2}}{2}\right) = - \left[\dfrac{x.(x+1)^{-2}}{2} - \int \dfrac{(x+1)^{-2}}{2} \, dx^* \right]$$

$$* \; d(x) = 1.dx$$

$$= - \left[\dfrac{x}{2(x+1)^2} + \dfrac{(x+1)^{-1}}{2} + C \right]$$

$$= -\left[\frac{x}{2(x+1)^2} + \frac{1}{2(x+1)} + C \right]$$

$$= -\left[\frac{x + x + 1}{2(x+1)^2} + C \right]$$

$$= -\frac{2x + 1}{2(x+1)^2} + C$$

You may like to try the above problem by using the substitution u=x+1. If so, note that $\frac{u-1}{u^3} = \frac{1}{u^2} - \frac{1}{u^3}$ splitting into partial fractions.

Chapter 12
FINANCIAL ARITHMETIC

When an individual, or company or government, lends or invests money they expect to earn a financial return. This return may take the form of interest or profit but in both cases it represents a reward for foregoing current consumption in return for future rewards. The difference between interest and profit is that the former is a fixed mandatory payment in return for a loan whilst the latter is the return to those who take a stake in a venture and risk their capital. Although we will discuss various techniques in the context of interest rates, these techniques are usually generally applicable to any type of financial return.

There are, of course, a plethora of different interest rates — bank deposit rates, bank lending rates, building society rates, treasury bill rate, central bank discount rate etc. This is because a particular interest rate reflects two elements:

$$r = i + p$$

where i = "pure" interest — the reward for parting with liquidity for a period of time.
and p = risk premium — the reward for the risk that the borrower may default or, where a financial asset exists, the risk that a forced sale results in loss.

Therefore, a particular interest rate will reflect the period for which the loan is made and the degree of risk attached. The greater either of these is, the greater will be the interest rate demanded.

Also, during a period of inflation the nominal rate of interest has to be greater than the rate of inflation in order that the lender receives a positive real rate of interest. In other words, only if the (nominal) rate of interest exceeds the rate of inflation will the purchasing power of the lender's money increase.

The basic tenet of what follows is that "MONEY NOW IS ALWAYS WORTH MORE THAN MONEY IN THE FUTURE". It must be stressed that this is true irrespective of whether inflation exists or not, because money now can be "invested" to earn interest and grow to a greater amount in the future. Inflation merely means that the nominal rate has to be higher if the investor is to earn a positive real return.

In this chapter we will deal with various interest rate calculations and in the following chapter we will relate these to the capital investment decisions of organisations.

12.1 SIMPLE INTEREST

Simple interest refers to a situation where the interest payment is a fixed amount. For example, suppose I put £100 in a building society which paid 10% p.a. simple interest on deposits. How much would I have at the end of 3 years?

			£
	Principal	=	100
Add	Simple interest for year 1	=	10
			110
Add	Simple interest for year 2	=	10
			120
Add	Simple interest for year 3	=	10
	Amount at end of 3 years		130

We could have performed the above calculation using the following formula:

$$A_n = P + nrP \quad \text{or} \quad P(1+nr)$$

where
P = Principal (the original sum invested)
n = number of time periods over which interest is calculated
r = rate of interest per time period as a proportion
A_n = Amount after n time periods

i.e. $A_3 = 100 + 3 \times 0.1 \times 100 = 130$

The formula is, of course, totally unnecessary but it serves to introduce the notation which we will employ.

More to the point, the calculation is totally unrealistic because building societies, in common with other financial institutions, pay compound interest not simple interest.

12.2.1 COMPOUND INTEREST

Compound interest is the normal method of calculating interest payments and differs from simple interest in that interest earned during previous periods itself earns interest. The above example would change in the following way if the building society paid compound interest:

			£
	Principal	=	100
Add	10% compound interest for year 1	=	10
			110
Add	10% compound interest for year 2		11
			121
Add	10% compound interest for year 3	=	12.10
	Amount at end of 3 years		133.10

In the case of compound interest we really do need a formula. Using the same notation as above:

$A_1 = 100(1+0.1) = 110 = P(1+r)$

$A_2 = 110(1+0.1) = 121 = A_1(1+r) = P(1+r)(1+r) = P(1+r)^2$

$A_3 = 121(1+0.1) = 133.10 = A_2(1+r) = P(1+r)^2(1+r) = P(1+r)^3$

It is obvious from the above that we can derive the following general formula:

$$A_n = P(1+r)^n$$

where A_n = Amount after n time periods

P = Principal

r = rate of interest as proportion

n = number of time periods

EXAMPLE 1

If I invested £100 at 10% p.a. (N.B. we will in future always assume compound interest), how much would I have at the end of 5 years?

Answer: $A_5 = 100(1+0.1)^5 = 100(1.1)^5 = 100 \times 1.6105$

$= £161.05$

The value of $(1+r)^n$ might also be found by using the compound interest tables which are printed at the end of this chapter (Appendix 12.1).

Examining bodies tend to differ in so far as some supply complete tables, some supply extracts from tables as part of the question, and others expect you to calculate the factors for yourself. Modern pocket calculators perform the necessary calculations more accurately than published tables which provide the factors for only a limited number of periods and interest rates.

It is probably advisable that you learn to carry out the calculations yourself and use the tables in the early stages to check your answers.

EXAMPLE 2

If I invested £250 in a bank deposit account for 10 years earning $10\frac{3}{4}\%$ for the first 5 years and $11\frac{1}{2}\%$ for the last 5 years, how much would I have at the end of the 10 years?

Answer:
$$A_{10} = 250\,(1+0.1075)^5\,(1+0.115)^5$$
$$= 250 \times 1.666 \times 1.059 = £441.07$$

EXAMPLE 3

If I invested £1000 in a building society at 12% p.a. compounded half-yearly, how much would I have at the end of one year?

Answer:
$$A_2 = 1000\,(1+0.06)^2 = £1,123.60$$
$$n=2,\ r=6\%$$

N.B. We have assumed that the building society pays 6% per half-year which is what would happen in practice. As the answer illustrates, 6% per half-year is not quite the same as 12% p.a. (see later).

EXAMPLE 4

If I invested £5000 in a bank deposit account at 8% p.a. compounded quarterly, how much would I have at the end of 5 years?

Answer:
$$A_{20} = 5000\,(1+0.02)^{20} = £7,429.74$$
$$r=2\%,\ n=20$$

12.2.2 Nominal and Effective rates of interest

Suppose that I borrowed £100 on my credit card which charges 2% per month on any outstanding balance. If I did not pay anything back for a whole year, how much would be outstanding at the end of the year?
$$A_{12} = 100\,(1+0.02)^{12} = £126.82$$

So, in the worst possible case, I would be charged £26.82 interest for borrowing £100 — an Effective Annual rate of interest of 26.82%.

A general formula for calculating the Effective Annual rate of interest is

Effective Annual Rate
or $= (1+r)^{\frac{12}{n}} - 1$
APR*

where r = rate per time period.
and   n = number of months in time period

*The Effective Annual rate is more commonly known as the Annual Percentage Rate and lenders are required under the Consumer Credit Act to quote it to potential borrowers.

12.2.3 Real and Money rates of interest

The Nominal rate of interest is the "named" or quoted rate of interest. Sometimes it is not the same as the Effective Annual rate of interest and the above example shows how the Effective Annual Rate can be calculated.

The Effective Annual Rate is, however, still only a monetary rate of interest; it shows the change in the money value as a result of the interest payment.

The "real" rate of interest is the nominal or money rate adjusted for inflation. So, if the nominal rate of interest was 15% then an inflation rate of 5% would imply a real rate of 10%. In other words, the increase in purchasing power would be 10% rather than 15%.

In fact we can be more precise than this. If you refer back to section 4.4.3.3 you will see that we "deflated" by multiplying by the ratio of the RPI at the base year to the RPI in the current year. If prices have risen by 5%, the RPI will have moved from 100 to 105, i.e. We need to multiply any amount of money by $\frac{100}{105}$ to reduce it to constant prices. This is the same as multiplying by $\frac{1}{1+i}$ where i is the inflation rate as a proportion.

It follows that:

$$\text{If} \quad A_1 = P(1+r) \qquad\qquad \text{where } r = \text{nominal rate}$$

$$\text{Increase in "real" terms} = P(1+r) \times \frac{1}{1+i} - P \qquad \text{where } i = \text{inflation rate}$$

$$= P\left[\frac{1+r}{1+i} - 1\right]$$

$$\text{"Real" rate of interest} = \frac{P\left[\dfrac{1+r}{1+i} - 1\right]}{P} = \frac{1+r}{1+i} - 1$$

$$= \frac{r-i}{1+i}$$

In the above example, the real rate would therefore be $\dfrac{0.15-0.05}{1.05} = 9.52\%$

12.3 PRESENT VALUE

When we calculate the amount to which a sum of money will grow in the future we use the formula:

$$A_n = P(1+r)^n$$

This formula can be re-arranged to give

$$\boxed{P = \frac{A_n}{(1+r)^n} \qquad \text{or} \qquad A_n(1+r)^{-n}}$$

where P = Present value of a sum of money A_n
        A_n = sum of money due n time periods
             hence
        r = rate per time period
        n = number of time periods

So P is the present value of a single sum of money A_n due n time periods hence given that money can be invested at a rate of interest r.

Put another way, P is the amount you would need to have today to be able to invest for n time periods at a rate r and end up with an amount A_n.

Obviously the present value of a future sum of money is always less than that future sum of money because money can be invested to earn interest. When we reduce the future sum of money to a present value by dividing it by $(1+r)^n$ or multiplying it by $(1+r)^{-n}$ we say that we are **discounting** the future sum.

We have already encountered compound interest tables which give the value of $(1+r)^n$. Values of $(1+r)^{-n}$ are known as discount factors and may be found using the present value or discounting table printed at the end of the chapter (Appendix 12.2). Again, it is a simple matter to calculate values of $(1+r)^{-n}$ on a pocket calculator and you should only use the tables to make sure you are carrying out the calculations correctly.

EXAMPLE 1
What is the present value of £1000 receivable 5 years from now given that money can be invested at 10% p.a.?

Answer:

$$PV = A_n(1+r)^{-n} = 1000(1+0.1)^{-5} = 1000 \times 0.62092 = £620.92$$

$$\text{or} \quad \frac{A_n}{(1+r)^n} = \frac{1000}{(1+0.1)^5} = \frac{1000}{1.61051} = £620.92$$

So, if we invested £620.92 for 5 years at 10% p.a. it would grow to £1000. We can, of course, check this using the compound interest formula:

$$A_n = P(1+r)^n = 620.92\,(1+0.1)^5 \simeq £1000$$

EXAMPLE 2
What is the present value of £1000 due two years from now and £2000 due four years from now, given that money can be invested at 8% p.a.?

$$PV = 1000(1.08)^{-2} + 2000(1.08)^{-4}$$
$$= 857.34 + 1470.06 = £2327.40$$

In other words, if I had £2327.40 today I could invest it at 8%, withdraw £1000 in two years time, withdraw £2000 in four years and the amount remaining would be zero. Let us check this using the compound interest formula:

$$\text{Amount after 2 years, } A_2 = 2327.40\,(1.08)^2 = 2714.68$$

$$\begin{array}{rr}
\text{Less withdrawal at end} & \\
\text{of second year} & 1000.00 \\
\hline
& 1714.68
\end{array}$$

$$\text{Amount after 4 years, } A_4 = 1714.68\,(1.08)^2 = \pounds2000$$

which when withdrawn leaves a zero balance.

EXAMPLE 3

How much would I need to invest today to give myself an income of £10,000 at the end of each of the next five years, given that I can obtain a rate of interest of 9%?

Answer:

$$\begin{array}{rlr}
& & \pounds \\
PV = & 10,000\,(1.09)^{-1} = & 9,174 \\
+ & 10,000\,(1.09)^{-2} = & 8,417 \\
+ & 10,000\,(1.09)^{-3} = & 7,722 \\
+ & 10,000\,(1.09)^{-4} = & 7,084 \\
+ & 10,000\,(1.09)^{-5} = & 6,499 \\
\hline
& & 38,896
\end{array}$$

In the next section we shall see that such a calculation can be performed more rapidly as the present value of an annuity.

12.4 ANNUITIES

An annuity is a fixed sum of money payable each year for a certain number of years. This is a rather restricted definition and, as we shall see, in order to apply the formulae that we develop it is only necessary that the payments occur at regular intervals. Furthermore, even if the sums of money are not absolutely constant the annuity formulae can still sometimes be used to ease computation.

12.4.1 Amount of an Annuity

Suppose I invest an amount a at the end of each of the next n years and earn a rate of interest r throughout the period, how much will I have accumulated at the end of the nth year?

DIAGRAM 12.1

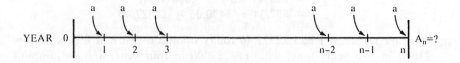

Diagram 12.1 represents what is happening. In order to use annuity tables, or the formulae relating to them, the annuity must be of the "shape" indicated. That is to say:—

(i)   the first payment must be made at the end of the first time period (year);
(ii) the last payment must be made at the end of the last time period (year);
(iii) the amount, a, must of course be constant; and
(iv) the amount, A_n, to which these sums of money grow occurs at the end of the last time period (year) **after** the last amount, a, is paid.

Using the formula for compound interest $(A_n=P(1+r)^n)$ and taking the payments in reverse order, the last amount, a, invested at the end of the last year will earn no interest so its value will remain as a.

The previous payment will earn one year's interest and so will grow to $a(1+r)$, the one before that will grow to $a(1+r)^2$ and so on. The first amount, a, is invested at the **end** of the first year and so it will earn interest for only (n–1) years and grow to $a(1+r)^{n-1}$.

The total amount accumulated by the end of the nth year will therefore be:

$$A_n = a + a(1+r) + a(1+r)^2 + a(1+r)^3 + \cdots + a(1+r)^{n-2} + a(1+r)^{n-1}$$

We can now simplify this equation as follows:

$$A_n = a\,[1+(1+r)+(1+r)^2 + \cdots (1+r)^{n-2} +(1+r)^{n-1}]$$

The term in the square brackets is a geometric progression which we can simplify as follows:

$$\text{Let}\quad S = 1+(1+r) + (1+r)^2 + \cdots (1+r)^{n-2} + (1+r)^{n-1}$$

$$\text{Then}\quad S(1+r) = (1+r) + (1+r)^2 + \cdots + (1+r)^{n-1} + (1+r)^n$$

$$\therefore\quad S(1+r)-S = -1 +(1+r)^n$$

$$\therefore\quad rS = (1+r)^n - 1$$

$$S = \frac{(1+r)^n - 1}{r}$$

This leads us to the formula for the compound amount of an annuity:

$$\boxed{A_n = a \left[\frac{(1+r)^n - 1}{r} \right]}$$

where
  a = fixed amount invested at the end of each year
  r = rate of interest per annum as proportion
  n = number of years
  A_n = the amount to which the annuity (a) will grow after n years at a rate of r per annum.

N.B. The first payment of the annuity at the end of the first time period and the last payment at the end of the last time period.

The values of n and r can be adjusted in the usual way to take account of non-annual compounding.

Values of $\left[\frac{(1+r)^n - 1}{r}\right]$ may be found from the table for the Compound Amount of an Annuity at the end of the chapter (Appendix 12.3) but, again, the recommendation is that you only use the table to check your calculations in the early stages.

EXAMPLE 1

If I pay £100 into a savings account on 31st Dec. 1980 and a further £100 on 31st Dec. each year thereafter, how much will I have accumulated by 1st Jan. 1990 if I earn 10% p.a. on my savings?

Answer:

This is a straightforward annuity but we must remember to count the year up to 31.12.1980 as the first time period.

DIAGRAM 12.2

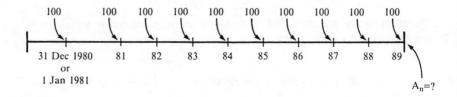

$$A_n = a \left[\frac{(1+r)^n - 1}{r}\right]$$

$$n = 10, \quad r = 0.1, \quad a = £100$$

$$A_{10} = 100 \left[\frac{(1+0.1)^{10} - 1}{0.1}\right] = 100 (15.9374) = £1,593.74$$

EXAMPLE 2

Suppose I paid £100 into a building society on 30th June 1980 and a further £50 every six months thereafter. If I receive 8% p.a. compounded half-yearly how much will I have accumulated by 1st Jan. 1985?

Answer:
This is rather more complicated. We can treat it as a £50 annuity and calculate how much the additional £50 in the first period will grow to but we need to be careful with the value of n.

DIAGRAM 12.3

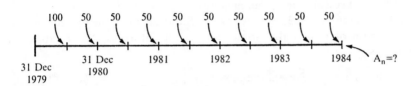

As the diagram illustrates we have a £50 annuity with n=10 and r=0.04 **plus** a single sum of £50 which will receive compound interest at 4% over 10 time periods.

$$\text{Therefore} \quad A_{10} = 50 \left[\frac{(1+0.04)^{10} - 1}{0.04} \right] + 50 (1+0.04)^{10}$$

$$= 50 (12.006107) + 50 (1.4802443)$$

$$= \underline{£674.32}$$

EXAMPLE 3
Suppose I pay £1000 into a bank deposit account on 1st Jan. 1980 and a further £1000 at the start of each year thereafter. If I receive 10% p.a., how much will I have in the account on 31st Dec. 1985?

Answer:
For the purpose of the calculation we can treat 1st Jan. of one year the same as 31st Dec. of the previous year.

DIAGRAM 12.4

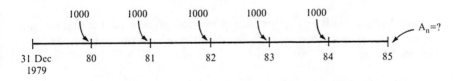

The diagram illustrates that we have the right "shape" for an annuity except we are missing £1000 at the end of the last time period.

The problem is overcome by assuming, for the purpose of applying the formula, that an extra £1000 is paid in at the end of the last time period and then deducting from our answer an appropriate amount. Since the £1000 has no time to earn interest we simply deduct £1000 to arrive at our answer.

i.e.
$$A_6 = 1000 \left[\frac{(1+0.1)^6 - 1}{0.1} \right] - 1000$$

$$= £6,715.61$$

12.4.2 Present value of an annuity

Earlier, in section 12.3, we saw that we could calculate the present value of a single sum of money due some time in the future by "discounting" that future sum.

i.e.
$$\text{Present value} = \frac{A_n}{(1+r)^n} \quad \text{or} \quad A_n (1+r)^{-n}$$

In example 3 in section 12.3 we calculated the present value of a stream of future cash flows of a constant amount. Such a stream is, of course, an annuity and in the same way that we derived a formula for the compound amount of an annuity so we can derive a formula for the present value of an annuity.

Again, in order to apply the formula or use the tables (Appendix 12.4) the "shape" of the annuity stream must be such that the first payment arises at the end of the first time period and the last payment at the end of the last time period. This time, however, we want to find the present value of the annuity payments at the start of the first time period.

DIAGRAM 12.5

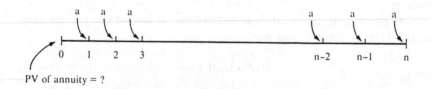

PV of annuity = ?

Using the formula $P = \frac{A_n}{(1+r)^n}$ for each individual payment, a, the first amount, a, will need to be discounted back one year, the second amount two years, and so on.

$$P = \frac{a}{(1+r)} + \frac{a}{(1+r)^2} + \frac{a}{(1+r)^3} + \cdots + \frac{a}{(1+r)^{n-1}} + \frac{a}{(1+r)^n}$$

$$= a \left[\frac{1}{(1+r)} + \frac{1}{(1+r)^2} + \cdots + \frac{1}{(1+r)^{n-1}} + \frac{1}{(1+r)^n} \right]$$

Again, we need to simplify the term in square brackets and, again, it is a geometric progression.

Let $S = \dfrac{1}{(1+r)} = \dfrac{1}{(1+r)^2} + \cdots\cdots + \dfrac{1}{(1+r)^{n-1}} + \dfrac{1}{(1+r)^n}$

Then $S.\dfrac{1}{(1+r)} = \dfrac{1}{(1+r)^2} + \cdots\cdots\cdots\cdots\cdots + \dfrac{1}{(1+r)^n} + \dfrac{1}{(1+r)^{n+1}}$

$\therefore\quad S - S.\dfrac{1}{(1+r)} = \dfrac{1}{(1+r)} - \dfrac{1}{(1+r)^{n+1}}$ all other terms cancelling.

$\therefore\quad \dfrac{S+rS-S}{(1+r)} = \dfrac{1}{(1+r)} - \dfrac{1}{(1+r)^{n+1}}$

$rS = 1 - \dfrac{1}{(1+r)^n}$ multiplying both sides by $(1+r)$

$= 1 - (1+r)^{-n}$

$\therefore\quad S = \dfrac{1 - (1+r)^{-n}}{r}$

Which means that the general formula for the present value of an annuity is

$$P = a\left[\frac{1 - (1+r)^{-n}}{r}\right]$$

where a = amount of the annuity at the end of each year (or time period)

r = rate of interest per time period or year

n = number of time periods or years

P = Present value of the annuity payments, a, arising over n time periods and given a rate of interest, r.

So the present value of an annuity can be regarded as the amount you would need to invest today, at a rate of interest r, in order to provide yourself with an income, a, at the end of each of the next n time periods.

In passing it is worth mentioning "perpetuities" or perpetual annuities which, as the name implies, are income streams or payments which carry on indefinitely. In such a situation the value of n is very large (infinity) and so the value of $(1+r)^{-n}$ or $\dfrac{1}{(1+r)^n}$ is very small and can be ignored. Therefore, the present value of a perpetuity reduces to $P = \dfrac{a}{r}$

EXAMPLE 1

How much would I need to invest today to give myself an income of £10,000 at the end of each of the next five years, given that I can obtain a rate of interest of 9%?

Answer:

This is the same question that we answered at the end of section 12.3 by finding the present value of each individual sum of £10,000 and adding them together.

Since the income flows are fixed in amount we can carry out the calculation more rapidly as below:

$$\text{PV of annuity} = a \left[\frac{1 - (1+r)^{-n}}{r} \right] = 10,000 \left[\frac{1 - (1.09)^{-5}}{0.09} \right]$$

$$= 10,000 \left[\frac{1 - 0.6499}{0.09} \right]$$

$$= 10,000(3.8897)$$

$$= £38,897$$

as previously.

EXAMPLE 2

An insurance company offers to sell you an annuity which would give you an income of £5000 p.a. for the next ten years (starting at the end of the year in which you buy the annuity and assuming that the income arises at the end of each year). How much would you be willing to pay for the annuity if you can currently obtain an interest rate of $7\frac{1}{2}\%$ p.a. on your money?

Answer:

$$P = a \left[\frac{1 - (1+r)^{-n}}{r} \right] = 5,000 \left[\frac{1 - (1.075)^{-10}}{0.075} \right]$$

$$= 5,000 \times 6.864 = £34,320$$

You would not pay more than £34,320 because this sum invested at $7\frac{1}{2}\%$ would provide you with an income of £5,000 p.a. for the next ten years.

N.B. You would, of course, be using your original £34,320 and the interest thereon to provide the income and you would have nothing left after ten years (as with the insurance company's offer).

EXAMPLE 3

How much would you be willing to pay for a $2\frac{1}{2}\%$ consul given that the current market rate for similar investments is 10%?

Answer:

This is another question of interest to Economists. A consul is an undated government stock. Stock with a nominal value of £100 yields an annual income of £2.50 until the government decides to redeem the stock.

Since interest rates are unlikely to ever fall below $2\frac{1}{2}\%$ p.a. the government will never redeem these stocks and so anyone who buys such stock is, in effect, purchasing a perpetual annuity of £2.50.

$$\frac{\text{PV of perpetual}}{\text{annuity}} = \frac{a}{r} = \frac{2.5}{0.10} = £25$$

The market price of such stock should therefore be £25 for stock with nominal value of £100. In passing, this illustrates the inverse relationship between the price of gilt-edged securities and market rates of interest.

12.5   Some business applications

The main reason for studying the techniques of compounding and discounting is that they are useful in the area of capital budgeting which is the subject of the next chapter. There are, however, a number of other situations in which these techniques can be helpful and some are mentioned below.

12.5.1   DEPRECIATION — The Diminishing Balance Method

There are a variety of methods of calculating depreciation charges; a favoured method, because it charges higher amounts in the early years of an asset's life, is the diminishing balance method. This method is to charge a constant percentage of the written down value of the asset.

For example, if an asset cost £100,000 and it had been decided to reduce the book value of the asset by 10% p.a. the depreciation charges would be calculated as follows:

	(£)
Cost of Asset	100,000
Depreciation Yr.1	10,000
Book value at end of Yr.1	90,000
Depreciation Yr.2	9,000
Book value at end of Yr.2	81,000
Depreciation Yr.3	8,100
Book value at end of Yr.3	72,900

etc, etc.

In theory this means that the asset will never be written off completely but in practice the final year's depreciation charge can be increased to write off the residual balance on the written down value of the asset.

Often, the percentage rate employed is decided by some rule of thumb but it is possible to be more scientific about it.

$$\text{If the asset cost an amount} = C \quad \text{and}$$
$$\text{life of asset} = n \text{ years} \quad \text{at the end of which}$$
$$\text{scrap value} = S \quad \text{and}$$
$$\text{\% depreciation charge} \atop \text{per annum} = r$$

	Depn.	VALUE at end of year		
Yr. 1	Cr		$C - Cr =$	$C(1-r)$
Yr. 2	$C(1-r)r$	$C(1-r) - C(1-r)r =$		$C(1-r)^2$
Yr. 3	$C(1-r)^2 r$	$C(1-r)^2 - C(1-r)^2 r =$		$C(1-r)^3$
Yr. X	$C(1-r)^{x-1}r$		$=$	$C(1-r)^x$
Yr. n	$C(1-r)^{n-1}r$		$=$	$C(1-r)^n$

The written down value at the end of the n years is $C(1-r)^n$ and this has to be equal to the scrap value.

$$\therefore \quad S = C(1-r)^n$$

$$\frac{S}{C} = (1-r)^n$$

$$\sqrt[n]{\frac{S}{C}} = 1-r$$

$$r = \left(1 - \sqrt[n]{\frac{S}{C}}\right) \times 100\%$$

where $\sqrt[n]{\frac{S}{C}}$ is the nth root of the ratio of scrap value to capital cost.

The above formula, then, can be used to find the appropriate rate under the diminishing balance method.

For example, suppose that we had an asset costing £100,000, likely to last 10 years at the end of which it is expected to have a scrap value of £1000. What rate of depreciation will reduce the value of the asset to £1000 over 10 years under the diminishing balance method?

$$r = 1 - \sqrt[n]{\frac{S}{C}} = 1 - \sqrt[10]{\frac{1,000}{100,000}} = 1 - \sqrt[10]{0.01}$$

$$= 1 - 0.631$$

$$= 0.369$$

36.9% ought to be written off each year.

Of course, the formula fails if there is no scrap figure but this can be overcome by assuming a tiny scrap value of say £1 which enables the formula to be employed.

12.5.2 Sinking funds

Depreciation is merely a bookkeeping device which charges the cost of an asset against profit over the lifetime of the asset.

If this were not done profits would be overstated and if those "profits" were distributed the business would be re-distributing its capital.

However, making a provision for depreciation does not, in itself, ensure that funds are available to replace an asset when it wears out. The funds will have been kept in the business but they might be invested in other fixed assets, stocks, giving credit to debtors, etc. To ensure that a certain amount of cash is available at some given time something else has to be done.

One way of ensuring that cash is available at some time in the future is to set up a sinking fund whereby the business invests equal annual sums into some sort of investment which matures at the time when the money is required. If the amount invested each year is a and the amount required is A_n after n years. Then, given a rate of interest r, we are back with the formula for the compound amount of an annuity.

i.e. $$A_n = a \left[\frac{(1+r)^n - 1}{r} \right]$$

We can very easily re-arrange this formula so that we can calculate the amount that has to be put into the sinking fund each year.

i.e. $$a = \frac{r A_n}{(1+r)^n - 1}$$

EXAMPLE

Suppose that a firm owns an asset which is expected to last for 5 more years. The asset has no scrap value and will cost £100,000 to replace. The firm has decided to set up a sinking fund into which equal annual investments will be made earning a return of 8%. How much will have to be paid in each year in order that the fund will provide for replacement of the asset?

Answer:
$$a = \frac{r A_n}{(1+r)^n - 1} = \frac{0.08 \times 100,000}{1.08^5 - 1} = \frac{8,000}{0.4693} = £17,046$$

N.B. We have assumed that the investments are made at the end of each year.

12.5.3 Amortisation schedules

Amortisation is the repayment of a loan, usually on an equal instalment basis. The virtue of spreading repayment in such a way is that it enables the borrower to provide for repayment on a regular basis from his income which may arise from productive use of the loan.

Suppose that the original loan is P and interest is calculated on the reducing balance at a rate r. If the principal, P, and the interest are to be paid in n equal instalments of an amount a then the problem is to find the amount a which has to be repaid at the end of each time period (year).

A little thought should convince you that this is the opposite situation to that described in the previous section. When we considered a sinking fund we were looking for the value of an annuity which would grow to the compound amount required. When we consider an amortisation schedule we are looking for the value of an annuity which will repay the loan plus interest over the scheduled number of years; this is the same thing as asking how much can be withdrawn each year if an amount P is invested at a rate r for n years. In other words, P is the present value of an annuity a over n years given a rate r and, once again, the formula is easily re-arranged to give the value of the annuity.

$$\text{Present Value of Annuity, } P = a \left[\frac{1-(1+r)^{-n}}{r} \right]$$

$$a = \frac{Pr}{1-(1+r)^{-n}}$$

EXAMPLE

Interest is charged at 10% p.a. on the reducing balance of a loan of £1000. The principal and interest are to be paid in ten equal instalments at the end of each of the ten years from the commencement of the loan. How much is each instalment?

Answer: $a = \dfrac{Pr}{1-(1+r)^{-n}} = \dfrac{1000 \times 0.1}{1-(1.1)^{-10}} = \dfrac{100}{0.6145} = £162.75$

The amortisation schedule below divides the ten annual instalments of £162.75 into interest and repayment components. The final amortisation payment does not exactly equal the outstanding loan due to rounding error but it is close enough to prove that the instalments do repay the £1000 loan and give the lender a return of 10% p.a. The division of the payment into interest and capital payments can be important for tax purposes as interest may be tax deductible for the borrower.

	Year	Total payment	Interest on balance of loan outstanding	Amortisation payment	Balance of loan outstanding
Start of Yr.1 →	0	—	—	—	1000.00
End of Yr.1 →	1	162.75	100 [1]	62.75	937.25
End of Yr.2 →	2	162.75	93.72 [2]	69.03	868.22
etc.	3	162.75	86.82	75.93	792.29
	4	162.75	79.23	83.52	708.77
	5	162.75	70.88	91.87	616.90
[1] 1000 × 0.1	6	162.75	61.69	101.06	515.84
= 100	7	162.75	51.58	111.17	404.67
[2] 937.25 × 0.1	8	162.75	40.47	122.28	282.39
= 93.72 etc.	9	162.75	28.24	134.51	147.88
	10	162.75	14.79	147.96	NIL

QUESTIONS

12.1   Draw a graph showing over a period of 15 years the growth in the value (i.e. principal plus interest) of £100 if invested at:
(a)   simple interest of 12% per annum;
(b)   compound interest of 8% per annum.

From the graph determine the year in which the total value will be equal under both (a) and (b) above.   *(ICMA)*

12.2   (a)   Calculate the annual effective rate of interest of:
6% compounded monthly;
6¼% compounded quarterly.

(b)   In 1964 the monthly average index of retail prices was 107, and in 1974 it was 208. Both values are relative to 16th January, 1962 = 100.

Calculate, in relation to the index for the period 1964–1974:
(i)   the annual compounded rate of change of the index of retail prices; and
(ii)   the annual compounded rate of change in the purchasing power of £1.   *(ICMA)*

12.3   In three years' time a considerable amount of the plant and machinery in your company's factory will need replacing. You estimate that a sum of £280,000 will be required for this.

(a)   If you were to set aside sufficient funds now to be invested at 12% per annum compounded quarterly (i.e. every three months),
(i)   what sum of money would you need, and
(ii)   what is the effective annual rate of interest?

(b)   If, again assuming that investments made during the three years will be at 12% per annum compounded quarterly, you decide instead to invest £4,000 at the end of every quarter, what additional sum needs to be set aside now in order to provide £280,000 at the end of the three years?   *(ICMA)*

12.4   (a)   In some compound interest calculations the formula

$$F = \left(A + \frac{p}{r} \right) R^t - \frac{p}{r}$$

is used.

You are required to re-arrange the formula to find p in terms of A, F, R, t and r, so that p is made the subject of the formula.
                                    (4 marks)

(b) A management accountant is considering the purchase of an annuity (i.e. a regular annual income) on retirement.

You are required to find the cost of an annuity of £2,500 for 15 years, paid in arrears, if compound interest is calculated at 9% per annum, and compounded

(i) annually; *(8 marks)*

(ii) each half-year. *(8 marks)*

Ignore administration charges and taxation. State any assumptions you have made. *(ICMA)*

*12.5 (a) A machine costing £25,650 depreciates to a scrap value of £500 in ten years.

You are required to calculate:

(i) the annual percentage rate of depreciation if the reducing balance method of depreciation is to be used; and

(ii) the book value at the end of the sixth year.

(b) It is estimated that a mine will yield an annual net return (i.e. after all operating costs) of £50,000 for the next 15 years. At the end of this time the property will be valueless.

Calculate the purchase price of the mine to yield a return of 12% per annum. *(ICMA)*

12.6 (a) If I put £1,000 in the bank on 1st January 1987 and at the beginning of each of the following five years, how much will I have accumulated by the end of 1992? Assume a rate of interest of 7½% throughout the period.

(b) Your firm is considering the purchase of a new machine which will generate net income of £5,000 p.a. over the next ten years (assume the income arises at the end of the year). The machine will cost £35,000 and money can be invested at 10% p.a. Should the machine be purchased?

(c) On the 1st January 1970 I deposited £1,000 in a bank account. On the 1st January 1971 a further £1,000 was deposited and each year after that £500 was deposited at the start of the year. If, on average, I receive 7% p.a. compound interest on my money how much will I have by 31.12.87?

12.7 (a) Your company has decided to set up a fund for its employees with an initial payment of £2,750 which is compounded six monthly over a four year period at 3.5% per six months.

Required:
(i) Calculate the size of the fund to two decimal places at the end of the four years. *(3 marks)*
(ii) Calculate the effective annual interest rate, to two decimal places. *(2 marks)*

(b) The company has purchased a piece of equipment for its production department at a cost of £37,500 on 1 April 1984. It is anticipated that this piece of equipment will be replaced after five years of use on 1 April 1989.

The equipment is purchased with a five year loan, which is compounded annually at 12%.

Required:
(i) Determine the size of the equal annual payments. *(3 marks)*
(ii) Display a table which shows the amount outstanding and interest for each year of the loan. *(4 marks)*

(c) If in (b) the £37,500 debt is compounded annually at 12% and is discharged on 1 April 1989 by using a Sinking Fund Method, under which five equal annual deposits are made starting on 1 April 1984 into the fund paying 8% annually.
(i) determine the size of the equal annual deposits in the sinking fund, and; *(3 marks)*
(ii) display a table which demonstrates the growth of the loan and the sinking fund. *(5 marks)*

Extract from Net Present Value Tables

Period	8% Discount Factor	12% Discount Factor
0	1.0000	1.0000
1	0.9259	0.8929
2	0.8573	0.7972
3	0.7938	0.7118
4	0.7350	0.6355
5	0.6806	0.5674

(20 marks)
(ACA)

APPENDIX 12.1

COMPOUND INTEREST TABLE (Value of $(1+r)^n$)

Period	1%	2%	3%	4%	5%	6%	7%	8%	9%
1	1.010	1.020	1.030	1.040	1.050	1.060	1.070	1.080	1.090
2	1.020	1.040	1.061	1.082	1.102	1.124	1.145	1.166	1.186
3	1.030	1.061	0.093	1.125	1.158	1.191	1.225	1.260	1.295
4	1.041	1.082	1.126	1.170	1.216	1.262	1.311	1.360	1.412
5	1.051	1.104	1.159	1.217	1.276	1.338	1.403	1.469	1.539
6	1.062	1.126	1.194	1.265	1.340	1.419	1.501	1.587	1.677
7	1.072	1.149	1.230	1.316	1.407	1.504	1.606	1.714	1.828
8	1.083	1.172	1.267	1.369	1.477	1.594	1.718	1.851	1.993
9	1.094	1.195	1.305	1.423	1.551	1.689	1.838	1.999	2.172
10	1.105	1.219	1.344	1.480	1.629	1.791	1.967	2.159	2.367
11	1.116	1.243	1.384	1.539	1.710	1.898	2.105	2.332	2.580
12	1.127	1.268	1.426	1.601	1.796	2.012	2.252	2.518	2.813
13	1.138	1.294	1.469	1.665	1.886	2.133	2.410	2.720	3.066
14	1.149	1.319	1.513	1.732	1.980	2.261	2.579	2.937	3.342
15	1.161	1.346	1.558	1.801	2.079	2.397	2.759	3.172	3.642
16	1.173	1.373	1.605	1.873	2.183	2.540	2.952	3.426	3.970
17	1.184	1.400	1.653	1.948	2.292	2.693	3.159	3.700	4.328
18	1.196	1.428	1.702	2.026	2.407	2.854	3.380	3.996	4.717
19	1.208	1.457	1.754	2.107	2.527	3.026	3.617	4.316	5.142
20	1.220	1.486	1.806	2.191	2.653	3.207	3.870	4.661	5.604
25	1.282	1.641	2.094	2.666	3.386	4.292	5.427	6.848	8.623
30	1.348	1.811	2.427	3.243	4.322	5.743	7.612	10.063	13.268

Period	10%	12%	14%	16%	18%	20%	24%	28%	32%
1	1.100	1.120	1.140	1.160	1.180	1.200	1.240	1.280	1.320
2	1.210	1.254	1.300	1.346	1.392	1.440	1.538	1.638	1.742
3	1.331	1.405	1.482	1.561	1.643	1.728	1.907	2.067	2.300
4	1.464	1.574	1.689	1.811	1.939	2.074	2.364	2.684	3.036
5	1.611	1.762	1.925	2.100	2.288	2.488	2.932	3.436	4.007
6	1.772	1.974	2.195	2.436	2.700	2.986	3.635	4.398	5.290
7	1.949	2.211	2.502	2.826	3.185	3.583	4.508	5.629	6.983
8	2.144	2.476	2.853	3.278	3.759	4.300	5.590	7.206	9.217
9	2.358	2.773	3.252	3.803	4.435	5.160	6.931	9.223	12.166
10	2.594	3.106	3.707	4.411	5.234	6.192	8.594	11.806	16.060
11	2.853	3.479	4.226	5.117	6.176	7.430	10.657	15.112	21.199
12	3.138	3.896	4.818	5.926	7.288	8.916	13.215	19.343	27.983
13	3.452	4.363	5.492	6.886	8.599	10.699	16.386	24.759	36.937
14	3.797	4.887	6.261	7.988	10.147	12.839	20.319	31.961	48.757
15	4.177	5.474	7.138	9.266	11.974	15.407	25.196	40.565	64.359
16	4.595	6.130	8.137	10.748	14.129	18.488	31.243	51.923	84.954
17	5.054	6.866	9.276	12.468	16.672	22.186	38.741	66.461	112.140
18	5.560	7.690	10.575	14.463	19.673	26.623	48.039	85.071	148.020
19	6.116	8.613	12.056	16.777	23.214	31.948	59.568	108.890	195.390
20	6.728	9.646	13.743	19.461	27.393	38.338	73.864	139.380	257.920
25	10.835	17.000	26.462	40.874	62.669	95.396	216.542	478.900	1033.600
30	17.449	29.960	50.950	85.850	143.371	237.376	634.820	1645.500	4142.100

APPENDIX 12.2

PRESENT VALUE TABLE (Value of $(1+r)^{-n}$)

Period	1%	2%	3%	4%	5%	6%	7%	8%	9%
1	0.990	0.980	0.971	0.962	0.952	0.943	0.935	0.926	0.917
2	0.980	0.961	0.943	0.925	0.907	0.890	0.873	0.857	0.842
3	0.971	0.942	0.915	0.889	0.864	0.840	0.816	0.794	0.772
4	0.961	0.924	0.889	0.855	0.823	0.792	0.763	0.735	0.708
5	0.951	0.906	0.863	0.822	0.784	0.747	0.713	0.681	0.650
6	0.942	0.888	0.838	0.790	0.746	0.705	0.666	0.630	0.596
7	0.933	0.871	0.813	0.760	0.711	0.665	0.623	0.583	0.547
8	0.923	0.853	0.789	0.731	0.677	0.627	0.582	0.540	0.502
9	0.914	0.837	0.766	0.703	0.645	0.592	0.544	0.500	0.460
10	0.905	0.820	0.744	0.676	0.614	0.558	0.508	0.463	0.422
11	0.896	0.804	0.722	0.650	0.585	0.527	0.475	0.429	0.388
12	0.887	0.788	0.701	0.625	0.557	0.497	0.444	0.397	0.356
13	0.879	0.773	0.681	0.601	0.530	0.469	0.415	0.368	0.326
14	0.870	0.758	0.661	0.577	0.505	0.442	0.388	0.340	0.299
15	0.861	0.743	0.642	0.555	0.481	0.417	0.362	0.315	0.275
16	0.853	0.728	0.623	0.534	0.458	0.394	0.339	0.292	0.252
17	0.844	0.714	0.605	0.513	0.436	0.371	0.317	0.270	0.231
18	0.836	0.700	0.587	0.494	0.416	0.350	0.296	0.250	0.212
19	0.828	0.686	0.570	0.475	0.396	0.331	0.276	0.232	0.194
20	0.820	0.673	0.554	0.456	0.377	0.312	0.258	0.215	0.178
25	0.780	0.610	0.478	0.375	0.295	0.233	0.184	0.146	0.116
30	0.742	0.552	0.412	0.308	0.231	0.174	0.131	0.099	0.075

Period	10%	12%	14%	16%	18%	20%	24%	28%	32%
1	0.909	0.893	0.877	0.862	0.847	0.833	0.806	0.781	0.758
2	0.826	0.797	0.769	0.743	0.718	0.694	0.650	0.610	0.574
3	0.751	0.712	0.675	0.641	0.609	0.579	0.524	0.477	0.435
4	0.683	0.636	0.592	0.552	0.516	0.482	0.423	0.373	0.329
5	0.621	0.567	0.519	0.476	0.437	0.402	0.341	0.291	0.250
6	0.564	0.507	0.456	0.410	0.370	0.335	0.275	0.227	0.189
7	0.513	0.452	0.400	0.354	0.314	0.279	0.222	0.178	0.143
8	0.467	0.404	0.351	0.305	0.266	0.233	0.179	0.139	0.108
9	0.424	0.361	0.308	0.263	0.226	0.194	0.144	0.108	0.082
10	0.386	0.322	0.270	0.227	0.191	0.162	0.116	0.085	0.062
11	0.350	0.287	0.237	0.195	0.162	0.135	0.094	0.066	0.047
12	0.319	0.257	0.208	0.168	0.137	0.112	0.076	0.052	0.036
13	0.290	0.229	0.182	0.145	0.116	0.093	0.061	0.040	0.027
14	0.263	0.205	0.160	0.125	0.099	0.078	0.049	0.032	0.021
15	0.239	0.183	0.140	0.108	0.084	0.065	0.040	0.025	0.016
16	0.218	0.163	0.123	0.093	0.071	0.054	0.032	0.019	0.012
17	0.198	0.146	0.108	0.080	0.060	0.045	0.026	0.015	0.009
18	0.180	0.130	0.095	0.089	0.051	0.038	0.021	0.012	0.007
19	0.164	0.116	0.083	0.060	0.043	0.031	0.017	0.009	0.005
20	0.149	0.104	0.073	0.051	0.037	0.026	0.014	0.007	0.004
25	0.092	0.059	0.038	0.024	0.016	0.010	0.005	0.002	0.001
30	0.057	0.033	0.020	0.012	0.007	0.004	0.002	0.001	0.000

APPENDIX 12.3

COMPOUND AMOUNT OF ANNUITY TABLE

$$\left(\text{Value of } \frac{(1+r)^n - 1}{r} \right)$$

Period	1%	2%	3%	4%	5%	6%	7%	8%	9%
1	1.000	1.000	1.000	1.000	1.000	1.000	1.000	1.000	1.000
2	2.010	2.020	2.030	2.040	2.050	2.060	2.070	2.080	2.090
3	3.030	3.060	3.091	3.122	3.152	3.184	3.215	3.246	3.278
4	4.060	4.122	4.184	4.246	4.310	4.375	4.440	4.506	4.573
5	5.101	5.204	5.309	5.416	5.526	5.637	5.751	5.867	5.985
6	6.152	6.308	6.468	6.633	6.802	6.975	7.153	7.336	7.523
7	7.214	7.434	7.662	7.898	8.142	8.394	8.654	8.923	9.200
8	8.286	8.583	8.892	9.214	9.549	9.897	10.260	10.637	11.028
9	9.369	9.755	10.159	10.583	11.027	11.491	11.978	12.488	13.021
10	10.462	10.950	11.464	12.006	12.578	13.181	13.816	14.487	15.193
11	11.567	12.169	12.808	13.486	14.207	14.972	15.784	16.645	17.560
12	12.683	13.412	14.192	15.026	15.917	16.870	17.888	18.977	20.141
13	13.809	14.680	15.618	16.627	17.713	18.882	20.141	21.495	22.953
14	14.947	15.974	17.086	18.292	19.599	21.051	22.550	24.215	26.019
15	16.097	17.293	18.599	20.024	21.579	23.276	25.129	27.152	29.361
16	17.258	18.639	20.157	21.825	23.657	25.673	27.888	30.324	33.003
17	18.430	20.012	21.762	23.698	25.840	28.213	30.840	33.750	36.974
18	19.615	21.412	23.414	25.645	28.132	30.906	33.999	37.450	41.301
19	20.811	22.841	25.117	27.671	30.539	33.760	37.379	41.446	46.018
20	22.019	24.297	26.870	29.778	33.066	36.786	40.995	45.762	51.160
25	28.243	32.030	36.459	41.646	47.727	54.865	63.249	73.106	84.701
30	34.785	40.568	47.575	56.805	66.439	79.058	94.461	113.283	136.308

Period	10%	12%	14%	16%	18%	20%	24%	28%	32%
1	1.000	1.000	1.000	1.000	1.000	1.000	1.000	1.000	1.000
2	2.100	2.120	2.140	2.160	2.180	2.200	2.240	2.280	2.320
3	3.310	3.374	3.440	3.506	3.572	3.640	3.778	3.918	4.062
4	4.641	4.770	4.921	5.066	5.215	5.368	5.684	6.016	6.392
5	6.105	6.353	6.610	6.877	7.154	7.442	8.048	8.700	9.398
6	7.716	8.115	8.536	8.977	9.442	9.930	10.980	12.136	13.406
7	9.487	10.089	10.730	11.414	12.142	12.916	14.615	16.534	18.696
8	11.436	12.300	13.233	14.240	15.327	16.499	19.123	22.163	25.678
9	13.579	14.776	16.085	17.518	19.086	20.799	24.712	29.369	34.895
10	15.937	17.549	19.337	21.321	23.521	25.959	31.643	38.592	47.062
11	18.531	20.655	23.044	25.733	28.755	32.150	40.238	50.399	63.122
12	21.384	24.133	27.271	30.850	34.931	39.580	50.985	65.510	84.320
13	24.523	28.029	32.089	36.786	42.219	48.497	64.110	84.853	112.303
14	27.975	32.393	37.581	43.672	50.818	59.196	80.496	109.612	149.240
15	31.772	37.280	43.842	51.660	60.965	72.035	100.815	141.303	197.997
16	35.950	42.753	50.980	60.925	72.939	87.442	126.011	181.870	262.36
17	40.545	48.884	59.118	71.673	87.068	105.931	157.253	233.790	347.31
18	45.599	55.750	68.394	84.141	103.740	128.117	195.994	300.250	459.45
19	51.159	63.440	78.969	98.603	123.414	154.740	244.033	385.320	607.47
20	57.275	72.052	91.025	115.380	146.628	186.688	303.601	494.210	802.86
25	98.347	133.334	181.871	249.214	342.603	471.981	898.092	1706.800	3226.80
30	164.494	241.333	356.787	530.312	790.948	1181.882	2640.916	5873.200	12941.00

APPENDIX 12.4

PRESENT VALUE OF ANNUITY TABLE

$$\left(\text{Value of } \frac{1 - (1+r)^{-n}}{r} \right)$$

Period	1%	2%	3%	4%	5%	6%	7%	8%	9%
1	0.990	0.980	0.971	0.962	0.952	0.943	0.935	0.926	0.917
2	1.970	1.942	1.913	1.886	1.859	1.833	1.808	1.783	1.759
3	2.941	2.884	2.829	2.775	2.723	2.673	2.624	2.577	2.531
4	3.902	3.808	3.717	3.630	3.546	3.465	3.387	3.312	3.240
5	4.853	4.713	4.580	4.452	4.329	4.212	4.100	3.993	3.890
6	5.795	5.601	5.417	5.242	5.076	4.917	4.766	4.623	4.486
7	6.728	6.472	6.230	6.002	5.786	5.582	5.389	5.206	5.033
8	7.652	7.325	7.020	6.733	6.463	6.210	5.971	5.747	5.535
9	8.566	8.162	7.786	7.435	7.108	6.802	6.515	6.247	5.995
10	9.471	8.983	8.530	8.111	7.722	7.360	7.024	6.710	6.418
11	10.368	9.787	9.253	8.760	8.306	7.887	7.499	7.139	6.805
12	11.255	10.575	9.954	9.385	8.863	8.384	7.943	7.536	7.161
13	12.134	11.348	10.635	9.986	9.394	8.853	8.358	7.904	7.487
14	13.004	12.106	11.296	10.563	9.899	9.295	8.745	8.244	7.786
15	13.865	12.849	11.938	11.118	10.380	9.712	9.108	8.559	8.060
16	14.718	13.578	12.561	11.652	10.838	10.106	9.447	8.851	8.312
17	15.562	14.292	13.166	12.166	11.274	10.477	9.763	9.122	8.544
18	16.398	14.992	13.754	12.659	11.690	10.828	10.059	9.372	8.756
19	17.226	15.678	14.324	13.134	12.085	11.158	10.336	9.604	8.950
20	18.046	16.351	14.877	13.590	12.462	11.470	10.594	9.818	9.128
25	22.023	19.523	17.413	15.622	14.094	12.783	11.654	10.675	9.823
30	25.808	22.397	19.600	17.292	15.373	13.765	12.409	11.258	10.274

Period	10%	12%	14%	16%	18%	20%	24%	28%	32%
1	0.909	0.893	0.877	0.862	0.847	0.833	0.806	0.781	0.758
2	1.736	1.690	1.647	1.605	1.566	1.528	1.457	1.392	1.332
3	2.487	2.402	2.322	2.246	2.174	2.106	1.981	1.868	1.766
4	3.170	3.037	2.914	2.798	2.690	2.589	2.404	2.241	2.096
5	3.791	3.605	3.433	3.274	3.127	2.991	2.745	2.532	2.345
6	4.355	4.111	3.889	3.685	3.498	3.326	3.020	2.759	2.534
7	4.868	4.564	4.288	4.039	3.812	3.605	3.242	2.937	2.678
8	5.335	4.968	4.639	4.344	4.078	3.837	3.421	3.076	2.786
9	5.759	5.328	4.946	4.607	4.303	4.031	3.566	3.184	2.868
10	6.145	5.650	5.216	4.883	4.494	4.193	3.682	3.269	2.930
11	6.495	5.938	5.453	5.029	4.656	4.327	3.776	3.335	2.978
12	6.814	6.194	5.660	5.197	4.793	4.439	3.851	3.387	3.013
13	7.103	6.424	5.842	5.342	4.910	4.533	3.912	3.427	3.040
14	7.367	6.628	6.002	5.468	5.008	4.611	3.962	3.459	3.061
15	7.606	6.811	6.142	5.575	5.092	4.675	4.001	3.483	3.076
16	7.824	6.974	6.265	5.669	5.162	4.730	4.033	3.503	3.088
17	8.022	7.120	5.373	5.749	4.222	4.775	4.059	3.518	3.097
18	8.201	7.250	6.467	5.818	5.273	4.812	4.080	3.529	3.104
19	8.365	7.366	6.550	5.877	5.316	4.844	4.097	3.539	3.109
20	8.514	7.469	6.623	5.929	5.353	4.870	4.110	3.546.	3.113
25	9.077	7.843	6.873	6.097	5.467	4.948	4.147	3.564	3.122
30	9.427	8.005	7.003	6.177	5.517	4.979	4.160	3.569	3.124

Chapter 13
CAPITAL INVESTMENT APPRAISAL

Investment involves the sacrifice of something now in return for some benefit in the future. For example, the decision to study for professional qualifications is a decision to invest, involving the sacrifice of current leisure time in return for higher future income.

More specifically, capital investment refers to expenditure by firms on fixed assets which, by definition, last for a long time and are expected to give a return in the form of higher revenue in the future. Of course, a firm's capital does not all get invested in fixed assets, part of it has to be used as working capital and is invested in current assets. Why then are we so concerned about investment in "fixed capital"?

In part it is because capital projects usually involve a large capital outlay but, probably, more importantly because the consequences of a wrong decision in the area of capital investment can haunt the firm for many years into the future.

Say a firm produces stocks of finished goods of a particular design, colour, or whatever. If demand for these goods does not materialise then the firm will be disappointed but not usually forced into liquidation. It can cut the price, sell in another market, perhaps change the design, etc. Profits will be reduced but there will usually be ways of mitigating the effects on the firm.

On the other hand, nowadays the fixed assets employed in most industries are highly specific in the sense that they may have great value to a particular firm, operating in a certain way, in a certain part of the country, in a certain industry. To any other firm these fixed assets may be useless and so their second-hand value is negligible. This means that if a firm builds a factory in a certain part of the country, buys a highly specialised computer system, purchases a press to stamp out a certain design, etc. it has very little chance of "cutting its losses" if it finds it has made a wrong decision. The firm will have to live with such mistakes for a very long time and that is why careful evaluation of capital projects is so important.

Merrett and Sykes[1] liken the difference between investment in fixed assets and investment in current assets to the risks involved in "making a false move in boxing compared to a mis-hit in tennis." The latter is a minor setback but the former may mean total disaster.

---

[1] "The Finance and Analysis of Capital Projects" by A.J. Merrett and Allen Sykes was first published in 1963 but probably remains the definitive work on the subject. A.J. Merrett and G. Lawson of Sheffield University were pioneers in promoting the use of DCF techniques in the UK.

The techniques of investment appraisal may be divided into two broad categories — discounted cash flow (DCF) techniques and non-discounting methods. As we have described it, the special feature of investment is that it involves costs and benefits which occur at different points in time. Investment appraisal must therefore address the problem of the time value of money so that cash inflows and outflows which occur at different points in time can be evaluated on a common basis. Discounting methods, based upon the principles described in the previous chapter, have long been recognised as being superior in this respect and during the last 25 years their use has become widespread. Nevertheless, various surveys have shown that non-discounting methods are still widely used albeit, most commonly, in conjunction with DCF techniques.

13.1 Non-discounting methods of investment appraisal

Despite Merrett and Sykes' contention that "conventional methods are inadequate substitutes for discounting methods in most circumstances and often produce capricious results", non-discounting methods are still employed; the simplest and most popular is payback.

13.1.1 PAYBACK METHOD

The payback period is the length of time it takes for an investment to "recover" its initial capital outlay. Suppose there were two alternative investments giving rise to the cash flows indicated below:

YEAR	Project A CASH FLOW (£)	Project B CASH FLOW (£)
0	−10,000	−10,000
1	+5,000	+8,000
2	+5,000	+1,000
3	—	+2,000
4	—	+2,000
5	—	+2,000

Project A, for example, involves a capital outlay of £10,000 at the start of the first year (denoted by year 0) and produces a positive cash inflow of £5,000 by the end of year 1 and a further £5,000 by the end of year 2. Project A therefore has a payback period of 2 years.

Assuming an even cash flow over the year, Project B has a payback period of 2½ years.

On the payback criterion, Project A would be considered superior because the payback period is shorter.

Although the example may be unrealistic it illustrates two defects of the payback method; Project B generates cash inflows after the payback period and also has a higher cash flow in the first year.

Advantages of payback method

(1) It is simple to apply and easy to understand. Where decisions about investment are taken by people who are unfamiliar with the more sophisticated techniques of investment appraisal, payback provides a non-technical basis for decision taking. Of course, although this may conform to reality, it is far from an ideal situation; investment appraisal is a complex business and the people who take investment decisions should be competent to do so.

(2) As with DCF techniques, payback considers cash flow rather than profit. This is generally accepted as the correct approach to investment appraisal because profit figures can be so ambiguous.

For example, consider the following investment project:

		(£)
Yr. 0	COST	−10,000
1	Profit	+1,000
2	..	+1,000
3	..	+2,000
4	..	+3,000
5	..	+3,000

The firm recovers its capital outlay over a five year period but it has earned no return on its capital investment. However, the profit figure will be after the deduction of a provision for depreciation of, let us say, £2,000 p.a. so that the actual cash flow would be:—

	CASH FLOW (£)
Yr. 0	−10,000
1	+3,000
2	+3,000
3	+4,000
4	+5,000
5	+5,000

When we consider the cash flow we see that the payback period is reduced to 3 years and the project does in fact earn a return over and above the depreciation. The provision for depreciation has no effect at all on cash flow, it is just a book-keeping device to avoid an overestimate of profit and possible capital depletion. To include the capital cost and the depreciation would be double-counting, the firm will only pay for the asset once. Since the firm has use of cash inflows (net of outflows) when they arise, it is cash flow rather than profit which is most important. Whether the firm decides to retain these funds in the business by making a provision for depreciation or whether it decides to distribute them as profit is an important question but irrelevant from the point of view of assessing the desirability of the investment project.

Another argument in favour of using cash flow rather than profit is that the latter can be affected by the chosen method of depreciation. Except in so far as it might affect the firm's tax liability, the method of depreciation will have no effect on the cash flows arising from a project and concentration on cash flow avoids any confusion arising from different methods of depreciation.

(3)   It is useful for firms that are short of cash. There is really little justification for this claimed advantage; firms exist to make profits not to be liquid. The implication of using payback to assess projects, where there is a liquidity problem, is that less profitable projects should be chosen because they have a shorter payback period. Such a policy is unlikely to benefit the firm in the long-run and liquidity problems are best tackled by other means.

(4)   Payback makes implicit assumptions about the riskiness of long-term forecasting. It is argued, quite reasonably, that the further ahead one tries to forecast cash flows the more likely the forecasts are to be wrong. It is then argued that by concentrating on the early cash flows up to the payback period the risk of forecasting errors is reduced. The problem with this is that it assumes that the forecasts are reliable up to the payback period and then the project suddenly collapses. There are situations where this can happen, one can imagine a new production process rendering old methods obsolete, but generally projects need to be assessed over the whole of their forecast life.

A related argument is to the effect that, because forecasting cash flows is subject to error, sophisticated discounting techniques are akin to using a sledgehammer to crack a nut and cruder methods such as payback are all that can be justified. This argument has virtually no foundation whatsoever. To abandon a scientific approach to business problems simply because all the facts cannot be known with absolute certainty is highly unprofessional. There are situations where investment appraisal techniques are of little use; for example, research by drug companies to find a cure for Aids or Cancer is in the nature of a gamble, the potential rewards are in every sense enormous but the likelihood of success is not quantifiable. But such situations are rare and in most cases the financial effects of projects will justify analysis using the best tools available.

(5)   Payback makes implicit assumptions about the time value of money. This is certainly true. By measuring the desirability of a project according to how quickly the initial capital outlay is recovered, payback implicitly assumes that money now is worth more than money in the future albeit very crudely. It was for this reason that there was a resurgence in the popularity of payback in the 1970s when inflation was at its peak.

Disadvantages of payback method
We have tended to be dismissive of the advantages of payback because, as Merrett & Sykes point out, payback can do nothing that DCF techniques cannot do much better.

Payback has its uses. It highlights one particular aspect of an investment project and it can usefully be used as a crude initial screening device to pick out obviously profitable or unprofitable projects which do not warrant further analysis. For example, if a firm was considering buying a comparatively cheap asset which had a useful life of 10 years and would pay for itself in six months it would not be worthwhile analysing the situation any further.

The deficiencies of payback are, however, too serious for it to be used as a method of investment appraisal except in a few situations. Research by R.H. Pike in 1983 showed that only 11% of the largest UK manufacturing and retailing companies used payback on its own and several studies point to the rapidly increasing use of DCF techniques.

The main disadvantages of payback were briefly mentioned earlier, they are:

(1) Payback ignores cash flows after the payback period. So, based solely on the payback criterion, project A would be considered superior to project B even though the latter generates income for many more years and has only a slightly longer payback period.

YEAR	Project A CASH FLOW £	Project B CASH FLOW £
0	−10,000	−10,000
1	+5,000	+5,000
2	+5,000	+4,000
3	—	+4,000
4	—	+4,000
5	—	+4,000
6	—	+4,000
7	—	+4,000
8	—	+4,000

A corollary of this is that payback discriminates against long-term projects; a firm which demands, say, a 3 year payback may miss out on highly profitable investments which may also be important to the long-term future of the firm.

(2) Payback ignores the time value of money. Except in the crude sense which we mentioned earlier, payback takes no account of the timing of cash flows.

	Project A CASH FLOW £	Project B CASH FLOW £
Yr. 0	−10,000	−10,000
1	+1,000	+9,000
2	+9,000	+1,000
	etc.	etc.

Again purely on the payback criterion, projects A and B would be judged equal but project B is clearly superior (ignoring what happens after payback) because it generates a higher cash inflow in the first year and, of course, this money can be invested to earn interest.

13.1.2 Accounting Rates of Return

There are a number of variants of this method of investment appraisal. The Return on Capital Employed (ROCE) is one variant and expresses profit as an annual percentage return on the capital investment. We have already mentioned that profit figures can be rather ambiguous and defining capital employed can also be a problem.

Another method, sometimes called the Book Rate of Return considers cash flow rather than profit and is defined as the surplus of revenue over cost expressed as an annual percentage return on the capital outlay.

	Project CASH FLOW (£)
Yr. 0	−10,000
1	+3,000
2	+3,000
3	+4,000
4	+5,000
5	+5,000

The total cash inflow is £20,000 over 5 years on an initial investment of £10,000. The book rate of return would therefore be

$$\frac{20,000 - 10,000}{10,000} \times \frac{1}{5} \times 100 = 20\%$$

The rate of return on the investment (however it is calculated) is then usually compared to the firm's "cost of capital" with some additional premium to cover the risk involved in the project. The cost of capital thus acts as a "hurdle rate" for investment projects; only projects which earn a return in excess of the cost of capital will be undertaken. The cost of capital is the rate of return which has to be given to the finance providers to obtain funds to finance the project. Where funds are obtained from a variety of sources the cost of capital is a weighted average of the costs of the various forms of finance. Even if a project is financed from retained profits, capital has a cost because unless retained earnings earn a return which satisfies the shareholder then he will sell his shares. In theory the market price of the shares would be driven down until the return to the shareholder was equivalent to the return that could be obtained on other investments carrying the same degree of risk.

It follows that even where profits are financed out of retained profits, in fact especially where projects are financed from retained profits, the real cost of undertaking a project is the opportunity cost in the form of the return that could be obtained on some other project within or outside the firm. It is necessary therefore for management to compare the return on internal investment to opportunities for investment outside the firm which carry similar degrees of risk.

The book rate of return has the advantage, compared to payback, that it does consider all the cash flows but it takes no account of the time value of money; both project A and B below would give a book rate of return of 20% but project B is clearly more desirable because cash inflow is greater early in the project's life and "money now is always worth more than money in the future".

	Project A (£)	Project B (£)
Yr. 0	−10,000	−10,000
1	+3,000	+16,000
2	+3,000	+1,000
3	+4,000	+1,000
4	+5,000	+1,000
5	+5,000	+1,000

Techniques for investment appraisal which do take adequate account of the time value of money are the DCF techniques to which we now turn.

13.2 Discounted Cash Flow techniques of investment appraisal
As the name implies DCF techniques consider cash flow which is generally regarded as more appropriate than profit which is an ambiguous concept. DCF techniques use, or make comparisons with, a firm's cost of capital. In practice, determining a firm's cost of capital can be extremely complicated but we will take it as given (as it usually will be in examination questions).

13.2.1 NET PRESENT VALUE METHOD
This is the classical economic technique and consists of reducing all the cash flows, positive and negative, to their present value equivalents by discounting

them at the firm's cost of capital. The Net Present Value (NPV) is the sum of the present values of the cash flows and if it is positive the project is worthwhile, if it is negative the project should be rejected. Projects may also be ranked according to the size of their NPV, the project with the larger NPV being deemed superior.

EXAMPLE
An investment project involves an initial capital outlay of £20,000 and will generate cash inflows of £5,000 at the end of each of the next 5 years. The cost of capital is 10%, should the project be undertaken?

Solution:

YEAR	CASH FLOW (£)	Discount factors* at 10%	Present Value of CASH FLOW
0	-20,000	1.0000	-20,000
1	+5,000	0.9091	+4,545
2	+5,000	0.8264	+4,132
3	+5,000	0.7513	+3,756
4	+5,000	0.6830	+3,415
5	+5,000	0.6209	+3,104
		NPV =	-1,048

*Remember we discount by multiplying by $(1+r)^{-n}$ or $\frac{1}{(1+r)^n}$ where r = rate of discount and n = number of time periods we wish to discount back. Values of $(1+r)^{-n}$ may be found from the table or by using a calculator.

The answer then is that the project should not be undertaken because the NPV is negative. The present value of the cash inflows (positive) is £18,952 which is £1,048 less than the capital cost of the project. This means that £18,952 invested at 10% would enable the investor to withdraw £4,545 at the end of the first year, £4,132 at the end of the second year, and so on; since the project requires an investment of £20,000 to generate such a cash flow it is clearly not worthwhile.

In passing, it should be noted that the arithmetic can be performed more rapidly, in this case, by evaluating an annuity of £5,000 over 5 years and deducting the capital cost of £20,000.

$$\text{ie.} \quad \text{PV of annuity} = a\left[\frac{1-(1+r)^{-n}}{r}\right]$$

$$= £5000\left[\frac{1-(1.1)^{-5}}{0.1}\right] = 5000 \times 3.791$$

$$= £18,954$$

$$NPV = 18,954 - 20,000$$
$$= -1,046 \text{ as before except for rounding errors.}$$

This method cannot, of course, be used when irregular cash flows are involved.

13.2.2 Internal Rate of Return Method

Another discounting method is the I.R.R. and it is known by a variety of names. Keynes called it the Marginal Efficiency of Capital, Joel Dean referred to it as discounted cash flow, and Merrett & Sykes call it simply the yield.

The I.R.R. is defined as the rate of "interest" which discounts the future net cash flows of a project into equality with its capital cost, i.e. the rate of discount which results in a zero NPV.

The IRR is therefore the break-even rate of return on the project; if the IRR is greater than the firm's cost of capital the project should be undertaken but if the yield on the project is less than the cost of capital the project should be rejected.

The logic of the IRR approach is that if at some rate of discount there is a positive NPV then this implies the rate of return offered by the project is greater than the rate of discount used. Similarly, if there is a negative NPV then the rate of return is less than the rate of discount. Therefore, the true rate of return, the IRR, is the rate of discount that produces a zero NPV.

The Net Present Value method and the Internal Rate of Return method are thus equivalent; a positive NPV implies that the IRR is greater than the cost of capital and a negative NPV implies that the cost of capital is greater than the IRR. It follows that both methods will give the same answer in deciding whether a project is worthwhile or not. When it is a question of choosing between competing alternatives, however, the two methods can produce different rankings for reasons explained later.

Although it is not a serious drawback, IRR is more difficult to calculate than NPV. Except where regular cash flows are involved, the IRR has to be found by a process of trial and error. To illustrate the method let us consider the same example we used to illustrate the calculation of NPV.

When we discounted at 10% the NPV was £-1048 which tells us that the IRR is less than 10%. If we did not have this information we would need to decide on a starting point, the book rate of return could be used to provide this.

As the next step we need to try a lower rate of discount, say 8%

YEAR	CASH FLOW (£)	Discount factors at 8%	Present Value of CASH FLOW
0	−20,000	1.0000	−20,000
1	+5,000	0.9259	4,630
2	+5,000	0.8573	4,287
3	+5,000	0.7938	3,969
4	+5,000	0.7350	3,675
5	+5,000	0.6806	3,403
		NPV =	−36

The NPV is still negative so the IRR is a little lower than 8% (in fact by comparison with the size of the cash flows the NPV of −36 is very close to zero and might be considered accurate enough in many circumstances).

As the next step we try a lower rate again, say 7%.

YEAR	CASH FLOW (£)	Discount factors at 7%	Present Value of CASH FLOW
0	−20,000	1.0000	−20,000
1	+5,000	0.9346	4,673
2	+5,000	0.8734	4,367
3	+5,000	0.8163	4,081
4	+5,000	0.7629	3,814
5	+5,000	0.7130	3,565
		NPV =	+500

The NPV is now positive so we know that the IRR is greater than 7% but less than 8% and nearer to the latter.

To get a more accurate answer we can resort to linear interpolation.

$$
\begin{aligned}
&\quad\quad\quad\quad\quad (£) \\
\text{NPV at } 8\% &= -36 \\
\text{NPV at } 7\% &= +500
\end{aligned}
$$

So, by linear interpolation, the IRR is

$$7\% + \frac{500}{536} \times 1\% = 7.9\%$$

because the IRR is $\frac{500}{536}$ ths of the way between 7% and 8%.

Alternatively, we can express this diagrammatically, and letting the IRR equal x, use similar triangles to solve for x. (see Diagram 13.1)

DIAGRAM 13.1

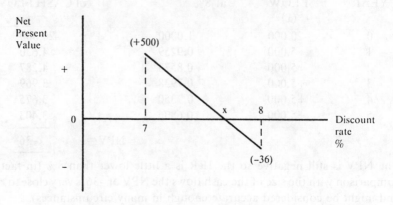

$$\frac{x - 7}{8 - x} = \frac{500}{36}$$

$$36x - 252 = 4000 - 500x$$
$$536x = 4252$$
$$x = \frac{4252}{536} = 7.9\% = \text{IRR.}$$

The answer to the problem then is that the project should not be undertaken because the IRR of 7.9% is less than the cost of capital of 10%.

It is worth noting that where the cash flows are constant, as here, the arithmetic can be reduced. Since the IRR is the rate of discount which reduces the PV of the cash inflows to the capital cost, we can write:

$$C = A \left[\frac{1 - (1+r)^{-n}}{r} \right]$$

where
$$C = \text{Capital cost}$$
$$A = \text{Amount of annuity}$$
$$r = \text{IRR}$$
$$n = \text{number of years or periods}$$

It follows that
$$\frac{C}{A} = \frac{1 - (1+r)^{-n}}{r}$$

and in the above example
$$\frac{C}{A} = \frac{20,000}{5,000} = 4.0000$$

So we need only find the value of r, for n=5, at which $\left[\frac{1 - (1+r)^{-n}}{r} \right]$ is equal to 4.0000.

From the tables for $\left[\dfrac{1-(1+r)^{-n}}{r}\right]$ or by calculation we find that the value of r is between 7% and 8% and linear interpolation would give the same result for the IRR as we obtained above.

13.2.3 **Mutually exclusive projects** — the ranking problem.

Most investment decisions involve either accepting or rejecting some project. The IRR and NPV methods will always give the same answer in such situations. There may be reasons why one method is preferred to the other, such as one method being more easily understood by decision takers, but the end result will be the same (except in very rare circumstances).

Frequently, however, investment decisions involve choosing between two, or more, investment opportunities — for example, leasing or buying machinery or utilizing land or buildings for different purposes. We mentioned earlier that projects can be ranked — projects with a large NPV or high IRR being better than those with low NPV or IRR. Unfortunately, ranking projects according to the size of their NPV does not always give the same order as when the projects are ranked according to the size of their IRR.

The reason that different answers can be obtained is that the NPV method assumes that the cash flows are invested at the cost of capital while the IRR method assumes that the cash flows are invested at the IRR. The reasons why rank orders can sometimes be reversed are illustrated by the following trivial and unrealistic, but revealing, examples:—

EXAMPLE 1

CASH FLOWS

		Project A	Project B	
Yr. 0		– 100	–10,000	
1		+500	+12,000	
NPV	=	+354	+909	(assuming cost of capital = 10%)
IRR	=	400%	20%	

In this case we see that A gives a much higher yield (IRR) while B has a much higher NPV. The rank orders are reversed because, in the case of project A, although £500 is a massive return on an investment of only £100 the NPV of £354 is small in absolute terms. On the other hand, project B gives a much lower yield but in absolute terms the NPV is considerably larger than for Project A.

The difference in rankings here is caused by the fact that the NPV method calculates the difference between the present value of the cash inflows and the capital cost, in absolute terms, but does not relate this quantity to the size of the capital outlay. If one accepts that larger capital outlays involve more risk then this is clearly a weakness of the NPV method since accepting projects with a higher NPV may lead firms into accepting more capital intensive projects which do not give a satisfactory return in relation to the capital outlay.

EXAMPLE 2

(£)

CASH FLOWS

	Project A	Project B	
Yr. 0	-10,000	-10,000	
1	15,000	5,758	
2	100	5,758	
3	100	5,758	
4	100	5,758	
5	100	5,758	
NPV =	+3,925	+11,827	(assuming cost of capital = 10%)
IRR =	51.5%	50%	

Here again the rankings are reversed, this time because of the timings of the cash flows. Project A gives the higher yield (IRR) but nearly all the cash inflow comes in the first year of the project. In fact, if we ignored the cash flows after the first year, project A would still be giving a yield of 50%. Project B gives a yield of 50%, as well, but it is spread evenly over the 5 years of the project and the total cash inflow, and hence NPV, is much higher than that for project A.

13.2.3.1 The Incremental Approach

The difficulties involved in analysing mutually exclusive projects can usually be resolved by adopting the incremental approach.

EXAMPLE

Suppose a firm is considering the installation of a new machine which will increase cash inflow by £1500 over each of the next five years. The machine can be bought for £3053 or it can be leased. If it is leased, the firm has to make an advance payment of £1000 each year and, to keep the example simple, a further £1000 at the end of the fifth year for removal and other costs. The firm's cost of capital is 10%.

As usual we assume that the other cash flows arise at the year end and the resultant net cash flows are therefore as follows:—

NET CASH FLOWS (£)

YEAR	LEASE	BUY	
0	−1000	−3053	
1	500	1500	
2	500	1500	
3	500	1500	
4	500	1500	
5	500	1500	
IRR =	41.2%	40%	
NPV =	£895	£2633	(assuming cost of capital at 10%)

We now have the dilemma that the rankings are reversed according to whether we adopt the NPV or the IRR criterion.

The incremental approach simply involves subtracting the net cash flows from each other to arrive at the incremental cash flow:—

YEAR	Incremental Cash Flow (£)
0	−2,053
1	+1,000
2	1,000
3	1,000
4	1,000
5	1,000
IRR =	39.5%
NPV =	£1,738

The question which the incremental cash flow poses is whether the increased cash inflows justify the higher capital outlay.

It is found that the NPV is positive and the IRR is higher than the cost of capital and so the firm would be advised to buy the machine.

The incremental approach, then, will resolve most difficulties with mutually exlusive projects but we must add certain caveats. The most obvious point is that incremental cash flow must be considered in the light of the project with which it is being compared. It is quite possible that the incremental cash flows could indicate that one of the options is desirable when in fact neither of them is desirable. Another point is that the incremental cash flows may involve a higher degree of risk and so the premium which is demanded over the cost of capital may be higher. Finally, although the incremental approach in the above example suggests that the NPV approach is the correct one because it gave the "correct" ranking for the original projects, the problem remains that the NPV takes no account of risk. In our example, if there was a strong possibility that a new machine might be invented that rendered others obsolete then leasing might still be the preferred option.

13.2.4 Which method is best?

As we said earlier, DCF techniques have long been recognised as superior to non-discounting methods because they take account of the time value of money.

Although they concede that there are situations in which the NPV method has advantages which make it superior to yield, Merrett & Sykes say "Our main conclusion is that, for the vast majority of simple capital budgeting decisions [the exceptions are discussed], we consider that yield is both technically and practically superior to net present value." Other experts disagree with this view and, although these techniques have been known about for over two hundred years, debate continues today about their relative merits.

Obviously we cannot do justice here to the various arguments but it is worthwhile mentioning some points which indicate the flavour of the debate.

(a) In most cases where the question involves accepting or rejecting a project both methods would produce the same answer. Nevertheless, supporters of IRR (including Merrett & Sykes) argue that, despite the fact that it is more complicated, IRR should be used because it is more easily understood by decision-takers. It is argued that businessmen have long tended to think in terms of rate of return on capital employed so that this can be considered in relation to the riskiness of the project. The IRR is "the rate of return per unit of capital outstanding in the project per unit of time" and so facilitates such comparisons while the NPV, being an absolute quantity, is a difficult concept for businessmen to understand.

(b) Supporters of the IRR method argue that the yield takes account of risk because it is related to the initial capital outlay and the time for which that capital is at risk (see examples, section 13.2.3). Where NPV is used, it is argued, there is a tendency for decision-takers to convert this into some sort of variant of yield. An example would be the Profitability Index.

Profitability Index Method

Instead of equating the cash flows with the original investment, as in the IRR method, the cash flows are discounted at the lowest acceptable rate (usually the cost of capital) and the resultant figure is divided by the original investment.

For example, if an investment of £10,000 was expected to produce annual cash flows of £3,500 over the next five years and the lowest acceptable rate was 15%, then

$$\text{P.V. of £3,500 for 5 years at 15\%} = 11,733$$
$$\text{Profitability Index} = \frac{11,733}{10,000} = 1.17$$

Merrett and Sykes dismiss such "eccentric perversion(s) of yield" as reproducing the disadvantages of yield while only imperfectly reproducing the advantages.

(c)   It is also argued that the IRR can be calculated without knowing the cost of capital. Since the cost of capital is often difficult to determine accurately this means that decision-takers can be presented with a single figure — the yield — which can be used to assess the project in the light of the decision-takers' estimates of the possible range of the cost of capital.

On the other hand, if the NPV method is used a number of NPVs have to be calculated to cover the range of the cost of capital and this can become confusing.

(d)   Supporters of the NPV method point to the ease of calculation and the clarity of the concept. As we have mentioned, there are situations where only the concept of NPV has any real relevance; for example, in placing a value on some financial or real asset, such as a security or a fixed asset, in terms of the future income stream which the asset will generate.

(e)   Supporters of the NPV method also argue that the NPV method is more easily adapted to take account of situations where the cost of capital changes in different periods.

(f)   Opponents of IRR point out that it can become meaningless in certain situations. This happens when there are very large negative cash flows in the later part of a project's life. This does not happen very often, negative cash flows can be quite consistent with a normal interpretation of the IRR and Merrett & Sykes show how to deal with those situations which create such problems. But it is not merely an academic problem, one can imagine situations where land has been used for mining or waste disposal and large outlays have to be made at the end of the project's life in order to satisfy environmentalists.

(g)   Finally, it is argued that the assumption under the NPV method that cash flows are reinvested at the cost of capital, while not absolutely accurate, is more reasonable than the assumption that they are reinvested at the IRR.

In conclusion, it is perhaps worth remembering that in practice firms tend to use more than one method, including non-discounting, methods, presumably recognising that different methods highlight different aspects of the investment decision.

QUESTIONS

13.1 The information below refers to three mutually exclusive investment projects.

YEAR	CASH FLOW (£'s)		
	Project A	Project B	Project C
0	-100,000	-100,000	-100,000
1	20,000	40,000	50,000
2	20,000	40,000	30,000
3	20,000	30,000	20,000
4	20,000	20,000	20,000
5	20,000	10,000	20,000
6	20,000	—	10,000
7	20,000	—	—
8	20,000	—	—
9	20,000	—	—

(a) Rank the above projects according to:-
  (i) Payback;
  (ii) book rate of return;
  (iii) net present value (assuming a cost of capital = 10%).

(b) Explain why the rankings are different.

(c) List the advantages of each of the above methods of investment appraisal.

13.2 A company has the opportunity of investing in a project which can be paid for in one lump sum or by making a down payment of £4,000 and two further payments of £4,000 in the following two years to make a total of £12,000. All payments would be made on 1st January of the year.

(a) If the interest rate applicable is 20% compound, what is the lump sum equivalent in present value terms of the £12,000?

(b) If the company has only £10,000 available on 1st January, to what level has the interest rate to rise before the payment of this lump sum would be acceptable?

Intermediate steps in your workings must be shown. *(ICMA)*

13.3 (a) An asset costing £40,000 is expected to have a useful life of 20 years after which its scrap value will be £4,000. If the reducing balance method of depreciation is to be used find the annual percentage rate of depreciation.

(b) It is estimated that an investment in a new process will cause the following cash flow:

	Net cash Inflow £	Net cash Outflow £
Now	—	60,000
End of year: 1	—	10,000
2	15,000	—
3	20,000	—
4	20,000	—
5	20,000	—
6	20,000	—

The firm wishes to earn at least 15% per annum on projects of this type.

Calculate the present values of the expected net cash inflows and outflows and comment on the course of action to be taken.

(ICMA)

13.4 Your company uses a machine in its production department which costs £12,000 at the beginning of 1983. The machine will be replaced after five years usage by a new machine at the end of 1988. During the five years of operation of the machine it is estimated that the net cash inflows at the beginning of each year will be as follows:

Year	1984	1985	1986	1987	1988
Net Cash Inflow (£)	6,600	6,000	4,500	(1,000)	(2,600)

Required:

(a) If the machine is being purchased with a five year loan, which is compounded annually at 15%, produce an amortization schedule for the five equal annual repayments of the loan. *(5 marks)*

(b) If the £12,000 debt, which is compounded annually at 15%, is to be discharged in 1988 by a sinking fund method, under which equal annual deposits will be made into a fund paying 10% annually, produce the schedule for the sinking fund. *(5 marks)*

(c) Calculate the net present value of the net cash flows over the five years of operation of the machine at the 10% and 15% discount rates. *(5 marks)*

(d) Determine the Internal Rate of Return and comment on and compare the three sets of results ignoring taxation with a view to making payment for the machine. *(5 marks)*

Extract from Net Present Value Tables

Period	10% Discount Factor	15% Discount Factor
0	1.0000	1.0000
1	0.9091	0.8696
2	0.8264	0.7561
3	0.7513	0.6575
4	0.6830	0.5718
5	0.6209	0.4972

(20 marks)
(ACA)

*13.5 Your company is about to undertake a new project which requires it to invest in a specialised machine costing £75,000. The project will last for five years, after which it is estimated that the scrap value of the machine will be £1,250, to be received at the end of the sixth year. It is necessary to inject money into the project at the end of each year to ensure that the machine is kept in proper working order for the next year of the project. The amount needed at the end of the first year is £1,000 and it is estimated that this amount needs to be increased by 10% at the end of each succeeding year over the period of the project.

The revenue produced from the project through the use of the machine is estimated to be £20,000 at the end of the first year, and this will increase by 7½% at the end of each succeeding year over the period of the project.

Required:
(a) Establish and tabulate the net cash flows for the project.
(5 marks)

(b) Establish the net present value of the project using a discount rate of 10%. *(4 marks)*

(c) Establish the net present value of the project using a discount rate of 15%. *(4 marks)*

(d) Establish the internal rate of return for the project by inter-polation using a diagram. *(5 marks)*

(e) Interpret the meaning of the internal rate of return that you have obtained in (d). *(2 marks)*

An extract from present value tables

Year	Interest Rate	
	10%	15%
1	0.9091	0.8696
2	0.8264	0.7561
3	0.7513	0.6575
4	0.6830	0.5718
5	0.6209	0.4972
6	0.5645	0.4323

(20 marks)
(ACA)

13.6 (a) Your company purchased an asset on 1 April 1979, the beginning of its financial year, for £50,000 and has depreciated its value each financial year at a rate of $7\frac{1}{2}\%$ on a reducing balance basis.

Required:
Determine the book value of the asset on 1 April 1984, by using compound interest methods. *(3 marks)*

(b) The company is about to purchase a large item of machinery estimated to cost £70,000 at the beginning of the next financial year. The book value at the end of the eighth year is estimated to be £40,000.

Required:
Calculate the percentage rate per annum, to the first place of decimals, to be used following the reducing balance method of depreciation. *(5 marks)*

(c) The company has recently run short of office accommodation and has had to rent space nearby for the Marketing Division. The annual rental for these extra premises is £30,000, which is payable in advance at the beginning of the year. It is envisaged that this arrangement will need to continue for some six years. The company decides to cover these circumstances by taking out an annuity at the beginning of the first year at 6.5% compounded annually.

Required:
Calculate the present value of the six years total rental. *(5 marks)*

(d) A recent survey of the machinery in the Production Division has revealed that an important piece of machinery will need replacement in the near future. The replacement cost price of this equipment is £29,000 and it is expected to be used for five full years after which time it will have a residual value of £5,000. The company has begun a financial investigation to determine whether to purchase the machine outright or to use hire purchase or to lease the machine. Hire purchase would require a down payment of £10,000 and equal instalments of £5,500 at the beginning of each subsequent year. Leasing requires a payment of £9,000 for the first year in advance. The payment for each subsequent year is reduced by $12\frac{1}{2}\%$ per annum (reducing balance method) over the life of the machine. There is no option to purchase the machine at the end of the lease.

Required:
Calculate the present value of the equipment if the current cost of capital is 11% and advise which method of acquisition should be used.

(7 marks)

The extract below from Present Value Tables is for your use.

Year	Discount Factor 11%
1	0.9009
2	0.8116
3	0.7312
4	0.6587
5	0.5935

(20 marks)
(ACA)

*13.7 An accountant is using the concept of net present value (NPV) to assess three alternative methods of paying for a new computer system which is expected to have a commercial life of eight years before replacement.

(a) Rent the system for eight years at £120,000 per annum, payable annually in advance, inclusive of all servicing and maintenance.

(b) Outright purchase for £0.5 million, with a service contract of £40,000 payable annually in advance. After eight years the system would have a re-sale value of 10% of its original purchase price.

(c) Hire purchase of a deposit of £150,000 and seven further annual payments of £100,000, inclusive of all servicing, after which time (i.e. after eight years) the company would own the system, then worth £50,000.

You are required to find which method is the most economical, assuming the cost of capital to be 15%, and comment on your answer.
(20 marks)
(ICMA)

*13.8 (a) A decision has been made in your company to purchase a new machine costing £40,000 for the production department, which is to be delivered and paid for on the first day of the next financial year. It is estimated that, in the first year of its use, the inflow of cash associated with this new machine will be £25,000. The outflow of cash for the corresponding period relating to this particular machine will be £10,000. (Note that cash inflows and outflows are to be considered as occurring at the end of the financial year.) Due to inflation the cash inflows are expected to rise by $7\frac{1}{2}\%$ per annum and cash outflows are expected to rise by 12% per annum. Unfortunately this type of machinery is not very reliable and its useful life in production terms will be five years, after which it is estimated that it will have a scrap value of £500, realisable in the following financial year.

Required:
(i)   Tabulate the net cash flows associated with this new machine over its life span.   *(5 marks)*
(ii) If the cost of capital is 15%, determine the net present value of the cash flows associated with this new machine.
                                                                    (3 marks)
(iii) Explain, as if to a layman, what your figure for the net present value of the cash flows associated with this new machine means.   *(3 marks)*

   (b) It has been decided to purchase the new machine by taking out a loan of £40,000 over the five years of its life. The loan is being compounded at an interest rate of $17\frac{1}{2}\%$ per annum. The loan is to be settled at the end of five years by a fund into which equal annual instalments are paid at the beginning of each year and on which interest compounds at 15% per annum.

Required:
Calculate the amount of each of the five equal annual instalments to be paid into the fund.   *(6 marks)*
                                                                        (ACA)

13.9 (a) One of your clients has a bank credit card and used it to pay £500 for an emergency repair to his car. The client can only repay at most £100 per month to the bank.

   The conditions for operating the credit card are that no interest is charged in the month that the repair takes place and thereafter the monthly interest is calculated at 2.5% of the opening balance.

Required:

Draw up a schedule showing the interest charged and the repayments made, if the first repayment is made in the month that the repair is charged. *(5 marks)*

(b) After his experience with the car your client decides to exchange it and borrow £3,000 from the bank to buy a new one.

The arrangement with the bank is for the client to make five equal annual repayments, being charged interest of 20% per annum on the amount of loan outstanding. Repayments take place on the anniversary of the original loan.

Required:

Determine the equal annual repayments and draw up a schedule showing the interest charged and repayments made. *(7 marks)*

(c) Your client operates a car-hire business acting as chauffeur. The client bought a new car at the beginning of 1986 for £12,000 and plans to sell it at the end of 1990 for £1,500. He estimates that his gross earnings during 1986 will be £9,000 and his expenses will be £4,500, both considered to be taken at the end of the year. He further estimates that his gross earnings will rise each subsequent year by $7\frac{1}{2}\%$ per annum whilst the expenses will rise correspondingly by 6% per annum.

Required:

(i) Determine the net cash flows for the five years from 1986 to 1990. *(3 marks)*

(ii) Establish the net present value for these five years of business assuming a 20% cost of capital. *(5 marks)*

(20 marks)

The extract below from present value tables is for your use.

Year	Discount Factor 20%
0	1.0000
1	0.8333
2	0.6944
3	0.5787
4	0.4823
5	0.4019

(ACA)

Chapter 14
MATRICES

Suppose that a manufacturer produces two products A and B from three raw materials x, y, and z such that:

A requires 2 units of x, 3 units of y, and 3 units of z;

B requires 5 units of x, 0 units of y, and 1 unit of z.

This information could be written in the form of a table as below:

	x	y	z
A	2	3	3
B	5	0	1

The company may wish to use this data to make many calculations such as the quantity of each product that can be made from a given supply of raw materials, the cost of the product given certain values for its components, etc.

Such calculations are often made easier by writing the numbers in the form of a rectangular array called a matrix and the matrix for the above product recipes would be written:

$$\begin{pmatrix} 2 & 3 & 3 \\ 5 & 0 & 1 \end{pmatrix}$$

Computers make extensive use of such matrices for storing data and for performing complex calculations.

In this chapter, operations on matrices will be examined and their use to solve simultaneous equations will be illustrated.

14.1 Operations on Matrices

14.1.1 Addition

If A is the matrix

$$\begin{bmatrix} a_{11} & \cdots & a_{1n} \\ \vdots & & \vdots \\ a_{m1} & & a_{mn} \end{bmatrix},$$

B is the matrix

$$\begin{bmatrix} b_{11} & \cdots & b_{1n} \\ \vdots & & \vdots \\ b_{m1} & & b_{mn} \end{bmatrix},$$

C is the matrix

$$\begin{bmatrix} c_{11} & \cdots & c_{1n} \\ \vdots & & \vdots \\ c_{m1} & & c_{mn} \end{bmatrix},$$

then if $\quad A + B = C$

$$C = \begin{bmatrix} a_{11} + b_{11} \cdots\cdots\cdots a_{1n} + b_{1n} \\ \vdots \qquad\qquad\qquad \vdots \\ a_{m1} + b_{m1} \qquad\qquad a_{mn} + b_{mn} \end{bmatrix}$$

by convention this is also written
$c_{ij} = a_{ij} + b_{ij}$ for each i and each j.

The addition of matrices is only defined for matrices of the same size, that is the matrices must each have the same number of rows and the same number of columns.

N.B. The number of rows does not have to be the same as the number of columns.

Example 1.1:
$$A = \begin{bmatrix} 1 & 2 \\ 4 & 2 \\ 3 & 1 \end{bmatrix}, \qquad B = \begin{bmatrix} 3 & 1 \\ 2 & 2 \\ 1 & 1 \end{bmatrix}$$

$$A + B = \begin{bmatrix} 1+3 & 2+1 \\ 4+2 & 2+2 \\ 3+1 & 1+1 \end{bmatrix} = \begin{bmatrix} 4 & 3 \\ 6 & 4 \\ 4 & 2 \end{bmatrix}$$

The two matrices can be added together because they have the same number of rows (three) and the same number of columns (two).

Example 1.2:
$$A = \begin{bmatrix} 1 & 2 \\ 4 & 2 \\ 3 & 1 \end{bmatrix}, \qquad B = \begin{bmatrix} 3 & 1 & 4 \\ 2 & 2 & 3 \\ 1 & 1 & 1 \end{bmatrix}$$

In this example, the addition of $A + B$ cannot be defined because although A and B have the same number of rows (three) they do not have the same number of columns.

14.1.2 Multiplication by a scalar

A matrix can be multiplied by a scalar (a single number) by multiplying each element in the matrix by the scalar.

If $\quad A = \begin{bmatrix} a_{11} & a_{12} \\ a_{21} & a_{22} \end{bmatrix} \quad$ and λ is any scalar

then if $\quad C = \lambda A$

$$C = \begin{bmatrix} \lambda a_{11} & \lambda a_{12} \\ \lambda a_{21} & \lambda a_{22} \end{bmatrix}$$

which can also be written

$$C_{ij} = \lambda a_{ij} \text{ for each i and each j.}$$

Example 2.1:

$$A = \begin{bmatrix} 6 & 3 \\ 3 & 9 \end{bmatrix}$$

if $\lambda = 2$

$$2A = \begin{bmatrix} 12 & 6 \\ 6 & 18 \end{bmatrix}$$

if $\lambda = \frac{1}{3}$

$$\frac{A}{3} = \begin{bmatrix} 2 & 1 \\ 1 & 3 \end{bmatrix}$$

14.1.3 MATRIX MULTIPLICATION

The multiplication (or product) of two matrices can only be defined if the number of columns in the first matrix equals the number of rows in the second matrix.

The resulting matrix will have the same number of rows as the first matrix and the same number of columns as the second matrix.

More generally, the product of an m × n matrix A with a p × q matrix B is an m × q matrix if n = p. If n ≠ p then the product is not defined.

Suppose $A = \begin{bmatrix} a_{11} & a_{12} \\ a_{21} & a_{22} \\ a_{31} & a_{23} \end{bmatrix}$ and $B = \begin{bmatrix} b_{11} & b_{12} & b_{13} & b_{14} \\ b_{21} & b_{22} & b_{23} & b_{24} \end{bmatrix}$

A is a 3 × 2 matrix,
B is a 2 × 4 matrix.

The product A.B can therefore be defined and will be a 3×4 matrix C with elements c_{ij}.

The product A.B is calculated for each element ij by obtaining the scalar product of the ith rows of A with the jth columns of B.

Thus, in the example above, the element

$$C_{24} = \text{scalar product of the 2nd row of A}$$
$$\text{with the 4th column of B}$$
$$= a_{21} b_{14} + a_{22} b_{24}$$

Written more generally:—

if $A = \begin{bmatrix} a_{11} \cdots a_{1n} \\ \vdots \\ a_{m1} \cdots a_{mn} \end{bmatrix}$ and $B = \begin{bmatrix} b_{11} \cdots b_{1q} \\ \vdots \\ b_{n1} \cdots b_{nq} \end{bmatrix}$

$$A.B = \begin{bmatrix} a_{11}b_{11} + \cdots + a_{1n}b_{n1} & \text{------} & a_{11}b_{1q} + \cdots + a_{1n}b_{nq} \\ \vdots & & \vdots \\ a_{m1}b_{11} + \cdots + a_{mn}b_{n1} & & a_{m1}b_{1q} + \cdots + a_{mn}b_{nq} \end{bmatrix}$$

Example 3.1:

$$A = \begin{bmatrix} 1 & 2 \\ 1 & 0 \end{bmatrix}, \qquad B = \begin{bmatrix} 2 & 3 \\ 4 & 2 \end{bmatrix}$$

$$A.B = \begin{bmatrix} 1.2+2.4 & 1.3+2.2 \\ 1.2+0.4 & 1.3+0.2 \end{bmatrix} = \begin{bmatrix} 10 & 7 \\ 2 & 3 \end{bmatrix}$$

There are a number of points to note:—

(i)   If the addition A+B is defined it does not follow that A.B is also defined.

(ii) If A.B is defined, B.A need not be defined.

(iii) If both A.B and B.A are defined then usually A.B ≠ B.A.

(iv) If A.B and B.A are defined and A.B = B.A then A and B are said to commute.

(v)   If A,B,C are three matrices such that

$$A = \begin{pmatrix} 2 & 3 \\ 1 & 2 \\ 2 & 1 \end{pmatrix}, \quad B = \begin{pmatrix} 2 & 3 \\ 1 & 1 \end{pmatrix}, \quad \text{and } C = \begin{pmatrix} 5 & -1 \\ -3 & 3 \end{pmatrix}$$

then
$$A.B = \begin{pmatrix} 2 & 3 \\ 1 & 2 \\ 2 & 1 \end{pmatrix} \begin{pmatrix} 2 & 3 \\ 1 & 1 \end{pmatrix} = \begin{pmatrix} 7 & 9 \\ 4 & 5 \\ 5 & 7 \end{pmatrix}$$

Therefore,
$$(A.B)C = \begin{pmatrix} 7 & 9 \\ 4 & 5 \\ 5 & 7 \end{pmatrix} \begin{pmatrix} 5 & -1 \\ -3 & 3 \end{pmatrix} = \begin{pmatrix} 8 & 20 \\ 5 & 11 \\ 4 & 16 \end{pmatrix}$$

also,
$$B.C = \begin{pmatrix} 2 & 3 \\ 1 & 1 \end{pmatrix} \begin{pmatrix} 5 & -1 \\ -3 & 3 \end{pmatrix} = \begin{pmatrix} 1 & 7 \\ 2 & 2 \end{pmatrix}$$

Therefore,
$$A(BC) = \begin{pmatrix} 2 & 3 \\ 1 & 2 \\ 2 & 1 \end{pmatrix} \begin{pmatrix} 1 & 7 \\ 2 & 2 \end{pmatrix} = \begin{pmatrix} 8 & 20 \\ 5 & 11 \\ 4 & 16 \end{pmatrix}$$

Therefore,   (AB)C = A(BC)

If the matrix multiplication ABC can be defined then the position of the brackets does not matter and the multiplication is said to be associative.

14.1.4 Zero matrix
A square matrix with all its elements zero is called the zero matrix 0.

Thus the 2×2 zero matrix

$$0 = \begin{pmatrix} 0 & 0 \\ 0 & 0 \end{pmatrix}$$

Any other matrix (A) multiplied by the zero matrix has the zero matrix as the product whatever the order of multiplication.

i.e. $A.0 = 0.A = 0$

If A and B are two matrices whose product is a zero matrix (A.B=0) it does not follow that either A or B must be zero nor that B.A=0.

For example, if $A = \begin{pmatrix} 2 & 1 \\ 2 & 1 \end{pmatrix}$, $B = \begin{pmatrix} 1 & 2 \\ -2 & -4 \end{pmatrix}$

then, $A.B = \begin{pmatrix} 2 & 1 \\ 2 & 1 \end{pmatrix} \begin{pmatrix} 1 & 2 \\ -2 & -4 \end{pmatrix} = \begin{pmatrix} 0 & 0 \\ 0 & 0 \end{pmatrix}$

But, $B.A = \begin{pmatrix} 1 & 2 \\ -2 & -4 \end{pmatrix} \begin{pmatrix} 2 & 1 \\ 2 & 1 \end{pmatrix} = \begin{pmatrix} 5 & 3 \\ -12 & -6 \end{pmatrix}$

14.1.5 Identity or Unit Matrix
A square matrix in which all the elements of the diagonal between the top left corner and the bottom right are ones and all the other elements are zeros is called the identity, or unit, matrix and is denoted by the letter I.

e.g. $\begin{pmatrix} 1 & 0 \\ 0 & 1 \end{pmatrix}$, $\begin{pmatrix} 1 & 0 & 0 \\ 0 & 1 & 0 \\ 0 & 0 & 1 \end{pmatrix}$, etc.

The product of any matrix A multiplied by the corresponding identity matrix will itself be A whatever the order of multiplication.

ie. $I.A = A.I = A$

For example,

if $A = \begin{pmatrix} 1 & 2 \\ 3 & 1 \\ 2 & 4 \end{pmatrix}$

$I.A = \begin{pmatrix} 1 & 0 & 0 \\ 0 & 1 & 0 \\ 0 & 0 & 1 \end{pmatrix} \begin{pmatrix} 1 & 2 \\ 3 & 1 \\ 2 & 4 \end{pmatrix} = \begin{pmatrix} 1 & 2 \\ 3 & 1 \\ 2 & 4 \end{pmatrix}$

$A.I = \begin{pmatrix} 1 & 2 \\ 3 & 1 \\ 2 & 4 \end{pmatrix} \begin{pmatrix} 1 & 0 \\ 0 & 1 \end{pmatrix} = \begin{pmatrix} 1 & 2 \\ 3 & 1 \\ 2 & 4 \end{pmatrix}$

14.1.6 The Inverse Matrix

If the product of matrices A and B is the identity matrix I, the B is called the inverse of A and can also be written as A^{-1}

For example, if $A = \begin{pmatrix} 5 & 3 \\ 3 & 2 \end{pmatrix}$ and $B = \begin{pmatrix} 2 & -3 \\ -3 & 5 \end{pmatrix}$

then $AB = \begin{pmatrix} 5 & 3 \\ 3 & 2 \end{pmatrix} \begin{pmatrix} 2 & -3 \\ -3 & 5 \end{pmatrix} = \begin{pmatrix} 10 & -9 & -15 & +15 \\ 6 & -6 & -9 & +10 \end{pmatrix}$

$$= \begin{pmatrix} 1 & 0 \\ 0 & 1 \end{pmatrix}$$

Therefore, $B = A^{-1}$

Additionally, $B.A = I$

$$A^{-1}A = I$$

Two points should be noted, firstly only a square matrix can have an inverse and secondly even if a matrix is square it may not have an inverse.

The inverse of a matrix A can be found by applying the series of changes to the rows of the identity matrix which when applied to A will transform it into the identity matrix.

There are two ways in which the rows can be changed:
1. Any row can be multiplied by a constant;
2. Any multiple of one row can be added to or subtracted from another row.

Using the previous example:

$$A = \begin{pmatrix} 5 & 3 \\ 3 & 2 \end{pmatrix}$$

The row transformations can be made more easily on A and the identity matrix if they are written in the form of a partitioned matrix as follows:

$$\left(\begin{array}{cc|cc} 5 & 3 & 1 & 0 \\ 3 & 2 & 0 & 1 \end{array} \right)$$

Subtracting $\frac{1}{2}$ times the second row from the first

$$\left(\begin{array}{cc|cc} \frac{1}{2} & 0 & 1 & -\frac{1}{2} \\ 3 & 2 & 0 & 1 \end{array} \right)$$

Subtracting 6 times row 1 from row 2

$$\left(\begin{array}{cc|cc} \frac{1}{2} & 0 & 1 & -\frac{1}{2} \\ 0 & 2 & -6 & 10 \end{array} \right)$$

Multiplying row 1 by 2

$$\left(\begin{array}{cc|cc} 1 & 0 & 2 & -3 \\ 0 & 2 & -6 & 10 \end{array} \right)$$

Multiplying row 2 by $\frac{1}{2}$

$$\left(\begin{array}{cc|cc} 1 & 0 & 2 & -3 \\ 0 & 1 & -3 & 5 \end{array} \right)$$

The matrix $\begin{pmatrix} 2 & -3 \\ -3 & 5 \end{pmatrix}$ is the inverse of A.

14.2 The Solution of Simultaneous Equations

It is possible, and often less time consuming, to solve simultaneous equations by using matrices.

Consider the following equations:

$$5x + 3y = 35$$
$$3x + 2y = 22$$

These can be written in matrix form as

$$\begin{pmatrix} 5 & 3 \\ 3 & 2 \end{pmatrix} \begin{pmatrix} x \\ y \end{pmatrix} = \begin{pmatrix} 35 \\ 22 \end{pmatrix}$$

If both sides of the equation are pre-multiplied by the inverse of $\begin{pmatrix} 5 & 3 \\ 3 & 2 \end{pmatrix}$, which is $\begin{pmatrix} 2 & -3 \\ -3 & 5 \end{pmatrix}$ from above, then the equation becomes

$$\begin{pmatrix} 2 & -3 \\ -3 & 5 \end{pmatrix} \begin{pmatrix} 5 & 3 \\ 3 & 2 \end{pmatrix} \begin{pmatrix} x \\ y \end{pmatrix} = \begin{pmatrix} 2 & -3 \\ -3 & 5 \end{pmatrix} \begin{pmatrix} 35 \\ 22 \end{pmatrix}$$

$$\begin{pmatrix} 1 & 0 \\ 0 & 1 \end{pmatrix} \begin{pmatrix} x \\ y \end{pmatrix} = \begin{pmatrix} 4 \\ 5 \end{pmatrix}$$

$$\begin{pmatrix} x \\ y \end{pmatrix} = \begin{pmatrix} 4 \\ 5 \end{pmatrix}$$

or $x = 4$, $y = 5$

More generally, if a set of simultaneous equations can be represented in matrix form as

$$A.X = B$$

then pre-multiplying by A^{-1} (the inverse of A)

$$A^{-1}.A.X = A^{-1}.B$$
$$I.X = A^{-1}.B$$
$$X = A^{-1}.B$$

14.2.1 Determinants

Finding an inverse can be cumbersome.

There is an alternative method which is most practical for a 2×2 matrix.

$$\text{Consider} \quad A = \begin{pmatrix} a_{11} & a_{12} \\ a_{21} & a_{22} \end{pmatrix}$$

the quantity $a_{11}.a_{22} - a_{12}.a_{21}$ is called the determinant, $|d|$, of the matrix and

$$A^{-1} = \frac{1}{|d|} \begin{pmatrix} a_{22} & -a_{12} \\ -a_{21} & a_{11} \end{pmatrix}$$

$$\text{Consider the matrix} \quad A = \begin{pmatrix} 4 & 3 \\ 2 & 2 \end{pmatrix}$$

$$|d| = 4 \times 2 - 3 \times 2 = 2$$

$$A^{-1} = \tfrac{1}{2} \begin{pmatrix} 2 & -3 \\ -2 & 4 \end{pmatrix}$$

$$= \begin{pmatrix} 1 & -\tfrac{3}{2} \\ -1 & 2 \end{pmatrix}$$

Note that the determinant of the matrix $\begin{pmatrix} 4 & 2 \\ 2 & 1 \end{pmatrix}$ is zero. If a matrix is to have an inverse then the determinant must be non-zero.

QUESTIONS

14.1 $\quad A = \begin{pmatrix} 2 & 1 \\ 3 & 2 \end{pmatrix}, \quad B = \begin{pmatrix} 3 & 1 \\ 2 & 3 \end{pmatrix}, \quad C = \begin{pmatrix} -1 & 2 \\ 1 & -6 \end{pmatrix}$

    (a) Find A + B
    (b) Find B + C
    (c) Find AB
    (d) Find AC
    (e) Find A^{-1}
    (f) Show that (AB)C = A(BC)
    (g) Show that BC ≠ CB

14.2 Two matrices are multiplied together:

$$\begin{bmatrix} 3 & 5 \\ 6 & 7 \end{bmatrix} Y = \begin{bmatrix} 2 & 5 \\ 1 & 7 \end{bmatrix}$$

which represents Y?

$$A \begin{bmatrix} 1 & 0 \\ 5 & 0 \end{bmatrix} \quad B \begin{bmatrix} \tfrac{2}{3} & 1 \\ \tfrac{1}{6} & 1 \end{bmatrix} \quad C \begin{bmatrix} 1 \\ 5 \end{bmatrix} \quad D \begin{bmatrix} \tfrac{16}{9} & -\tfrac{5}{9} \\ \tfrac{35}{9} & -\tfrac{16}{9} \end{bmatrix} \quad E \begin{bmatrix} -1 & 0 \\ 1 & 1 \end{bmatrix}$$

(CIMA)

14.3   Matrix X is defined as $\begin{pmatrix} 3 & 5 \\ 2 & 3 \end{pmatrix}$

X^{-1} equals

A $\begin{pmatrix} 3 & 5 \\ -2 & -3 \end{pmatrix}$ B $\begin{pmatrix} 3 & 2 \\ 5 & 3 \end{pmatrix}$ C $\begin{pmatrix} 2 & 3 \\ 3 & 5 \end{pmatrix}$ D $\begin{pmatrix} -3 & 5 \\ 2 & -3 \end{pmatrix}$

E   none of these.   *(CIMA)*

14.4   Solve the following simultaneous equations
$$2x + y = 7$$
$$3x + 2y = 12$$
(Hint: Use the inverse found in 14.1)

14.5   Use the matrix method to solve the following equations
$$x + 2y + z = 0$$
$$3x + 2y + z = 2$$
$$2x + 3y + 2z = 2$$

14.6   Check by row transpositions that
$A = \begin{pmatrix} 4 & 2 \\ 2 & 1 \end{pmatrix}$ does not have an inverse.

14.7   A manufacturer produces two products A and B from two raw materials x and y.
To produce 20 units of A and 25 units of B requires 115 Kg. of x and 120 Kg. of y.
To produce 30 units of A and 20 units of B requires 120 Kg. of x and 110 Kg. of y.
Use the matrix method to calculate the quantities of x and y per unit of A and of B.

14.8   (a)   There are three types of breakfast meal available in supermarkets known as brand BM1, brand BM2, and brand BM3. In order to assess the market, a survey was carried out by one of the manufacturers. After the first month the survey revealed that 20% of the customers purchasing brand BM1 switched to BM2 and 10% of the customers purchasing brand BM1 switched to BM3. Similarly after the first month of the customers purchasing brand BM2, 25% switched to BM1 and 10% switched to BM3 and of the customers purchasing brand BM3 5% switched to BM1 and 15% switched to BM2.

Required:

(i) Display in a matrix S, the patterns of retentions and transfers of customers from the first to the second month, expressing percentages in decimal form. *(2 marks)*

(ii) Multiply matrix S by itself (that is form S^2). *(5 marks)*

(iii) Interpret the results you obtain in part (ii) with regard to customer brand loyalty. *(3 marks)*

(b) In any one week your company can sell x items at a price of £(43,750 – 112.5x) per item, whilst incurring marginal costs of £(200 – x)x per item.

Required:

(i) Determine the formula for total revenue for one week. *(2 marks)*

(ii) If marginal revenue is the gradient of the total revenue curve, determine the formula for marginal revenue for one week. *(2 marks)*

(iii) Determine the number of items per week where marginal revenue is the same as marginal costs. *(4 marks)*

(iv) Interpret the results from part (iii). *(2 marks)*

(Total 20 marks) (ACA)

14.9 (a) The quantity of a commodity demanded or supplied is represented by q tonnes and £p represents its price. The demand equation is $2p - q = 15$ and the supply equation is $-p + 3q = 5$.

Required:

(i) Express these equations in matrix form. *(2 marks)*

(ii) Using matrix methods establish the values of p and q which satisfy the demand and supply equations simultaneously. *(6 marks)*

(b) Another demand equation is given by $q = 2p^3 - 21p^2 + 36p + 9$.

Required:
Using the method of differential calculus establish the maximum demand and its corresponding price. *(8 marks)*

(c) Elasticity of demand is given by the expression

$$\left(\frac{dq}{dp}\right) \cdot \frac{p}{q}$$

Required:

If the demand function is given by $q = \dfrac{90}{p^3}$, show that the elasticity of demand is constant.

(4 marks)

(Total 20 marks)

(ACA)

14.10 (a) **Required:**

(i) Calculate the rates of interest that give a break-even position if the equation for net present value (£P) is given by $P = 192 - 28r + r^2$ where r is the discount factor. (3 marks)

(ii) Explain the significance of the values of r that you obtain in part (i) with respect to "profit" and "loss" in the context of net present value. (3 marks)

* (b) Socsport p.l.c. is a company in the wholesale trade selling sports-wear and stocks two brands, A and B, of football kit, each consisting of a shirt, a pair of shorts and a pair of socks.

The costs for Brand A are £5.75 for a shirt, £3.99 for a pair of shorts and £1.85 for a pair of socks and those for Brand B are £6.25 for a shirt, £4.48 for a pair of shorts and £1.97 for a pair of socks. Three customers X, Y, Z demand the following combinations of Brands; X, 36 kits of Brand A and 48 kits of Brand B; Y, 24 kits of Brand A and 72 kits of Brand B; Z, 60 kits of Brand A.

Required:

(i) Express the costs of Brands A and B in matrix form, then the demands of the customers, X, Y, Z in matrix form.

(4 marks)

(ii) By forming the product of the two matrices that you obtain in the previous part deduce the detailed costs to each of the customers. (5 marks)

(c) As a result of recent price increases Z has ceased to be a customer of Socsport but the demands of X and Y remain the same. Socsport no longer stocks socks of either brand.

Required:

Re-express the demands of X and Y in matrix form and find its inverse matrix. (5 marks)

(Total 20 marks)

(ACA)

*14.11 (a) A zoo car park charges £1 for a motorcycle, £2 for a car and £10 for a coach. Write down this data as a column matrix C.

(2 marks)

(b) The number of vehicles using the car park last weekend is given by the matrix V, where

$$V = \begin{array}{c} \\ \text{Saturday} \\ \text{Sunday} \end{array} \begin{array}{ccc} \text{motor-} & & \\ \text{cycle} & \text{car} & \text{coach} \\ \left(\begin{array}{ccc} 84 & 337 & 38 \\ 62 & 291 & 43 \end{array} \right) \end{array}$$

(i) Which of the products CV and VC can be evaluated?

(2 marks)

(ii) Let this product be Y, evaluate Y, and state its meaning.

(6 marks)

(c) To become cost-effective the car park must generate more revenue at weekends. It has been suggested that three options be considered:

1. Increase the charges by 50% for both days
2. Double the charges for Saturdays
3. Double the charges for Sundays

The matrix X is defined so that the product XY gives the actual revenue for last weekend and the hypothetical revenue which might have been obtained for each of the three possible options.

Write down the matrix X, evaluate XY, and interpret your result.

(10 marks)
(Total 20 marks)
(CIMA)

Chapter 15
LINEAR PROGRAMMING

Many business decisions involve seeking the optimum use of limited resources. One way of establishing this is through controlled experimentation but this is usually expensive and frequently not practical. A model is a way to represent the real world without disturbing the existing situation. In many instances a linear relationship can be defined between the variables of the problem. The formulation and solution of simultaneous equations is an example of a linear relationship model. The features of such a model are that there are as many equations as variables and a unique solution.

There are a more complex category of problems in which the optimum solution does not necessarily involve the full utilisation of all resources and so the formulation of the model involves inequality relationships. In addition there will usually be more variables than relationships between them. This means that there will be several solutions which satisfy the relationships. The purpose of the model is to find the conditions under which a quantity called the objective function can be maximized (or minimized) under the defined constraints.

15.1 Graphical Solution
When the number of variables is just two the solution to the problem can be found graphically.

Consider the following problem:-

$$\text{Maximize } Z = 2x_1 - 4x_2$$

within the constraints

$$3x_1 + 5x_2 \geqslant 15$$
$$4x_1 + 9x_2 \leqslant 36$$
$$x_1, x_2 \geqslant 0$$

For a detailed explanation see Appendix A on Page 385.

Solution:
STEP 1
Draw the x_1, x_2 plane. The $x_1, x_2 \geqslant 0$ conditions restrict the solution to the positive quadrant.

STEP 2
Draw the line $3x_1 + 5x_2 = 15$. Any values of x_1, x_2 in the area between the origin and this line fail to satisfy the constraint $3x_1 + 5x_2 \geqslant 15$

DIAGRAM 15.1

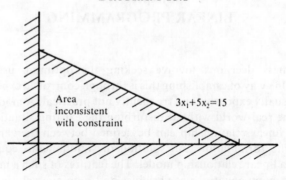

Area inconsistent with constraint

$3x_1+5x_2=15$

STEP 3

Draw the line $4x_1 + 9x_2 = 36$. Only values of x_1, x_2 in the area between the origin and this line satisfy the constraint $4x_1 + 9x_2 \leq 36$. But part of this area has already been excluded in Step 2.

The valid solution area satisfying both constraints is indicated by the shaded area in Diagram 15.2.

DIAGRAM 15.2

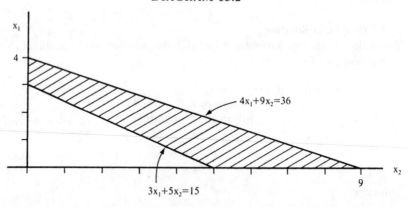

x_1

4

$4x_1+9x_2=36$

x_2

9

$3x_1+5x_2=15$

STEP 4

The maximizing function $Z = 2x_1 - 4x_2$ is now considered.

Draw the line $2x_1 - 4x_2 = 0$, as shown in Diagram 15.3. This is a straight line through the origin and the value of $Z=0$. For any other value of Z the line $Z = 2x_1 - 4x_2$ will be a straight line parallel to this line. From Diagram 15.3 it can be seen that Z can have any positive value up to $Z = 18$ whilst staying within the feasible region of values for x_1, x_2. Thus $Z = 18$ is the maximum value and occurs at the point $x_1 = 9$, $x_2 = 0$.

DIAGRAM 15.3

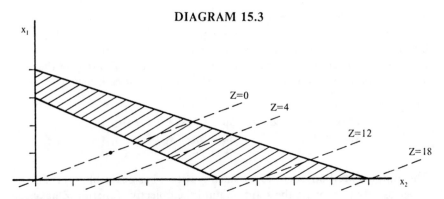

The above example illustrates two general points:-
1.   The optimal solution occurred at an extreme point (corner) of the feasible region.
2.   Any line joining two points on the boundary of the region lies wholly within the region. The region of permissible solutions is called CONVEX.

15.2   The Simplex Method
The graphical solution to linear programming problems is only useful with two variables. The Simplex method is an algebraic approach suitable for programming on a computer and hence for solving large problems. The use of the Simplex method will be described as a generalised iterative procedure and illustrated at each step by considering the following production problem.

A manufacturer has two machines on which he makes two products X_1 and X_2.

1 Kg of X_1 requires 3 units of capacity on machine 1
                    and 5 units of capacity on machine 2
1 Kg of X_2 requires 5 units of capacity on machine 1
                    and 2 units of capacity on machine 2

The weekly capacities available are machine 1 – 15 units and machine 2 – 10 units. The gross margin is £50/Kg on X_1, and £30/Kg on X_2. What quantity of each product should he make to maximise gross margin?

The first step is to describe the problem as a mathematical model. This can be done in the form:-

$$\text{Maximize} \quad Z \; = \; 50x_1 + 30x_2$$
$$\text{subject to} \quad 3x_1 + 5x_2 \leqslant 15$$
$$5x_1 + 2x_2 \leqslant 10$$
$$x_1 \geqslant 0$$
$$x_2 \geqslant 0$$

where x_1 = Quantity of X_1 produced per week in kilograms
          x_2 = Quantity of X_2 produced per week in kilograms

To facilitate the mathematical analysis it is necessary to convert the inequality constraints into equality equations. This is achieved by the introduction of an additional variable to each constraint, this is called a slack variable. To ensure such slack variables do not affect the solution they are added to the maximising function Z with a zero profit coefficient.

The problem can then be restated as:-

$$\text{Maximize} \quad Z = 50x_1 + 30x_2 + 0.x_3 + 0x_4$$
$$\text{subject to} \quad 3x_1 + 5x_2 + x_3 \qquad\qquad = 15$$
$$5x_1 + 2x_2 \qquad\qquad + x_4 = 10$$

The Simplex Method operates by starting with a basic feasible solution and progressively improving the solution until the objective function Z has been maximised.

STEP 1
An initial basic solution is required. This is achieved by a solution to produce nothing. Applying this to the production example

$$x_1 = 0, \ x_2 = 0$$
$$\text{thus} \quad x_3 = 15 \text{ and } x_4 = 10$$

STEP 2
This information is displayed as a Simplex tableau in the following format:-

		variables					
		x_1	x_2	x_3	x_4		
basic variables in current solution	x_3	3	5	1	0	15	value of each basic variable
	x_4	5	2	0	1	10	
	Z	–50	–30	0	0	0	value of Z

Each row of the tableau represents an equation. The first row represents the constraint on machine 1, $3x_1 + 5x_2 + x_3 = 15$, the second row represents the constraint on machine 2 and the bottom row represents the objective function $Z = 50x_1 + 30x_2$, rewritten as $Z - 50x_1 - 30x_2 = 0$.

In each constraint equation there is only one variable with a positive value, e.g. in row 1, $x_3 = 15$. $x_1 = 0$, $x_2 = 0$ and x_4 is not part of the equation. The variables taking positive values are called basic variables. The variables taking zero values are called non-basic variables. The principle that the Simplex Method is based upon is that the number of variables with positive values in the optimal solution will be not more than the number of constraints.

STEP 3

The procedure to improve the value of Z involves removing one of the basic variables in the solution and replacing it with one of the non-basic variables.

The non-basic variable to enter the solution is the variable with the largest negative coefficient in the Z row.

The reason for this is that it is the variable for which each unit increase gives the maximum increase to the value of Z (which is the aim of the solution).

In the example, x_1 is the non-basic variable selected to enter the solution because every kilo of x_1 produced will increase Z by £50 whereas each kilo of x_2 would only increase Z by £30.

To decide which variable to remove from the solution, consider the effect of introducing x_1. Every kilo of x_1 will require 3 units of capacity on machine 1 which has total capacity of 15 units so the maximum production of x_1 from machine 1 could be 5Kg.

On machine 2 the maximum possible output of x_1 is only 2 kilos because each kilo requires 5 units from a machine with 10 units of capacity.

If $x_1 = 2$ kilo then all capacity will be used on machine 2 and x_4 the slack variable in equation 2 will be zero. It will therefore depart from the basic solution.

More generally,
To decide the basic variable to leave the solution, calculate the ratio

$$\frac{\textbf{value of the basic variable}}{\textbf{coefficient of the entering variable}} \quad \textbf{for each equation,}$$

the variable to depart is the basic variable of the equation with the minimum ratio, ignoring zero and negative ratios.

Referring again to the example, the ratio for equation 1 is

$$\frac{\text{value of basic variable } x_3}{\text{coefficient of } x_1 \text{ in equation 1}} = \frac{15}{3} = 5$$

The ratio for equation 2 is

$$\frac{\text{value of basic variable } x_4}{\text{coefficient of } x_1 \text{ in equation 2}} = \frac{10}{5} = 2$$

Equation 2 has the minimum ratio and therefore the basic variable x_4 will be removed.

STEP 4

To calculate the next tableau, first identify the 'pivot' element of the current tableau. This is the element at the intersection of the row of the departing variable and the column of the entering variable.

In the example this is the element 5 in row 2 (x_4 is the departing variable) and column 1 (x_1 is the entering variable).

Divide this row by the pivot element to obtain a one in the pivot position.

Then by addition or subtraction of multiples of this new row produce zeros elsewhere in the column of the pivot element.

In the example this is achieved by
i.   dividing row 2 by 5
ii. subtracting 3 times new row 2 from row 1
iii. adding 50 times new row 2 to the Z row.

This gives a new tableau

	x_1	x_2	x_3	x_4	
x_3	0	$^{19}/_5$	1	$-^3/_5$	9
x_1	1	$^2/_5$	0	$^1/_5$	2
Z	0	-10	0	10	100

STEP 5

Examine the Z row to see if one or more of the non-basic variables has a negative coefficient and if so repeat steps 3 and 4 to produce another tableau. When a tableau has been produced without any negative coefficients in the Z row an optimal solution has been reached.

In the example the coefficient of the non-basic variable $x_2 = -10$, therefore the value of Z can be improved by introducing x_2 to the basic solution.

To determine which basic variable departs we calculate the ratios in step 3.

$$\text{For row 1} \qquad 9 \div \frac{19}{5} = \frac{45}{19}$$

$$\text{For row 2} \qquad 2 \div \frac{2}{5} = 5$$

Row 1 has the minimum ratio and therefore x_3 will be the departing variable.

The pivot element is the intersection of row 1 and column of $x_2 = {}^{19}/_5$.

The next tableau is achieved by
i.   dividing row 1 by $\frac{5}{19}$
ii. subtracting $\frac{2}{5}$ times new row 1 from row 2
iii. add 10 times new row 1 to the Z row.

The next tableau is

	x_1	x_2	x_3	x_4	
x_2	0	1	$\frac{5}{19}$	$-\frac{3}{19}$	$\frac{45}{19}$
x_1	1	0	$-\frac{2}{19}$	$\frac{5}{19}$	$\frac{20}{19}$
Z	0	0	$\frac{50}{19}$	$\frac{160}{19}$	$\frac{2350}{19}$

There is no negative coefficient in the Z row so the optimal solution has been reached.

The solution to the production problem is to make $\frac{45}{19}$ Kg of x_2 and $\frac{20}{19}$ Kg of x_1 which will provide gross margin of $£\frac{2350}{19}$.

15.2.1   Post-optimality Analysis
As well as calculating the optimal solution, the Simplex Method provides additional information to identify
—   the increase in the objective function which can be achieved by increasing the limit of a constrained resource.
—   the range over which the coefficient of a variable in the objective function can change without changing the optimum solution.

Effect of changing the limit of a constraint
The coefficients of the slack variables in the Z row are called the shadow prices and represent the effect on the objective function of each additional unit of change to the constraint to which each is associated.

In the example used above the slack variable x_3 is associated with machine 1. The shadow price of x_3 from the final tableau is $\frac{50}{19}$. This means that if the capacity of machine 1 was increased by 1 unit from its present limit of 15 the gross margin could be increased by $£\frac{50}{19}$.

The new solution is obtained by adding each element in the column of the appropriate slack variable to the solution value of the row.

Thus the new solution from increasing the capacity of machine 1
new x_2 output $= \frac{5}{19} + \frac{45}{19} = \frac{50}{19}$ Kilo
new x_1 output $= -\frac{2}{19} + \frac{20}{19} = \frac{18}{19}$ Kilo

Similarly for a unit increase in capacity of machine 2 (for which x_4 is the slack variable).

the output of x_2 will reduce by $\frac{3}{19}$ Kilo
the output of x_1 will increase by $\frac{5}{19}$ Kilo
and the gross margin will increase by $£^{160}/_{19}$.

There is a limit to which a resource constraint can be increased and the shadow price remains a valid assessment of the increase in the objective function.

In the case of machine 1 every unit increase in capacity enables an increase to the objective function by $£^{50}/_{19}$ by increasing the amount of x_2 produced and reducing the quantity of x_1 by $\frac{2}{19}$ Kg/unit increase in capacity. The original solution is $x_1 = {}^{20}/_9$ and so the capacity of machine 1 can be increased by 10 units which would change the solution to

$$x_2 = \frac{45}{19} + \frac{10 \times 5}{19} = \frac{90}{19}$$

$$x_1 = \frac{20}{19} - \frac{10 \times 2}{19} = 0$$

The shadow price would not apply to any further increase in capacity because x_1 cannot go negative.

Similarly the capacity on machine 2 could be increased by 15 units, the output of x_1 increased by $15 \times \dfrac{5}{19} = \dfrac{75}{19}$ Kilo, the output of x_2 decreased by $15 \times \dfrac{3}{19}$ Kilo to zero and the increase to the objective function would be

$$£ \frac{160 \times 15}{19} = £ \frac{2400}{19}$$

15.2.2 Sensitivity of the coefficients in the objective function

It is possible to calculate the extent of the change to a coefficient of the objective function which could be made without changing the optimal solution (although the value of the objective function would obviously be changed).

In the production example the gross margin of x_1 is £50/Kg and of x_2 is £30/Kg. In considering the optimal production mix it may be important to consider the range over which the gross margins can vary without changing the optimal solution.

For each variable calculate the ratios of

$$\frac{\text{the shadow price of the non-basic variable}}{\text{coefficient in variable row of the same column}}$$

This is most easily understood by a practical illustration using the production problem

For x_1

$$\frac{\text{the shadow price in } x_3 \text{ column}}{\text{coefficient of } x_1 \text{ row in } x_3 \text{ column}} = \frac{50}{19} \div \frac{-2}{19} = -25$$

$$\frac{\text{the shadow price in } x_4 \text{ column}}{\text{coefficient of } x_1 \text{ row in } x_4 \text{ column}} = \frac{150}{19} \div \frac{5}{19} = 32$$

The lower limit of the change to the gross margin of x_1 is the most restrictive negative ratio.

The upper limit of the change to the gross margin of x_1 is the most restrictive positive ratio.

This means for x_1 the optimal solution is valid for gross margins

between   £50 − £25   =   £25
and   £50 + £32   =   £82

It is suggested that the reader demonstrates that the optimal solution is valid for x_2 in the range £−23.33 to £40. (In practice, of course, x_2 would not be produced to be sold at a negative gross margin.)

More generally, if no negative ratio exists, there is no lower limit and if no positive ratio exists, there is no upper limit.

15.2.3 Mixed Inequalities
The previous example only involved constraints which were "less than or equal to" and the addition of slack variables to convert the inequalities into equations provided an immediate initial basic feasible solution (which was to produce nothing).

Consider the following model to represent a linear programming problem:-

$$\text{Maximize} \quad Z = 3x_1 + 8x_2$$
$$\text{subject to} \quad 3x_1 + 4x_2 \leqslant 20$$
$$x_1 + 3x_2 \geqslant 6$$
$$x_1 \geqslant 0$$
$$x_2 \geqslant 0$$

Adding slack variables the model can be re-stated as

$$\text{Maximize} \quad Z = 3x_1 + 8x_2$$
$$\text{subject to} \quad 3x_1 + 4x_2 + x_3 = 20$$
$$x_1 + 3x_2 - x_4 = 6$$
$$x_1, x_2, x_3, x_4 \text{ each} \geqslant 0$$

x_4 must be deducted from the left hand side because of the "greater than or equal to" constraint. It represents the amount by which $x_1 + 3x_2$ exceeds 6.

There is not an obvious initial basic feasible solution and so an artificial variable x_A is added to the second equation.

$$x_1 + 3x_2 - x_4 + x_A = 6 \quad (*)$$

To obtain a solution to the problem it is necessary to ensure that x_A will eventually disappear. This is achieved by giving the artificial variable a high cost coefficient of M where M represents a large unspecified number.

The objective function can now be modified to

maximize $Z' = Z - Mx_A$, then substituting

for x_A from equation $(*)$ $Z' = 3x_1 + 8x_2 - M(6 - x_1 - 3x_2 + x_4)$

$$Z' = (3 + M)x_1 + (8 + 3M)x_2 - Mx_4 - 6M$$

There is now an immediate basic feasible solution $x_3 = 20$, $x_A = 6$

The initial Simplex tableau can now be written as

	x_1	x_2	x_3	x_4	$_A$	
x_3	3	4	1	0	0	20
x_A	1	3	0	-1	1	6
Z'	-M-3	-3M-8	0	M	0	-6M

$-3M-8$ is the most negative coefficient in the Z' row and so x_2 will be the entering variable.

For row 1 $\dfrac{\text{value of basic variable } x_3}{\text{coefficient of } x_2} = \dfrac{20}{4} = 5$

For row 2 $\dfrac{\text{value of basic variable } x_A}{\text{coefficient of } x_2} = \dfrac{6}{3} = 2$

The row with the minimum ratio is row 2 and so x_A is the departing variable.

Tableau 2

	x_1	x_2	x_3	x_4	x_A	
x_3	$5/3$	0	1	$4/3$	$-4/3$	12
x_2	$1/3$	1	0	$-1/3$	$1/3$	2
Z'	$-1/3$	0	0	$-8/3$	$M+8/3$	16

All references to the artificial variables can now be ignored because the Simplex process improves the value of the objective function at each iteration and an artificial variable will never be considered for re-entry because of its high cost coefficient.

Tableau 3.

	x_1	x_2	x_3	x_4	
x_4	$5/4$	0	$3/4$	1	9
x_2	$3/4$	1	$1/4$	0	5
Z	3	0	2	0	40

The optimal solution is $x_1 = 0$, $x_2 = 5$, giving a value of $Z = 40$.

15.2.4 Minimisation Problems

Many linear programming problems are concerned with optimising the use of resources to minimise costs rather than maximising profit. This is achieved by modifying the model to maximise $Z^1 = -Z$. In addition to this modification the model will probably involve "greater than or equal to" constraints as well as or instead of "less than or equal to" constraints. The linear programming model to minimize an objective function will then be set up using an appropriate number of artificial variables as described in the previous section.

QUESTIONS

15.1 A confectionery manufacturer makes two kinds of chocolate bar, A and B, each of which requires three stages of production: mixing, cooking, and boxing. The number of minutes required to complete each process for a box of chocolate bars is as follows:

	Mixing	Cooking	Boxing
A	1.25	0.5	1.5
B	1.2	1.5	0.5

All the production equipment is available for eight hours each day. Accountants have calculated that the contribution on each box of A is £0.50 and on B is £1. The equipment may be used to produce A and B simultaneously. All production may be sold.

You are required to:

(a) state the objective function in mathematical terms, assuming the manufacturer wishes to maximise contribution.　*(2 marks)*

(b) state all the constraints (equations/inequalities) which are relevant to this production problem.　*(4 marks)*

(c) graph the constraints, shading any unwanted regions, and determine the optimum production position.　*(8 marks)*

(d) find the contribution which is generated by this optimum position.　*(2 marks)*

(e) comment on any assumptions and practical limitations of this method of analysis. *(4 marks)*

(Total 20 marks) (ICMA)

15.2 A manufacturer can make two products, X and Y, on a particular machine. One unit of each product has the following requirements:—

	Raw Material	Machine Time	Labour
X	4 tonnes	2 hrs.	1 hr.
Y	1 tonne	1 hr.	1 hr.

The availability of resources each week is
90 tonnes of raw material
50 hours of machine time
40 hours of labour.

The contribution is £4 per unit of X and £3 per unit of Y.

(a) State the objective function to maximise weekly contribution.

(b) State the equations/inequalities which describe the production conditions.

(c) Draw a graph of these equations/inequalities.

(d) Find the quantities of X and Y which should be produced each week to maximise profit and state the optimum value of the objective function.

*15.3 Solve the above problem using the simplex method and check your answer with the solution to question 2.

15.4 A manufacturer produces two alloys A_1, A_2 which are both made with different proportions of two metals M_1, M_2 as shown.

Metal	Proportion of Metal		Daily Supply (tonnes)
	A_1	A_2	
M_1	0.5	0.25	10
M_2	0.5	0.75	15

If the net profit per tonne of A_1 is £30 and of A_2 is £25, maximize the daily profit in manufacturing the two alloys.

Chapter 16
NETWORK ANALYSIS

INTRODUCTION
The term Network Analysis has long been used by electrical engineers to describe the study of electrical networks but it is only comparatively recently that the tools of network theory have come to be used in other contexts as diverse as planning construction projects and open-heart surgery.

As a branch of Operations Research, Network Analysis has developed from PERT and CPM.

PERT is an acronym for Programme Evaluation and Review Technique which was developed by the US Navy and CPM stands for Critical Path Method which was again developed in America by du Pont in the late 1950s. The term Network Analysis has now come to mean the various methods which have developed from what were originally rather different techniques.

The use of network analysis in such a wide range of situations derives from its applicability to any operation which involves the co-ordination of a number of diverse activities to achieve some objective. We often perform such operations in our everyday lives routinely and without constructing a network; take, for example, the making of a cup of tea — we could represent this operation in the form of a network as in Diagram 16.1.

DIAGRAM 16.1

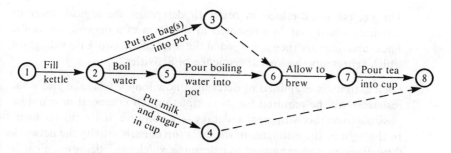

In the network, lines represent activities and the circles, or nodes, represent the start or end of an activity. The network represents the logic of the operation; for example, we cannot boil the water until we have filled the kettle, we cannot pour the water into the pot until it has boiled, and so on. Notice the use of dotted arrows between "events" 3, 6 and 4, 8; these are dummy activities. Dummy activities are not actual activities, they merely preserve the logic of the network. For example, the dotted arrow between events 3 and 6 merely indicates that the tea bags have to be in the pot before we allow the tea to brew.

One other thing to notice is that most tasks can be broken down further. For example, the first task of filling the kettle might be further sub-divided as in Diagram 16.2.

DIAGRAM 16.2

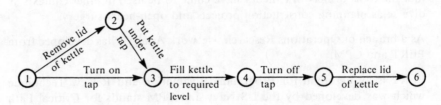

So how far does one go in sub-dividing activities? Well, it is simply a matter of commonsense; some tasks are so well understood and routine that there is no need to analyse in detail the various activities required for their completion. When we are concerned with more complex tasks, say some sort of construction project, the degree of detail required will, of course, depend upon the level of management concerned.

It is in the management of large scale projects, where the co-ordination of many diverse activities is necessary, that Network Analysis is most useful in planning and controlling the operation. Network Analysis examines a project in three stages:

(i)   The project is examined in order to determine the logical order of activities which may be presented in the form of a dependency table. These activities are then arranged in the form of a network flow diagram which represents the logical sequence of activities.

(ii) Each activity is examined to determine how long it will take and what resources will be required for its completion. Of course, it may not be possible to do this with great accuracy — a point we shall return to later. In the light of the estimates of the duration of each activity the network flow diagram is re-examined to determine which activities are critical in determining the completion of the project — the critical path.

(iii) The length of time that each activity will take and the resources required for its completion will usually be inter-related; if more resources are committed to a particular activity then it will usually be possible to complete that activity more quickly. The final step is therefore to examine the allocation of resources to see if it can be improved in some way. This raises the question of what we mean by an improvement. If there is a heavy penalty for late completion then the objective will be to complete the project within the time allowed and this may involve increasing the resources used on the critical jobs at least. If resources are limited the objective may be to complete the job as quickly as possible without exceeding the limitations on resources and this may mean that the total duration of the project will be longer than originally envisaged. Another objective might be to complete the project with the minimum variation in the size of the work force. Most usually, however, the objective is to maximise profit and this will usually involve comparing the extra cost involved in completing the job more quickly with the savings or extra revenue which this will generate.

Most small and even medium sized projects can be performed without any formal network analysis. Construction site managers, for example, are so experienced that they know instinctively which jobs are critical, when it is necessary to move men and machines from one job to another, whether it is worthwhile paying overtime to complete some activity more quickly, and so on. With large scale projects, however, it is not possible for management to maintain an overall view without the techniques of Network Analysis. Although we drew a network flow diagram for making a cup of tea quite easily a similar diagram for, say, the construction of a channel tunnel would be impossible without the formalised procedures to which we now turn.

Let us suppose that we are a small company planning the construction of a building. The company personnel consist of

> 4 Labourers
> 3 Bricklayers
> 2 Joiners
> 2 Tilers
> 2 Electricians
> 2 Plumbers
> 2 Plasterers
> 2 Painters

16.1 DEPENDENCY TABLE
The first task is to make a list of all the activities and the activities upon which they depend. Although we do not need the information just yet, let us also make a note of the duration of, and resources required for, each activity.

Job Reference	Job	Preceding Jobs	Normal Duration (days)	Resources needed
A	Get bricks, drains, pipes	—	21	—
B	Get concrete mix ready	—	3	—
C	Get timber	—	10	—
D	Get electrical fittings and wire	—	10	—
E	Get sanitary fittings	—	17	—
F	Excavate foundations and ducts	—	4	2 labourers
G	Concrete foundations, ducts, floors	B,F	2	4 labourers
H	Build walls to roof level	A,G	6	3 labourers, 3 bricklayers
J	Lay drains	A,G	2	2 labourers
K	Erect roof timbers	C,H	2	2 joiners
L	Place roof coverings	K	3	2 tilers
M	Install electric wiring	D,L	4	2 electricians
N	Fit external doors and glaze	K	2	2 joiners
P	Install plumbing	E,K,J	4	2 plumbers
Q	Plaster walls and ceilings	M,N,P	5	1 labourer, 1 plasterer
R	Fix joinery	Q	5	2 joiners
S	Fix door fittings	R	1	1 joiner
T	Fix sanitary fittings	Q	2	2 plumbers
U	Paint	S,T	8	2 painters

The next step is to construct a network flow diagram and there are a few simple rules to follow.

16.2 NETWORK FLOW DIAGRAMS

An **activity** is represented by an arrow; the arrowhead indicates the end of the activity but the length of the arrow has no significance. A job or activity is defined as "an operation or process consuming time and possibly other resources".

The beginning or end of an activity is called an **event** and is denoted by a numbered circle called a node. An event is formally defined as "a state in the progress of a project after the completion of all preceding activities but before the start of any succeeding activity."

The symbols used to denote activities and events are therefore as follows:

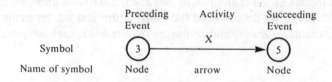

	Preceding Event	Activity	Succeeding Event
Symbol	③	X ⟶	⑤
Name of symbol	Node	arrow	Node

It is usual to label the activities with letters and events with numbers. Succeeding events must have higher numbers than preceding events (the numbering cannot be performed until after the network has been constructed) and activities may be labelled by the relevant numbers in addition to the letter. For example, the activity above could be labelled simply X or $X_{3,5}$. If the latter approach is adopted the activity can be identified by its events as well as its label.

The following conventions should be followed in constructing the network flow diagram:

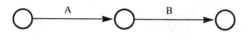

This means that activity B cannot start until activity A has been completed.

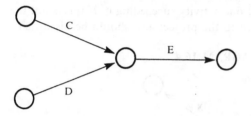

This means that E cannot start until both C and D have been completed.

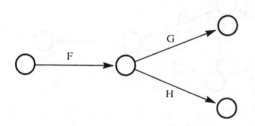

This means that neither G nor H can start until F has been completed.

Dummy activities
Dummy activities are of zero duration, they represent no work and are merely introduced to maintain the logic of the network. Dummy activities are represented by dotted arrows.

If you refer back to the diagram at the start of the chapter you will see that we used a dummy activity between events 3 and 6 to indicate that, although no task was performed, the tea could not brew until the tea bags were in the pot.

Some common mistakes — looping and dangling
A **loop,** such as illustrated in Diagram 16.3, is logically impossible because it implies that activity A must both precede and follow activity C. The sequential numbering system mentioned later will always detect such loops because according to the 'i,j rule' the number of the succeeding event (j) must

always be greater than the number of its preceding event (i).

DIAGRAM 16.3

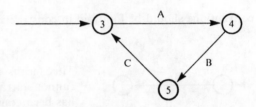

A **dangler** is an activity such as X or Y in Diagram 16.4. They can be avoided by the rule that every event except the first or last must have at least one activity preceding it and at least one activity succeeding it. If this is not the case then the activity is irrelevant to the project and should be discarded.

DIAGRAM 16.4

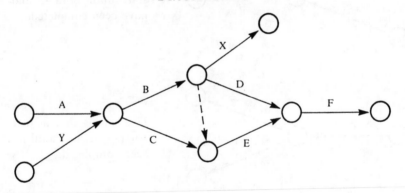

There is one other important rule and that is that there should be only one start event and one end event. Observance of this rule would allow us to get rid of the dangler, Y, in the above diagram by re-drawing the early part as in Diagram 16.5.

DIAGRAM 16.5

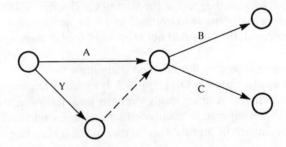

16.2.1 Drawing the network flow diagram

Armed with the above rules we can now attempt to draw the network for the dependency table in section 16.1.

There will normally be several ways of representing the network, there is no unique answer and usually several attempts will be necessary before a logically consistent network is constructed.

Drawing such diagrams quickly and neatly is a matter of practice so initially a lot of paper and patience is necessary. Two tips from the experts are

(i) Try to avoid arrows which cross, and
(ii) Try to avoid backward-sloping arrows.

You should now try to draw the diagram to represent the dependency table or, at least, check the sequence of activities in Diagram 16.6.

DIAGRAM 16.6

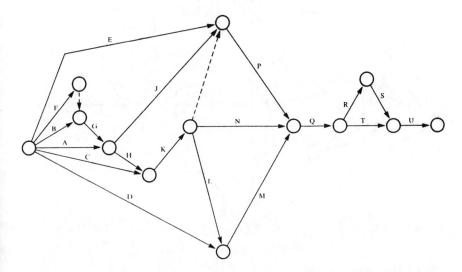

16.2.2 Numbering the Nodes

When all the activities have been built into a closed network, numbers can be allocated to the events. The nodes which represent the events are numbered sequentially from the beginning to the end of the network according to the "i,j" rule. The "i,j" rule simply means that the number at the end of an activity (j) must be greater than the number at the start of the activity (i). This is very simple and means that several different numbering systems will be equally appropriate. Try numbering the diagram above; you probably won't need it but there is a standard method for tackling the problem known as Fulkerson's routine.

Fulkerson's Routine

(a) An "initial" event is one which has arrows emerging from it but none entering it. Find the initial event and number it '1'.

(b) Now, delete all the arrows emerging from all numbered events. This will create at least one new initial event.

(c) Number all the new initial events '2', '3', and so on; the order in which they are numbered is not important.

(d) Again delete the emergent arrows and continue in this way until the final event is reached; the final event is one which has no arrows emerging from it.

One numbering system which obeys the "i, j" rule is indicated in Diagram 16.7.

DIAGRAM 16.7

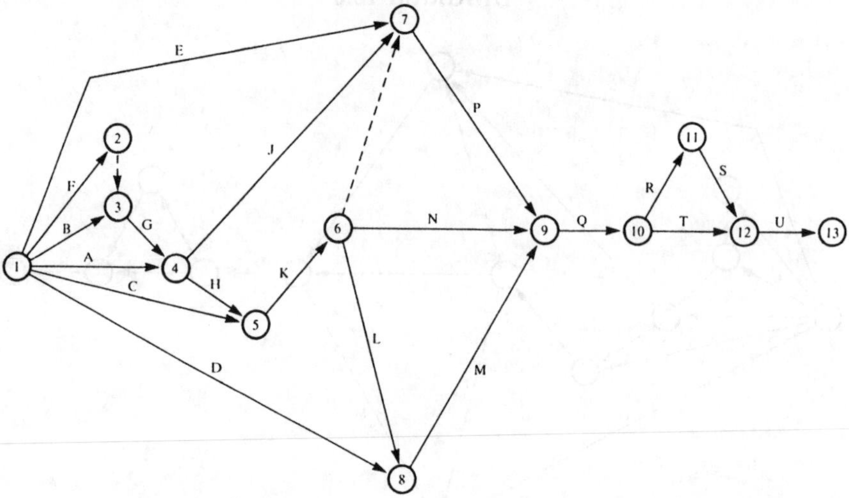

16.3 The Critical Path

When we consider the duration of each activity, the total duration of the project will be governed by the duration of the critical activities. Consider the simple network in Diagram 16.8 in which the duration of each activity in days has been entered next to the arrow representing it.

The total duration of the project will be 32 days and the critical activities are those represented by the heavy arrows. These activities are critical in the sense that if they are not completed on time the whole project will be delayed and, conversely, if they can be speeded up then the whole project can be completed more quickly. Identification of these activities therefore enables management to pay close attention to the activities which are most important.

DIAGRAM 16.8

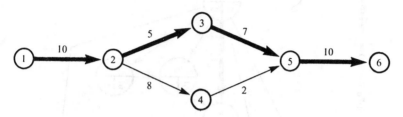

The path which joins these critical activities is called the critical path (there may be more than one) and it is the longest path through the network. In small networks the critical path can usually be found by trial and error; in the above example there was only one other path (duration of 30 days) but finding all the alternative paths in a large network would be tedious and so a systematic procedure is needed. The procedure is based upon a study of the earliest and latest times at which each event can occur.

FORWARD PASS

The method of finding the earliest time at which an event can take place (EET) is sometimes called a forward pass and is:

> To the earliest time of each immediately preceding event, add the duration of the job which connects it and select the highest of the values obtained.

> N.B. The EET for the initial event is taken to be zero.

BACKWARD PASS

To find the latest time at which each event can occur if the project is to be completed on time (LET), we perform a backward pass:

> From the latest time of each immediately succeeding event, subtract the duration of the job which connects it and select the lowest of the values obtained.

> N.B. When starting the backward pass take the latest event time for the final event as being the same as found by the forward pass.

> The latest event time for the first event will be zero (the same as its earliest event time) and this provides a check on the arithmetic.

It is convenient to record the earliest and latest event times on the network flow diagram. To do this the node can be divided into three sections which can be used as indicated.

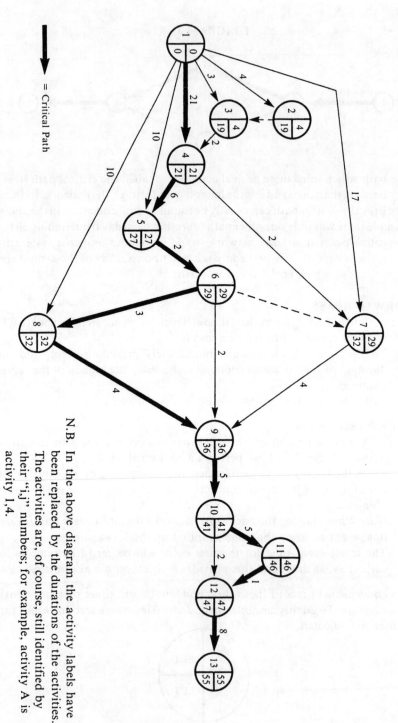

DIAGRAM 16.9

= Critical Path

N.B. In the above diagram the activity labels have been replaced by the durations of the activities. The activities are, of course, still identified by their "i,j" numbers; for example, activity A is activity 1,4.

At this point you would be well advised to draw the network for the dependency table as in section 16.2.2 and calculate the earliest and latest event times by the method just described. The answer is in Diagram 16.9.

We said earlier that the critical path links those critical activities which govern the length of the whole project. If these activities are not started on time the duration of the whole project will be increased and, conversely, if they can be speeded up the duration of the project can be reduced. It follows that these critical activities must have the same earliest and latest event times. The critical path can therefore be identified by finding those activities where EET = LET

i.e.   Critical Path: 1, 4, 5, 6, 8, 9, 10, 11, 12, 13
            or   A, H, K, L, M, Q, R, S, U.
            and the total duration of the project is 55 days.

The Critical Path, then, links events which have the same earliest and latest event times. Unfortunately, this is a **necessary** but **not a sufficient** condition. Consider the last part of the network flow diagram that we have just completed, shown separately in Diagram 16.10.

DIAGRAM 16.10

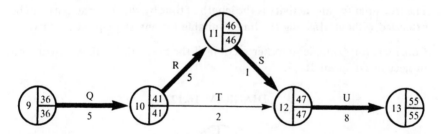

The Critical Path is, as we said, Q.R.S.U. but why is not Q.T.U. a critical path? The path Q.T.U. does fulfil the condition that it links events with the same earliest and latest event times but activity T is not critical because its duration is only 2 days while R and S have a combined duration of 6 days. The difference of 4 days is called a "float" and it means that activity T could take 4 days longer or start 4 days late without delaying the start of activity U.

So, to be more precise, the Critical Path is the set of activities with zero float (total float — see below), i.e. the set of jobs with the greatest overall duration.

16.3.1   Calculating the floats
There are several types of float which can be calculated but the most commonly used are total float and free float. The latter is more accurately called Early Free float but "early" is usually omitted.

Total float

The total float for any activity is the length of time by which the activity can be extended **without affecting the total duration of the project.** In other words, the length of time by which it can be extended before it becomes critical.

If we consider activity T in our network diagram, repeated in Diagram 16.11. The earliest time at which activity T can start is after day 41 and the latest time at which it can finish is day 47. As the activity has a duration of only 2 days there are 4 spare days available and the total float is 4 days. The calculation is thus according to the formula:

TOTAL FLOAT for activity i,j = LET_j – (EET_i + duration of activity)

∴ TOTAL FLOAT for activity 10,12 = 47 – (41 + 2) = 4 days

DIAGRAM 16.11

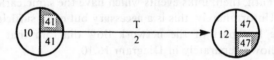

Free Float

The free float for any activity is the length of time by which the activity can be extended **without affecting the time available for any subsequent activity.**

Consider, for example, another section of the network for the construction project in Diagram 16.12.

DIAGRAM 16.12

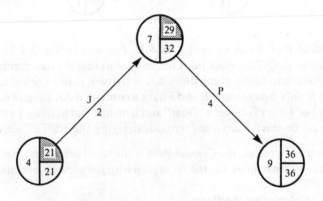

The earliest time at which activity J can start is after day 21 and the latest time at which it can finish is day 32. This means there is a time span of 11 days in which it can be completed and, since the activity takes only 2 days, there is a total float of 9 days.

Now consider activity P. The earliest that P can start is after day 29 and the latest it can finish is day 36. Since P takes 4 days, there is a total float of 3 days.

However, if activity J absorbed all of its float it would not be completed until day 32 and activity P could not start until then. Since P takes 4 days and must be completed by day 36 this would mean that activity P would now have no float at all.

On the other hand, if activity J only absorbed 6 days out of its total float of 9 days then there would still be 3 days float on activity P.

So, while activity J does have a total float of 9 days only 6 days can be used without decreasing the float for succeeding activities. In other words, the free float on activity J is only 6 days out of its total float of 9 days. The free float for any activity may be calculated from the formula:

Free Float for activity i,j = EET_j – (EET_i + duration of activity)
∴ Free Float for activity 4,7 = 29 – (21 + 2) = 6 days

The floats can be calculated directly from the network flow diagram as in the above examples. From the point of view of monitoring the project and as an aid to resource allocation, however, it is useful to prepare a full tabulation such as below.

1 Job Reference	2 Event nos. i	3 j	4 Duration (days)	5 EET i	6 j	7 LET i	8 j	9 Total Float (days)	10 Free Float (days)
A	1	4	21	0	21	0	21	0	0
B	1	3	3	0	4	0	19	16	1
C	1	5	10	0	27	0	27	17	17
D	1	8	10	0	32	0	32	22	22
E	1	7	17	0	29	0	32	15	12
F	1	2	4	0	4	0	19	15	0
G	3	4	2	4	21	19	21	15	15
H	4	5	6	21	27	21	27	0	0
J	4	7	2	21	29	21	32	9	6
K	5	6	2	27	29	27	29	0	0
L	6	8	3	29	32	29	32	0	0
M	8	9	4	32	36	32	36	0	0
N	6	9	2	29	36	29	36	5	5
P	7	9	4	29	36	32	36	3	3
Q	9	10	5	36	41	36	41	0	0
R	10	11	5	41	46	41	46	0	0
S	11	12	1	46	47	46	47	0	0
T	10	12	2	41	47	41	47	4	4
U	12	13	8	47	55	47	55	0	0

Col.9 = Col.8 — (Col.5 + Col.4)
Col.10 = Col.6 — (Col.5 + Col.4)

As we said earlier, the activities with zero total float make up the critical path.

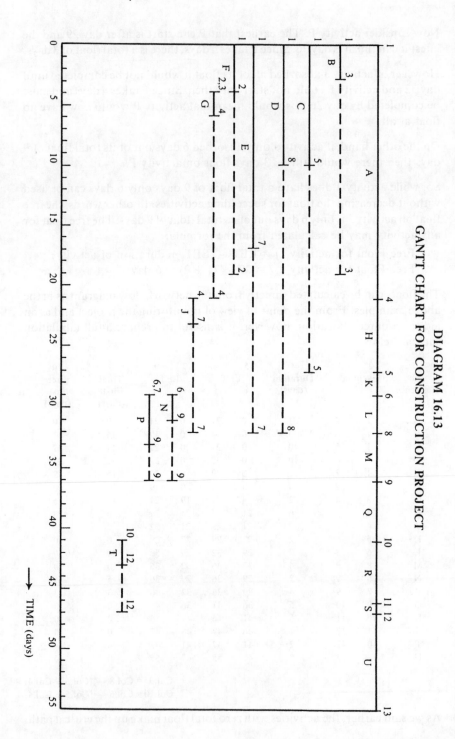

DIAGRAM 16.13
GANTT CHART FOR CONSTRUCTION PROJECT

16.3.2 GANTT CHARTS

The information contained in the above table is sometimes better presented in the form of a Gantt chart which facilitates the comparison of planned with actual performance. A Gantt chart for the construction project is shown in Diagram 16.13.

The Gantt Chart is constructed on the assumption that each activity is started at the earliest possible time. The critical activities are shown at the top of the chart and the length of the critical path corresponds to the total time of the project which is shown as the horizontal scale for the chart.

The activities are identified by their i,j numbers and their labels. Non-critical activities are shown below the critical path and the solid line represents the duration of the activity while the dotted line shows the total float associated with the activity. Taking activity J as an example:—

The solid line indicates that the earliest time at which J can start is after day 21 and the duration of activity J is 2 days. The dotted line shows that activity J must be completed (event 7) by day 32, i.e. a total float of 9 days. Notice that activities G and P have two event numbers at the start which indicate dummy activities. For example, the numbers 2,3 at the beginning of activity G indicate that events 2 and 3 must take place before G can commence.

When a non-critical activity depends only on the completion of one other non-critical activity, the two activities are usually shown as one line on the Gantt chart. For example, if the activities X, Y, and Z formed part of a network as shown in Diagram 16.14.

DIAGRAM 16.14

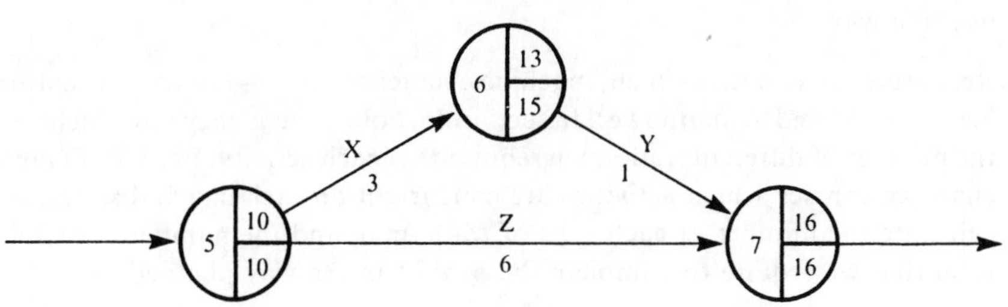

The relevant part of the Gantt chart would appear as in Diagram 16.15.

DIAGRAM 16.15

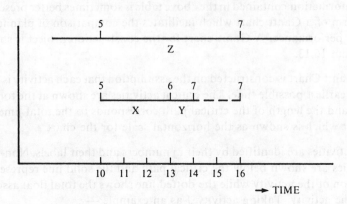

Each of the activities, X and Y, have a total float of 2 and are non-critical. Y has a free float of 2 and, when they are combined, X and Y together have a total float of 2 which can be absorbed by either activity.

In order to monitor the progress of the project, the actual amount of work completed can be added to the Gantt chart. The extent to which each activity has been completed at a particular time can be shown as another bar or line adjacent to, or superimposed upon, the line indicating the planned performance. The chart can be up-dated on a daily basis so that the project manager can see at a glance which activities are ahead of, on, or behind schedule. The project manager may then have to consider shifting resources to those activities which are critical because they lie on the critical path or have become critical because they have fallen so far behind that their float has been used up. Gantt charts are therefore a useful tool in resource allocation.

16.4 Resource Allocation
The implicit assumption in everything that we have done so far has been that there are sufficient resources available to be able to carry out the project in the way that has been planned. This may not be the case and even if it is it may be that the project can be performed more profitably by re-allocating resources in some way.

Resources are various — men, machines, materials etc. — but most attention has been devoted to manpower. In section 16.1 our dependency table included the number of different tradesmen required for each activity. From our Gantt chart we can see which activities are concurrent on each day and so we can calculate the number of each type of tradesman and the number of men in total that we require to complete the project in the way planned.

LABOUR REQUIREMENTS:—

Day	Labourers	Bricklayers	Joiners	Tilers	Electricians	Plumbers	Plasterers	Painters	Total
1–4	2								2
5–6	4								4
22–23	5	3							8
24–27	3	3							6
28–29			2						2
30–31			2	2		2			6
32				2		2			4
33					2	2			4
34–36					2				2
37–41	1						1		2
42–43			2			2			4
44–46			2						2
47			1						1
48–55								2	2

This information can be presented in the form of a resource profile, such as in Diagram 16.16, with the resource limitations superimposed. From the profile we can see that the limit of what is available is exceeded for only two days in the case of labourers. This "overload" occurs on days 22 and 23 and from the Gantt chart we can see that this happens because activities H and J are both scheduled to start on day 22. Activity H is a critical activity and so it cannot be re-scheduled without increasing the duration of the project.

Activity H will be completed by day 27 so if we can re-schedule activity J to start after this then the overload may be avoided. If we re-schedule activity J for days 28 and 29 it will run concurrent with activity K but this requires 2 joiners so we will avoid the overload on labourers. We will have used up all of activity J's free float (see section 16.3.1) but activities J and P will still have a combined float of 3 days which can be taken up by either activity.

The lengthy periods of inactivity for all the tradesmen would be a matter for concern; one would like a reasonably smooth level of labour utilization and, in practice, the firm would have several projects so that these periods of inactivity could be used up in servicing other projects. It does, however, indicate the problems which arise due to demarcation lines between different trades. A more flexible labour force would certainly make network planning much easier.

16.5 THE COST-TIME RELATIONSHIP

If a project can be completed more quickly then benefits may accrue in the form of reduced overheads, avoidance of penalty clauses for late completion, and so on.

Usually, however, completing the project more quickly will require more resources to be committed to it and this will increase the cost. So the increased

DIAGRAM 16.16

RESOURCE PROFILE FOR CONSTRUCTION PROJECT

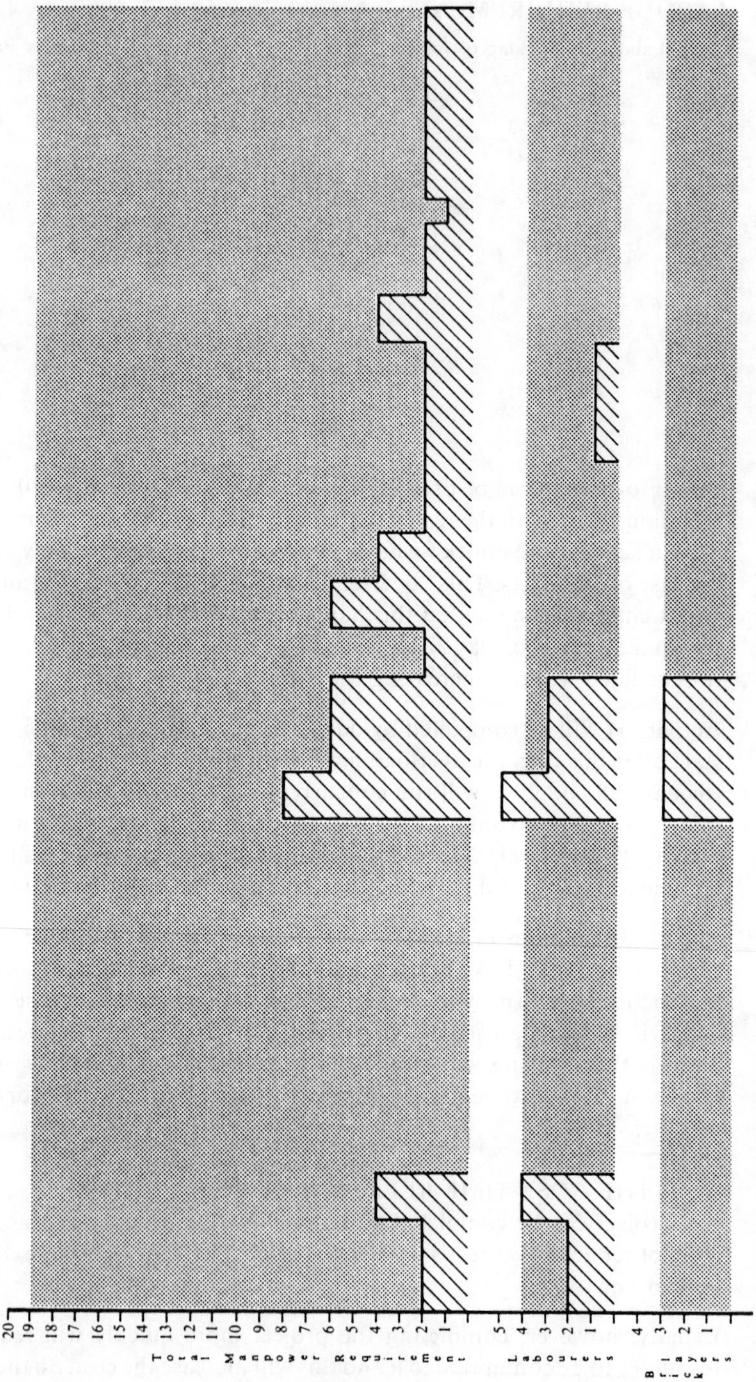

NUMBER OF MEN ⟵

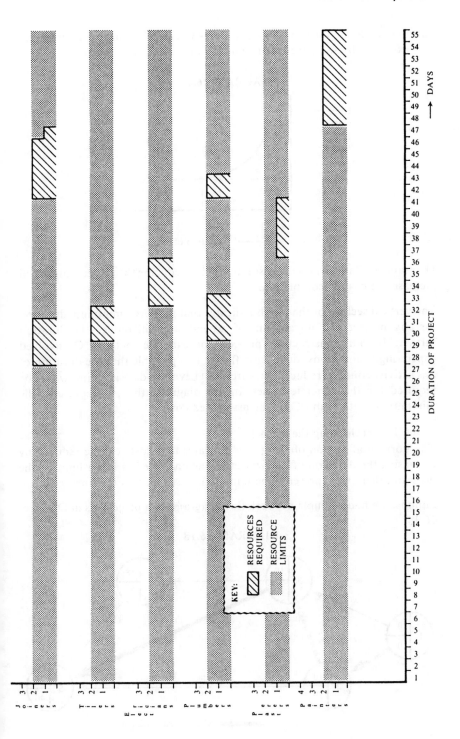

cost of completing the project more quickly will only be worthwhile as long as it is exceeded by the benefits of reducing the length of the project.

DIAGRAM 16.17

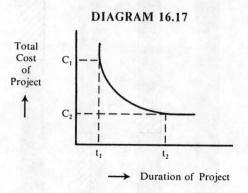

Diagram 16.17 illustrates the assumption that reducing the project length will increase the cost of completion.

The vertical section of the graph indicates that there is a minimum duration for any project and no amount of expenditure will reduce the duration further. In our construction project, for example, activity G involved concreting foundations, ducts, and floors; it is possible that the duration of this activity could be reduced but surely not beyond 1 day since time would be required for the concrete to set. In our diagram, then, t_1 represents the minimum duration and C_1 is the associated cost.

16.5.1   Accelerating the project

The horizontal section of the graph indicates that costs can be reduced by increasing the duration of the project but again there is a lower limit. In the diagram, then, C_2 represents the minimum cost and t_2 is the time required.

Suppose we had a simple network flow diagram for a project, as in Diagram 16.18.

DIAGRAM 16.18

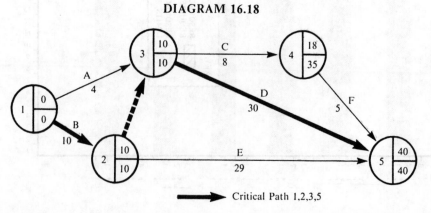

Critical Path 1,2,3,5

If we want to reduce the duration of the project then we have to concentrate on the critical activities. Obviously we want to reduce the duration at the lowest cost so we choose the critical activity with the lowest cost of acceleration per unit of time and reduce it as far as possible without making it non-critical.

As the duration of the project is reduced, other critical paths may emerge and it is then necessary to reduce each of the critical paths by equal amounts. If any one of the critical paths cannot be reduced further then there is no point in reducing the others and the minimum time for the project (at minimum cost) has been reached.

Suppose we ascertained the following time and cost estimates for the project illustrated in Diagram 16.18.

JOBS WHICH CAN BE ACCELERATED		COST OF ACCELERATION £/day	CRASH TIME (i.e. minimum duration)
LABEL	i j		
B	1 – 2	70	7
A	1 – 3	50	3
E	2 – 5	65	27
C	3 – 4	20	6
D	3 – 5	60	25

Suppose, further, that we need to reduce the duration of the project from its current length of 40 days to, say, 34 days.

STEP 1: The critical activity with the lowest cost of acceleration is D and this could be reduced by 5 days.
However, we only reduce it by one day because activity E now becomes critical. If we reduced D by more than one day it would become non-critical.
There are now two critical paths: 1, 2, 3, 5 and 1, 2, 5.

STEP 2: Two critical paths now have to be reduced in step. The cheapest way of reducing both is by accelerating activity B.
We can accelerate B by a maximum of 3 days and it does not make any other activities critical.

STEP 3: The only way now of reducing the duration of the project is by reducing activities D and E in step. We can still reduce D by 4 more days but we can only reduce E by 2 days to its crash time of 27 days. Therefore, we reduce D and E by 2 days which reduces the duration of the project to 34 days.

The network is now as in Diagram 16.19.

DIAGRAM 16.19

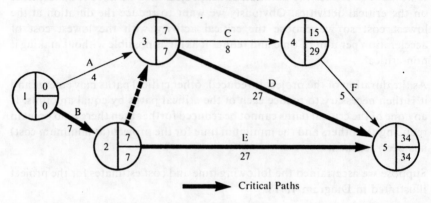

➤ Critical Paths

Activities A, C, D and F can all be reduced further but since B and E cannot be reduced further there is no point. 34 days is thus the minimum duration of the project which is achieved at an extra cost of £520 as shown below.

SUMMARY:—

Step	Job Accelerated	No. of days	Cost/Day (£)	Cost of Acceleration (£)	Cumulative Cost (£)	COMMENT
1	D	1	60	60	60	E becomes critical
2	B	3	70	210	270	crash time reached
3	D and E	2	125	250	520	goal achieved and no more reductions possible

16.5.2 The Optimum duration

We said earlier that the cost of completing a project can be reduced by increasing its duration. So, C_2 represents the minimum cost and t_2 is the time required.

DIAGRAM 16.20

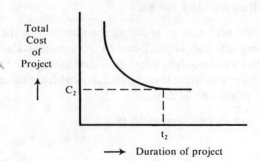

➤ Duration of project

Suppose in the example in section 16.5 the firm had to pay some penalty, say overhead costs for the hire of special machinery at £75 per day, in addition to the costs already referred to. Apart from this penalty cost let us assume that there is no deadline for completion.

Every day that can be saved reduces overheads by £75. Therefore, as long as it costs less than £75 to speed up the project it will be worthwhile doing so because the total cost of the project will fall.

However, once the cost of speeding up the project exceeds £75 the saving on overhead is outweighed by the cost of acceleration and the total cost rises.

In our example, then, the lowest cost occurs after Step 2 when 4 days have been saved and the optimum, or best, duration for the project is therefore 36 days.

To prove the point, suppose the cost of the project when it was scheduled to take 40 days was £5,000. We could produce the following cost schedule:

Duration (days)	Saving on Overhead cost at £75/day	Cost/Day of Reduction	Cost of Reduction	Total Cost
	(£)	(£)	(£)	(£)
40	—	—	—	5000
39	−75	60	+60	4985
36	−225	70	+210	4970
34	−150	125	+250	5070

So, in this case, the total cost would fall to a minimum of £4970 at the optimum duration of 36 days and would then rise (unlike in the diagram where it remains at the minimum value as the duration increases).

16.6 Models under uncertainty

So far we have assumed that the duration of each activity can be forecast accurately. In common with all forecasts, estimates of job durations are subject to uncertainty. It was one of the distinguishing features of PERT that it attempted to associate probabilities with the estimates of job durations and to incorporate these into probability estimates for the duration of the whole project. The various assumptions implicit in PERT and other techniques for dealing with uncertainty have generated much academic controversey and, for practical purposes, what follows should be treated with some circumspection.

It is assumed that the duration of any activity follows the Beta-distribution such that the expected duration, t_E, is given by:

$$t_E = \frac{a + 4m + b}{6}$$

where   a = the optimistic estimate;
m = the most likely estimate; and
b = the pessimistic estimate

with a variance, $V(t) = \left(\frac{b-a}{6}\right)^2$

This expected duration, t_E, is then used for the network analysis.

When the critical path has been found, it is assumed that the variance of the duration of the whole project is the sum of the variances along the critical path (no account is taken of the variances of non-critical activities).

When considering variations in the duration of the project the normal distribution is usually taken as a reasonable approximation to the Beta-distribution.

EXAMPLE:

Suppose that the construction project we studied earlier has to be completed within 60 days because heavy penalty charges are payable after that time.

Three estimates of the duration of each activity are obtained — optimistic, most likely, and pessimistic — and from these the expected duration and variance of each activity are calculated as in the following table.

| | ESTIMATED DURATION (DAYS) | | | | Variance of |
Job Reference	Optimistic (a)	Most likely (m)	Pessimistic (b)	Expected Duration $t_E = \frac{a+4m+b}{6}$	Expected Duration $V(t) = \left(\frac{b-a}{6}\right)^2$
A	17	21	25	21	1.78
B	1	3	5	3	0.44
C	4	11	12	10	1.78
D	8	10	12	10	0.44
E	15	16	23	17	1.78
F	2	4	6	4	0.44
G	1	2	3	2	0.11
H	4	6	8	6	0.44
J	1	2	3	2	0.11
K	1	2	3	2	0.11
L	2	3	4	3	0.11
M	2	4	6	4	0.44
N	1	2	3	2	0.11
P	2	4	6	4	0.44
Q	3	4	11	5	1.78
R	4	5	6	5	0.11
S	½	1	1½	1	0.03
T	1	2	3	2	0.11
U	6	7	14	8	1.78

The expected durations (t_E) are those that we use in calculating the critical path and since they are the same as the normal durations that we used earlier the critical path would be A, H, K, L, M, Q, R, S, U.

If we now sum the expected durations of the activities on the critical path we will obtain the expected duration of the critical path and if we sum the variances of the critical activities we will obtain the variance of the duration for the whole project:

Critical Activities	Expected Duration t_E	Variance of Expected Duration $V(t)$
A	21	1.78
H	6	0.44
K	2	0.11
L	3	0.11
M	4	0.44
Q	5	1.78
R	5	0.11
S	1	0.03
U	8	1.78
	55	6.58

If we now assume that the total duration of the project is distributed normally with a mean of 55 days and a standard deviation of $\sqrt{6.58} = 2.57$ days then we can work out the probability of the project taking more than 60 days in the usual way, viz:

60 days is 5 days above the mean of 55 days.

$$5 \text{ days} = \frac{5}{2.57} = 1.95 \text{ standard deviations above the mean}$$

From the normal tables, the probability of the duration being more than 1.95 standard deviations above the mean = 0.5 – 0.4744 = 0.0256 so there is just over a 2½% chance of the firm having to pay the penalty charges.

QUESTIONS

16.1 Consider the dependency table below:

Activity	Duration (Days)	Preceding Activities
A	4	—
B	7	A
C	7	A
D	6	A
E	2	C
F	5	C
G	9	C
H	6	B,E
J	6	D,F
K	9	H,G,J.

You are required to:
(a) Draw the network flow diagram.
(b) State the critical path and its duration.
(c) Prepare a table showing the floats associated with each activity.
(d) Draw a Gantt chart to illustrate the project.

16.2 The following network flow diagram and cost information refers to a construction project.

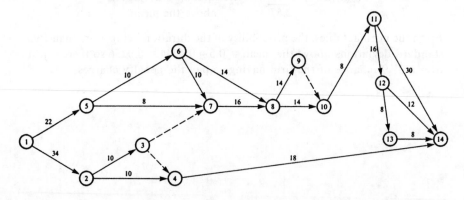

N.B. The numbers on the arrows refer to the durations of the activities in days.

Jobs which can be accelerated i j	Cost of acceleration £/day	Crash time (days)
2 – 3	250	8
10 – 11	300	4
11 – 12	400	10
12 – 13	200	4
13 – 14	250	6
11 – 14	200	24

Required:
(a) Determine the critical path.
(b) If the job is not completed by the end of day 106 then the company has to pay a penalty of £8,500 and has to continue renting a piece of specialised machinery at a cost of £300 per day. What is the most money the company can save by completing on day 106?
(c) Explain why it is not worth completing before day 106.

16.3 Consider the following schedule of activities and related information for the construction of a new plant.

Activity	Expected time months	variance	Expected cost £000's
1,2	4	1	5
2,3	2	1	3
3,5	3	1	4
2,4	6	2	9
1,6	2	1	2
6,5	5	1	12
4,5	9	5	20
6,7	7	8	7
7,8	10	16	14
5,8	1	1	4

You should assume that the cost and time required for one activity are not dependent upon the cost and time of any other activity and variations are expected to follow a normal distribution.

You are required to calculate:
(a) the critical path;
(b) the expected cost of constructing the plant;
(c) the expected time required to build the plant;
(d) the standard deviation of the expected time;
(e) the probability of completing the plant in 24 months or less.

(ICMA)

(Quantatitive Techniques paper)

*16.4 The following arrow diagram, time and cost estimates are given:

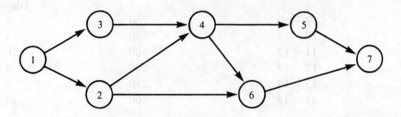

Activity	Normal cost per day £	Additional cost per day of saving one day £	Normal duration in days	Maximum number of days that could be saved
1–2	100	900	9	6
1–3	400	600	7	2
2–4	700	900	12	6
2–6	700	1,200	10	8
3–4	600	700	12	8
4–5	500	800	6	2
4–6	700	1,900	7	1
5–7	300	500	14	4
6–7	400	700	8	5

Overhead costs are at the rate of £190 per day. The time taken to complete each activity can be reduced below the normal, up to the maximum given, by incurring an additional cost for each day saved.

You are required to calculate:
(a) normal time and normal cost of completion;
(b) minimum time and the associated cost;
(c) minimum cost and the time required. *(ICMA)*

(Quantitative Techniques paper)

*16.5 Consider the activities required to complete the processing of a customer's order:

Activity	Preceding activities	Average time in days	Normal variable cost per day £
1 Receipt of order, checking credit rating, etc.	—	2	5
2 Preparation of material specification, availability of material, etc.	1	4	10
3 Inspection, packing, etc.	2	1	7
4 Arrangement of transport facilities, etc.	1	5	5
5 Delivery	3, 4	3	2

The time for activities 1, 3 and 5 are fixed; for activity 2 there is a 0.5 probability that it will require 2 days and a 0.5 probability that it will require 6 days; for activity 4 a 0.7 probability of taking 4 days, 0.2 of taking 6 days, and 0.1 of taking 10 days.

You are required to:

(a) draw the network (it is very simple), clearly indicating the meaning of any symbols that you use;

(b) indicate the critical path, calculate average duration and variable cost under normal conditions;

(c) calculate the minimum and maximum times and the probabilities associated with them.

(ICMA)

(Quantitative Techniques paper)

APPENDIX A

Take the situation where we have two products which we will call X_1 and X_2, supposing the contribution for $X_1 = £2$ per unit and for $X_2 = £4$ per unit and that each unit requires materials and labour as follows:—

$$X_1 = 3 \text{ kgs of material}$$
$$X_2 = 5 \text{ kgs of material}$$ same material

$$X_1 = 4 \text{ hours of labour}$$
$$X_2 = 9 \text{ hours of labour}$$ same type of labour

In addition, in any single week there is a limit to the total amount of labour available which is 36 hours. Furthermore, in any production period the firm must use 15 kgs or more of material to have an economic mix.

If we wanted to maximize the contributions made by the two products X_1 and X_2 we could formulate what is called an objective function as follows: Maximize $Z = 2x_1 + 4x_2$.

However, this is not the whole picture since we have constraints to take account of in respect of materials and labour, so we write:—

subject to: $3x_1 + 5x_2 \geqslant 15$ (materials constraint)

$4x_1 + 9x_2 \leqslant 36$ (labour constraint)

$x_1, x_2 \geqslant 0$ (This simply states that the production solution must be positive i.e. greater than zero).

The Linear Program should be stated thus:—

Maximize $Z = 2x_1 + 4x_2$ OBJECTIVE FUNCTION

s.t. $3x_1 + 5x_2 \geqslant 15$ MATERIAL CONSTRAINT

$4x_1 + 9x_2 \leqslant 36$ LABOUR CONSTRAINT

where $x_1, x_2 \geqslant 0$

ANSWERS TO QUESTIONS

1.1 (a) 440

      (b) 2040

      (c) 0.00690

      (d) 0.00680

      (e) 4880 (rounding so last significant figure is even)

      (f) 2710

      (g) 6000

      (h) 6.52 (rounding so last significant figure is even)

1.2 (i)   56

      (ii) 34

      (iii) 550

      (iv) 3136

      (v) 37

      (vi) 1904

      (vii) 4.44

      (viii) 4.75

1.3 (a)

SRI LANKA
G.D.P. by origin
(1,000 millions of Rupees at current prices)

	1972	1973	1974
Agriculture	4	5	8
Wholesale and retail trade	2	2	3
Manufacturing	2	2	2
Transport, storage, communications	1	2	2
Construction	1	1	1
Public Admin. & Defence	1	1	1
All other	2	3	3
	13	15	20

(b)

YEAR	1972	1973	1974
Actual Total	12,807	15,265	19,806
Rounded Total	13,000	15,000	20,000
Absolute error	193	265	194
Percentage error	$\frac{193}{13,000} \times 100 = 1.5\%$	$\frac{265}{15,000} \times 100 = 1.8\%$	$\frac{194}{20,000} \times 100 = 1.0\%$

(c) The relative error is more informative than the absolute error because the size of the error is related to the value of the estimated figure. An error of, say, 10 in an estimated figure of 100 is obviously more important than an error of 10 in a figure of 1,000 and the relative errors of 10% and 1% illustrate this fact.

(d) Systematic error occurs when the errors produced are consistently in one direction so that answers are biassed.

If, for example, the figures for 1972 were as follows:

Actual Figure	Rounded Figure	Error
4,499	4,000	−499
1,499	1,000	−499
1,499	1,000	−499
1,499	1,000	−499
499	0	−499
499	0	−499
2,499	2,000	−499
12,493	9,000	−3493

It can be seen that by rounding to the nearest 1,000 the total is massively undervalued with a relative error of 39%.

(e) (i) The increase in GDP at current prices (rather than constant prices) means that there may have been an increase in the volume of production and/or an increase in the prices of the output. Only if the growth of output in money terms is greater than the rate of inflation can we conclude that there has been a real volume increase. Without information about the changes in prices it is impossible to be sure whether the increase is due to inflation or a real growth in output.

(ii) The classification of transport, storage, and communications in one category is rather unusual and the "all other" category is the second largest suggesting that some subdivision would be more informative.

(f) The number of significant digits in a number indicate the degree of accuracy in the data. For example, the number 4,119 contains four significant figures and suggests that the actual figure may lie between 4119.5 and 4118.5. When rounded to one significant figure, the number 4,000 suggests that the actual figure may lie between 4,500 and 3,500 with a much greater possible error.

2.1 (1) There are a number of reasons why the conclusions are likely to be biassed.

No information is available for a high proportion of households, the reason for this may be that the "housewife" was busy at the time pursuing 'household duties', e.g. shopping.

The visits were not spread evenly over the time period, over 50% of the calls taking place between 10 and 12. It may be that this is a time when housewives are more, or less, busy than usual.

If a housewife is asked whether she was working or not there will probably be a tendency for her to say yes even if she was not working at the time (in the same way as people will always under-estimate how much they spend on cigarettes). etc., etc.

(2)

HOUR	8–9	9–10	10–11	11–12	12–1
Proportion of housewives working	$\dfrac{21}{33}$	$\dfrac{21}{36}$	$\dfrac{54}{93}$	$\dfrac{36}{63}$	$\dfrac{9}{18}$
%	64	58	58	57	50

This suggests that housewives are busiest between 8–9.

(3) See Section 6.3 in text, before attempting this part of the question.

$$\sigma_p = \sqrt{\frac{P(100-P)}{n}} = \sqrt{\frac{58\times 42}{243}} = 0.032$$

95% confidence limits are $p \pm 2\ \sigma_p$ $= 0.58 \pm 2 \times 0.032$
$= 0.516 \text{ to } 0.644$

This means that from the sample, housewives are working for between 51.6% and 64.4% of the time and only 1 time in 20 (5%) would we expect this sample estimate to be inaccurate.

2.2 (a)(1) The figures in the table relate to a grand total of 400. To construct a quota sample of 100 we simply have to scale the figures down by dividing by 4:—

		Age 21 – 40	41 and over	TOTAL
MALE	Smoker	15	11	26
	Non-Smoker	10	7	17
FEMALE	Smoker	17	14	31
	Non-Smoker	15	11	26

(2)

			TOTAL
MALE	{	Smoker	26
		Non-Smoker	17
FEMALE	{	Smoker	31
		Non-Smoker	26
			100

(3)   See Text.

(b)   This is a question which requires careful thought so that the selection procedure does not introduce bias.

List the companies and number from 00 to 79.

Take the random numbers in pairs rejecting numbers greater than 79 and select the company with the corresponding number on the list.

Thus, the first three companies selected would be numbers 46, 37, 15.

3.1   (a)

Number of rejects	frequency
3	2
7	1
8	1
9	1
11	1
12	1
13	2
15	1
16	1
17	2
18	1
19	2
20	2
21	2
22	6
23	5
24	5
25	2
26	3
27	2
28	3
29	1
30	1
31	1
33	1
	50

(b)

Number of rejects per time period	frequency
0 – under 5	2
5 – under 10	3
10 – under 15	4
15 – under 20	7
20 – under 25	20
25 – under 30	11
30 – under 35	3
	50

3.2 See section 3.2.3.4 where histogram is reproduced.

3.4 (c) Median salary ≃ £10,770

(d) Assuming reasonable symmetry we can multiply the median salary by the number of employees to give to total annual salary bill as
99 × £10,770 ≃ £1,066,230.

3.6 **SOCIAL SECURITY BENEFITS — GREAT BRITAIN**

YEAR	1964		1983	
	Recipients (thousands)	% of all recipients	Recipients (thousands)	% of all recipients
Retirement pension [1]	6158	45.6	9326	26.3
Widows' benefit	596	4.4	406	1.1
Unemployment benefit	172	1.3	906	2.6
Supplementary benefit	1958	14.5	4349	12.3
Sickness and invalidity benefit	819	6.1	1075	3.0
Child benefit [2]	3794	28.1	6919	19.5
Rent rebate	N/A	—	3900	11.0
Rent allowance	N/A	—	1080	3.0
Rate rebate	N/A	—	7530	21.2
	13497	100	35491	100

NOTES: (1) Includes non-contributory retirement pension.
(2) Prior to 1979 this came under Family Allowance.
N/A — not available

Source: 'UK in Figures' – Government Statistical Service

3.8

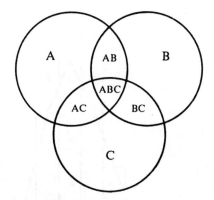

If we use the notation corresponding to the above diagram.

$$
\begin{aligned}
AC &= 15 \\
B &= 65 \\
C &= 51 \\
AB + ABC &= 15 \\
A + B + AB &= 117 \\
B + C + BC &= 128
\end{aligned}
$$

$$A + B + C + AB + AC + BC + ABC = 200$$

Manipulation of the equations gives the following answers:—
(a) $ABC = 5$
(b) $A + B + C = 158$
(c) $A + AB + AC + ABC = 72$
(d) $A = 42$
(e) $AB = 10$

3.9   It must be remembered that the AREA of each rectangle must be proportional to the frequency. Therefore, we need to calculate the frequency density before plotting the histogram. This is done below together with the cumulative frequency which is required for the ogive.

Weekly Wage £	Class Width	Frequency	Frequency Density (class width = 5)	Cumulative Frequency
31 – 36	5	6	6	6
36 – 41	5	8	8	14
41 – 46	5	12	12	26
46 – 51	5	18	18	44
51 – 56	5	25	25	69
56 – 61	5	30	30	99
61 – 66	5	24	24	123
66 – 71	5	14	14	137
71 – 75	4	6	7.5	143
75 – 81	6	3	2.5	146

(a)   See graphs.

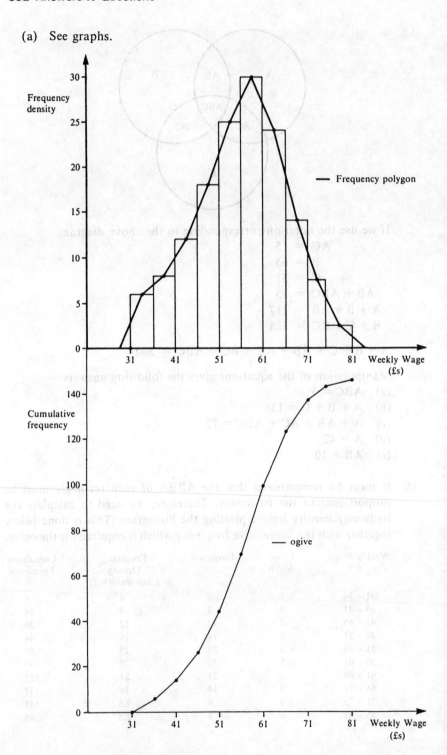

(b) This information is best presented in the form of a component bar chart:

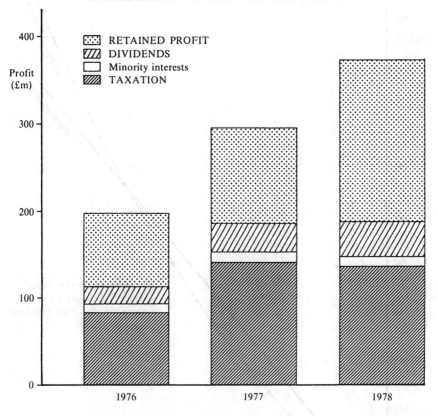

LARGE BANK — PROFIT DISTRIBUTION

3.10 (a) Simple interest   12% p.a. gives an interest payment of £12 p.a. on a principal of £100.

The amount after 15 years would be $100 + 15 \times 12 = £280$. This can be represented by a straight line on the graph.

(b) As we shall see later we may calculate the amount after n years from the formula $A_n = P(1+r)^n$.

For the moment, we can simply add the interest to the amount at the start of each year as follows:

year	1	2	3	4	5	6	7	8	9	10	11	12	13	14	15
Value at end of year	108	116.6	126	136	146.9	158.7	171.4	185.1	199.9	215.9	233.2	251.8	272	293.7	317.2

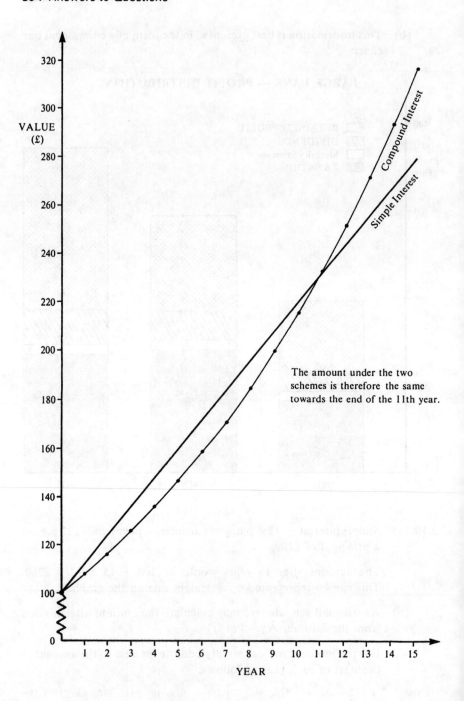

The amount under the two schemes is therefore the same towards the end of the 11th year.

3.11 (a) TOTAL COST $= 10,000 + 7.5x$
where x = volume of output/sales.

If we let the demand curve be represented by the equation
$x = a + bp$ where p = price
$400 = a + b.40$
$800 = a + b.20$
which gives $b = -20$ and $a = 1200$

The demand curve is therefore $x = 1200 - 20p \left(p = 60 - \dfrac{x}{20} \right)$

Total revenue $= x.p = (1200 - 20p)p$

$$= 60x - \frac{x^2}{20}$$

Profit = Total Revenue – Total Cost
$$= 60x - \frac{x^2}{20} - 10,000 - 7.5x$$
$$= 52.5x - \frac{x^2}{20} - 10,000$$

(b)

OUTPUT	0	200	400	600	800	1000	1200
TC	10,000	11,500	13,000	14,500	16,000	17,500	19,000
TR	0	10,000	16,000	18,000	16,000	10,000	0
PROFIT	-10,000	-1,500	3,000	3,500	0	-7,500	-19,000

(c) From the graph overleaf, the maximum profit is at 525 units per week.

$$p = 60 - \frac{1}{20} x = 60 - \frac{1}{20} \cdot 525 = £33.75$$

$$\text{Profit} = 52.5x - \frac{x^2}{20} - 10,000 \backsimeq £3,780$$

N.B. Later in the text we shall see that we could arrive at this answer by calculus

$$\text{Profit} = 52.5x - \frac{x^2}{20} - 10,000$$

$$\frac{dp}{dx} = 52.5 - \frac{x}{10} = 0 \text{ at max. or min.}$$

$$\therefore \quad x = 525$$

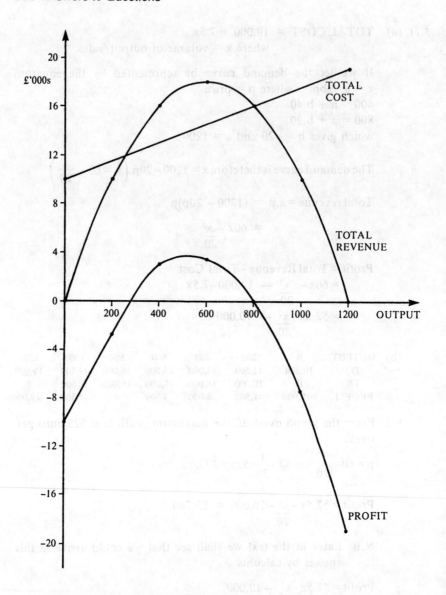

3.12

Month	Sales 1983	Sales 1984	MAT 1984	Sales 1985	MAT 1985	Cumulative Sales 1984	Cumulative Sales 1985
J	200	240	2760	270	3040	240	270
F	200	230	2790	280	3090	470	550
M	210	230	2810	270	3130	700	820
A	220	250	2840	280	3160	950	1100
M	210	230	2860	290	3220	1180	1390
J	250	270	2880	300	3250	1450	1690
J	260	280	2900	320	3290	1730	2010
A	250	280	2930	300	3310	2010	2310
S	240	250	2940	220	3280	2260	2530
O	220	240	2960	210	3250	2500	2740
N	230	250	2980	200	3200	2750	2940
D	230	260	3010	200	3140	3010	3140
	2720	3010		3140			

Units of sales are a better measure of performance than the value of sales because the latter will automatically increase if prices rise as a result of inflation.

The main feature of the Z-chart overleaf is the alarming fall in the MAT, confirmed by the dip in monthly sales, towards the end of 1985. The fall in the MAT shows that the decrease in monthly figures is not merely a seasonal variation but a drop in the general upward trend of sales.

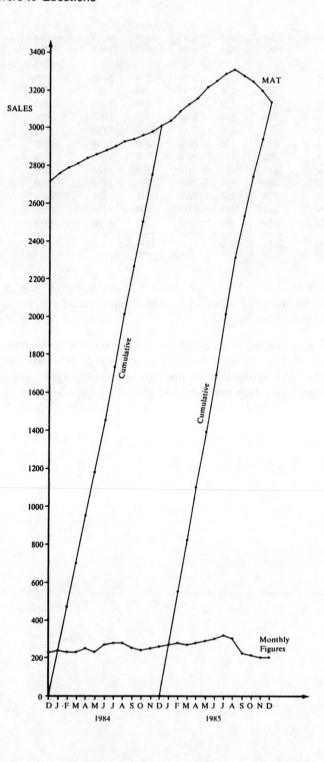

3.14 (a)

Value of Debt (Mid-point)	Frequency	Cumulative Frequency	Cumulative Frequency %	Total Value of Debts	Cumulative Value of Debts	Cumulative Value %
5	4,000	4,000	80	20,000	20,000	22.4
30	800	4,800	96	24,000	44,000	49.3
125	150	4,950	99	18,750	62,750	70.3
350	40	4,990	99.8	14,000	76,750	86.0
1250	10	5,000	100.0	12,500	89,250	100.0
	5,000			89,250		

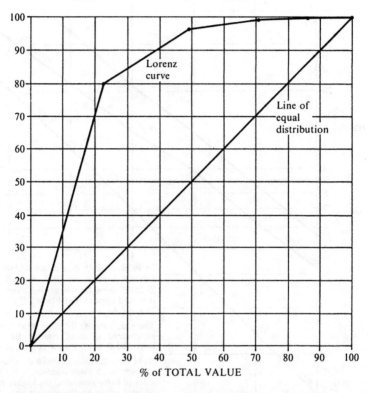

(b) The table, and curve, reveal that 80% of the debtors account for only 22.4% of the total debts, or 20% of debtors covers 77.6% of the debts. Even worse, 1% of the debtors (50 debtors) account for about 30% of the debts and 50% of the debts are covered by only 4% of the debtors.

Because the debts are concentrated in a few hands, the firm will be vulnerable to bad debts which could create liquidity problems (& profitability). Obviously, the firm should monitor the large debts closely. In particular, the firm might examine the age profile of the larger debts and maybe increase discounts as an incentive for early payment.

3.15

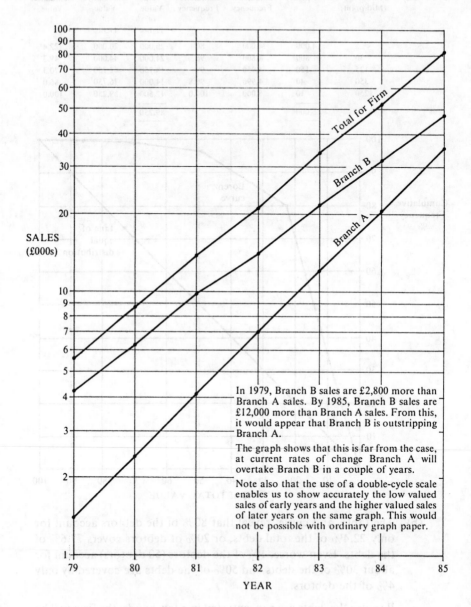

SALES
(£000s)

In 1979, Branch B sales are £2,800 more than Branch A sales. By 1985, Branch B sales are £12,000 more than Branch A sales. From this, it would appear that Branch B is outstripping Branch A.

The graph shows that this is far from the case, at current rates of change Branch A will overtake Branch B in a couple of years.

Note also that the use of a double-cycle scale enables us to show accurately the low valued sales of early years and the higher valued sales of later years on the same graph. This would not be possible with ordinary graph paper.

YEAR

4.1 (a) Construction of cumulative frequency curve should give a median $\simeq$ £6,100.

(b) $$\text{Median} = 6,000 + \frac{20}{232} \times 1,000 = £6,086$$

4.2 (a) Geometrical construction on histogram should give a mode $\simeq$ £6,250.

(b) $$\text{Mode} = 6,000 + \frac{48}{48+122} \times 1,000 = £6,282$$

4.3 $\bar{x} = 34.3$, $M_d = 29$

x	$|x-\bar{x}|$	$|x-M_d|$
5	29.3	24
14	20.3	15
16	18.3	13
19	15.3	10
26	8.3	3
32	2.3	3
45	10.7	16
56	21.7	27
62	27.7	33
68	33.7	39
	187.6	183

(i) $$\text{Mean deviation from } \bar{x} = \frac{187.6}{10} = 18.76$$

(ii) $$\text{Mean deviation from } M_d = \frac{183}{10} = 18.3$$

(iii) The answer in both cases is 18.3 because 5 values go up by 3 miles and 5 values go down by 3 miles in both cases.

(iv) Either the one at 26 or the one at 32 miles distance from the market because the mean deviation is at a minimum at both these shops. In practice the question would be a little more complicated and, amongst other things, would depend upon whether the total distance between the depot and the other shops and the market is at a minimum when the mean deviation of distances from the depot is at a minimum.

4.4 (a)

Weekly earnings (£)	Number of workers	Mid-point		
	f	x	fx	fx²
20–30	5	25	125	3,125
30–40	26	35	910	31,850
40–50	41	45	1,845	83,025
50–60	58	55	3,190	175,450
60–70	48	65	3,120	202,800
70–80	18	75	1,350	101,250
80–90	4	85	340	28,900
	200		10,880	626,400

(i) Median is the value of the 100th observation

$$= 50 + \frac{28}{58} \times 10 = £54.83$$

(ii) $$\bar{x} = \frac{\Sigma fx}{\Sigma f} = \frac{10,880}{200} = £54.40$$

$$S_x = \sqrt{\text{mean } x^2 - (\text{mean } x)^2}$$

$$= \sqrt{\frac{626,400}{200} - (54.40)^2} = \sqrt{3132 - 2959.36} = \sqrt{172.64}$$

$$= £13.14$$

Coefficient of variation $= \dfrac{S_x}{\bar{x}} = \dfrac{13.14}{54.4} = 0.242 = 24.2\%$

(b) The median value of weekly earnings is £54.83 and this means that half the workers earn more than this while the other half earn less.

The coefficient of variation relates the variability in the data to the mean value. A standard deviation of, say, £20 in another group's wages would indicate greater variation but if the mean value of that group's earnings were £100 the coefficient of variation would, in fact, be only 20% which is less than 24.2%.

4.5 (a)

CLASS	FREQUENCY
510 < 520	7
520 < 530	10
530 < 540	12
540 < 550	7
550 < 560	4
	40

(b) All the classes are of equal width so the histogram is straightforward.

(c) The usual geometrical construction gives a modal value of 533 components.

(d) $\bar{x} = \dfrac{\Sigma fx}{\Sigma f}$ where x is mid-point of class

$\quad\quad = \dfrac{21,310}{40} = 533$ components

(e) Standard deviation $= \sqrt{\text{mean } x^2 - (\text{mean } x)^2} = 12$ components.

(f) The fact that the mean and mode coincide suggests that the distribution is reasonably symmetrical, a glance at the histogram confirms this fact. The range of 510–560 is only about 4 standard deviations which suggests that the data is concentrated round the central values.

4.6 (a)

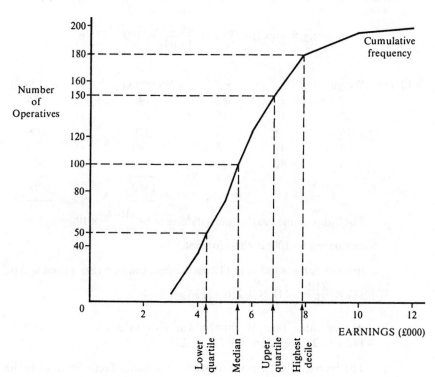

(b) From the graph,

$$\text{Median} \simeq £5,500$$
$$\text{Upper quartile} \simeq £6,800$$
$$\text{Lower quartile} \simeq £4,350$$
$$\text{Highest decile} \simeq £7,900$$

$$\text{Quartile deviation} = \frac{\text{Upper quartile} - \text{Lower quartile}}{2}$$

$$= \frac{6800 - 4350}{2}$$

$$\simeq £1,125$$

(c) From the table, the distribution appears to be slightly skewed with the mean greater than the median. Estimate of mean about £5,700.

4.9

YEAR	1972	1973	1974	1975	1976	1977	1978	1979	1980	1981	1982	1983
Index of Real Wages	89.5	100	102.6	95.3	103.4	111.7	111.7	113.7	115.6	120.6	121.6	126.4

e.g. Index for 1980 is $\dfrac{68.26}{59.04} \times 100 = 115.6$

4.10 (a)

Weight	P_0	P_1	Weight$\times P_0$	Weight$\times P_1$
7	20	22	140	154
20	12	15	240	300
15	8	7.2	120	108
2	40	38	80	76
10	80	104	800	1040
			1380	1678

The index in one year's time will have to be $\dfrac{1678}{1380} \times 100 = 121.6$ compared to 100 at the moment.

But the current index is 112 so the index in one year's time will be

$$112 \times \frac{121.6}{100} = 112 \times 1.216 = 136$$

(b) At the same rate of change, the FPI in 3 years' time will be $112 \times 1.216 \times 1.216 \times 1.216 = 201$

(c) The increase in the price of meat is the major factor in causing the rise in the FPI. Milk and eggs both fall in price. If people spend less on meat and more on milk and eggs in the coming year, a current weighted index would be lower than the base weighted index calculated above.

(d) A current weighted index might understate the effect of price changes because people may reduce consumption of higher priced items and switch to those items which have fallen in price.

4.11 (a) There is no single answer to this question, various aspects of the data might usefully be illustrated in a variety of ways. However, the question suggests that whatever figures are chosen should be deflated and the inclusion of numbers of employees indicates that the figures might be related to the size of the workforce.

There is a defect in the question in so far as the Index of prices relates to the calendar year while the accounting information appears to relate to the financial/tax year.

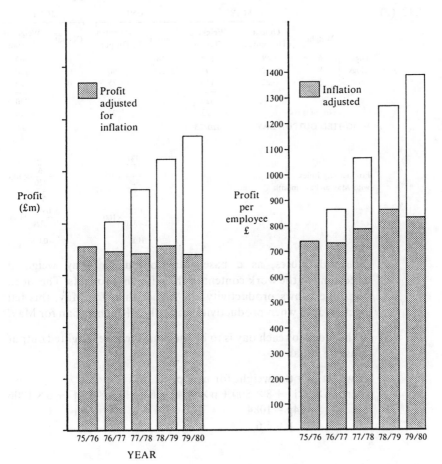

Year	Index of Retail Prices	Pre-Tax Profit (£m)	Pre-Tax Profit at constant prices (£m)	Profit/Employee (£)	Profit/Employee at constant prices (£)
1975/6	100	36.10	36.10	735	735
1976/7	116.5	40.59	34.84	855	734
1977/8	135.0	46.52	34.46	1060	786
1978/9	146.2	52.61	35.98	1260	862
1979/80	165.8	57.25	34.53	1380	832

(b) The visual display is more easily understood than the table of raw figures. The display makes it clear that while profit and profit/employee have increased impressively throughout the period, the inflation adjusted figures have shown more modest increases and have both fallen during 79/80. A lengthening of the scale would exaggerate this effect and make it more apparent but could, perhaps, be misleading (see section on visual display of data 3.4.6).

4.12 (a)

	Weight	MAY Output (Thousands)	MAY Weighted Output	JUNE Output	JUNE Weighted Output	JULY Output	JULY Weighted Output
Togs	6	19	114	16	96	10	60
Clogs	8	12	96	20	160	15	120
Pegs	5	22	110	15	75	10	50
			320		331		230
No. of days			23		22		16
WEIGHTED OUTPUT/DAY			320/23		331/22		230/16

Productivity Index with May as base month	100	$\dfrac{\frac{331}{22}}{\frac{320}{23}} \times 100$	$\dfrac{\frac{230}{16}}{\frac{320}{23}} \times 100$
		$= \dfrac{331 \times 23}{22 \times 320} \times 100$	$= \dfrac{230 \times 23}{16 \times 320} \times 100$
		$= 108$	$= 103$

The index uses, as a base, May output per day weighted according to the work content of the different products. The index for June shows productivity 8% higher than for May, this fell back in July when productivity was only 3% higher than for May.

(b) If the index for each day is to be the same then the weighted output must be equal.

If we let p = the weight for new pegs
then $6 \times 921 + 8 \times 800 + p \times 1042 = 6 \times 811 + 8 \times 747 + p \times 1206$
$164p = 1084$
$\therefore \quad p = 6.6$

4.13 (a)

Laspeyre's Price Index $= \dfrac{\sum P_n q_0}{\sum P_0 q_0} \times 100$

Laspeyre's Quantity Index $= \dfrac{\sum q_n P_0}{\sum q_0 P_0} \times 100$ where p_0 = prices in base year etc.

Using subscripts to denote the relevant years.

YEAR	1973		1974		1975						
	p_3	q_3	p_4	q_4	p_5	q_5	$p_3 q_3$	$p_3 q_4$	$p_3 q_5$	$p_4 q_3$	$p_5 q_3$
Sugar	10	2	11	2	29	1.5	20	20	15	22	58
Bread	11	4	12	4	16	4	44	44	44	48	64
Tea	8	2	9	3	10	4	16	24	32	18	20
Milk	5	20	5	21	5.5	19	100	105	95	100	110
Butter	9	3	10	3	13	2	27	27	18	30	39
							207	220	204	218	291

	1974	1975
Price Indices	$\dfrac{218}{207} \times 100 = 105$	$\dfrac{291}{207} \times 100 = 141$
Quantity Indices	$\dfrac{220}{207} \times 100 = 106$	$\dfrac{204}{207} \times 100 = 99$

(b) Obviously, a survey based on food items will not represent a reasonable assessment of changes in the cost of living except by sheer accident. All the other items such as fuel, light, heat, rent, entertainment etc. must be taken into account. Even as an index measuring the cost of food the survey would be inadequate since too few items are included and many substitute items e.g. margarine, coffee are excluded.

Since the survey is limited to the South of England it would, of course, not be useful to measure national changes because consumption patterns and prices are different in the North.

4.14

		1981	1982	1983
(a)	Base weighted price index	100	124.27	130.65
(b)	Current weighted price index	100	125.70	133.28
(c)	see text			

5.1 (1) A batch of 300 would contain 200 from X and 100 from Y
Number of defectives $= 18 + 12 = 30$
Proportion of defectives $= \dfrac{30}{300} = 0.10$

(2) $\text{Prob}\begin{pmatrix}1\text{ defective}\\ \text{in sample}\end{pmatrix} = P\begin{pmatrix}1\text{st is defective}\\ \text{and 2nd OK}\\ \text{and 3rd OK}\end{pmatrix} + P\begin{pmatrix}1\text{st is OK,}\\ \text{2nd is defective}\\ \text{and 3rd is OK}\end{pmatrix} + P\begin{pmatrix}1\text{st is OK,}\\ \text{2nd is OK,}\\ \text{and 3rd is}\\ \text{defective}\end{pmatrix}$

$$= (0.1)(0.9)(0.9) + (0.9)(0.1)(0.9) + (0.9)(0.9)(0.1)$$
$$= 3.(0.1)(0.9)^2 = 0.243$$

(3) $P(A \text{ and } B) = P(A) \times P(B/A)$

So, $P\begin{pmatrix}\text{item is from Y and defective}\end{pmatrix} = P\begin{pmatrix}\text{item is defective}\end{pmatrix} \times P\begin{pmatrix}\text{item is from Y}\\ \text{given it is}\\ \text{defective}\end{pmatrix}$

Also, $P\begin{pmatrix}\text{item is from Y and defective}\end{pmatrix} = P\begin{pmatrix}\text{item is from Y}\end{pmatrix} \times P\begin{pmatrix}\text{item is defective}\\ \text{given it is from Y}\end{pmatrix}$

$$= \frac{1}{3} \times 0.12 = 0.04$$

So, $0.04 = 0.10 \times P \begin{pmatrix}\text{item is from Y given it is defective}\end{pmatrix}$

$\therefore \; P\begin{pmatrix}\text{item is from Y}\\ \text{given it is defective}\end{pmatrix} = \dfrac{0.04}{0.10} = 0.4$

(4) In a batch of 300, 200 would be from X and 100 from Y

Defectives from Y would be $200 \times \dfrac{9}{100} = 18$

Defectives from Y would be $100 \times \dfrac{12}{100} = 12$

Repair costs would be $9 \times 2 + 6 \times 3 = £36$
Replacement costs would be $15 \times 7 \qquad = £105$
$\qquad\qquad\qquad$ Total cost $\qquad\qquad = £141$

5.2 (a) (i) $P(A \text{ and } B) = P(A) \times P(B)$
$$= 0.4 \times 0.4 = 0.16$$

(ii) $P\begin{pmatrix}\text{exactly}\\ \text{one sale}\end{pmatrix} = P\begin{pmatrix}1\text{st is sale,}\\ \text{2nd is not}\end{pmatrix} + P\begin{pmatrix}\text{2nd is sale}\\ 1\text{st is not}\end{pmatrix}$

$$= 0.4 \times 0.6 + 0.4 \times 0.6 = 0.48$$

(iii) $P\begin{pmatrix}\text{A or B}\\ \text{or}\\ \text{both}\end{pmatrix} = P(A) + P(B) - P(AB)$

$$= 0.4 + 0.4 - 0.16 = 0.64$$

(b) Let A = success in finding oil
and B = favourable result from test drill.

Then, $P(A) = 0.6$
$P(B/A) = 0.7$

We need to know $P(A/B)$

$$P(A/B) = \frac{P(B/A) \times P(A)}{P(B)}$$

$P(B)$ is the probability of a favourable result for a test drill =

$$P \begin{pmatrix} \text{favourable result} \\ \text{if there is oil} \end{pmatrix} + P \begin{pmatrix} \text{favourable result} \\ \text{if there is no oil} \end{pmatrix}$$

$$= 0.7 \times 0.6 + 0.3 \times 0.4 = 0.54$$

$$\therefore \quad P(A/B) = \frac{0.7 \times 0.6}{0.54} = 0.78$$

5.3 (a) See text

(b) (i) A simple random sample would be appropriate. However, if it is suspected that different colour codes (or suppliers) indicate different quality the sample could be stratified to reflect the different quantities in the population.

(ii) $P(\text{red}) = 150/1000 = 0.15$
$P(X) = 400/1000 = 0.4$
$P(\text{red and } X) = 100/1000 = 0.1$
$P(\text{red or } X) = (150 + 400 - 100)/1000 = 0.45$

(iii) $P(\text{Same Supplier})$

$$= \frac{400}{1000} \times \frac{399}{999} + \frac{400}{1000} \times \frac{399}{999}$$

$$+ \frac{200}{1000} \times \frac{199}{999} = 0.3594$$

(iv) $P(\text{not red}/Y) = \frac{160}{200} = 0.8$

5.4 1. $P(A+B+C) = P(A) \times P(B) \times P(C)$

(i)   P (no defects) $= 0.7 \times 0.7 \times 0.65 = 0.3185$

(ii) $P \begin{pmatrix} \text{one minor} \\ \text{and two} \\ \text{major defects} \end{pmatrix} = P \begin{pmatrix} \text{Minor on shaping,} \\ \text{majors on plating} \\ \text{and finishing} \end{pmatrix} + P \begin{pmatrix} \text{Minor on plating,} \\ \text{majors on shaping} \\ \text{and finishing} \end{pmatrix} + P \begin{pmatrix} \text{Minor on finishi} \\ \text{majors on shap} \\ \text{and plating} \end{pmatrix}$

$\qquad = (0.2\times0.2\times0.15) + (0.1\times0.1\times0.5) + (0.1\times0.2\times0.2)$

$\qquad = 0.006 + 0.0015 + 0.004 = 0.0115$

(iii) $P \begin{pmatrix} \text{two defects} \\ \text{of any type} \end{pmatrix} = P \begin{pmatrix} \text{defect on shaping} \\ \text{and plating,} \\ \text{OK on finishing} \end{pmatrix} + P \begin{pmatrix} \text{defect on shaping} \\ \text{and finishing,} \\ \text{OK on plating} \end{pmatrix} + P \begin{pmatrix} \text{defect on finish} \\ \text{and plating,} \\ \text{OK on shaping} \end{pmatrix}$

$\qquad = (0.3\times0.3\times0.65) + (0.3\times0.7\times0.35) + (0.7\times0.3\times0.35)$

$\qquad = 0.2055$

2. $P \begin{pmatrix} \text{no defects} \end{pmatrix}$ $\qquad = 0.7 \times 0.65 \quad = 0.455$

$P \begin{pmatrix} \text{1 minor on shaping} \\ \text{and OK on finishing} \end{pmatrix} = 0.2 \times 0.65 \quad = 0.130$

$P \begin{pmatrix} \text{1 minor on finishing} \end{pmatrix} = 0.2 \times 0.7 \quad = 0.140$

$P \begin{pmatrix} \text{2 minor on shaping} \\ \text{and finishing} \end{pmatrix} = 0.2 \times 0.2 \quad = 0.04$

$P \begin{pmatrix} \text{1 major on shaping} \end{pmatrix} = 0.10 \times 0.65 = 0.065$

$P \begin{pmatrix} \text{1 major on finishing} \end{pmatrix} = 0.15 \times 0.70 = 0.105$

$P \begin{pmatrix} \text{1 minor on shaping} \\ \text{and 1 major on finishing} \end{pmatrix} = 0.2 \times 0.15 \quad = 0.030$

$P \begin{pmatrix} \text{1 major on shaping} \\ \text{and 1 minor on finishing} \end{pmatrix} = 0.1 \times 0.2 \quad = 0.02$

$P \begin{pmatrix} \text{2 major} \end{pmatrix}$ $\qquad = 0.1 \times 0.15 \quad = \underline{0.015}$

$\qquad\qquad\qquad\qquad\qquad\qquad\qquad 1\cdot000$

Total cost of repair in batch of $1{,}000 = 455 \times 0 + 130 \times 1$
$+ 140 \times 1 + 40 \times 2 + 65 \times 5 + 105 \times 5$
$+ 30 \times 6 + 20 \times 6 + 15 \times 10$
$= £1650$

$\therefore$ Average cost of repairs $= £1.65$ per item produced.

5.5 (a) See text.

(b) (i) Expected Sales = $400 \times 0.3 + 500 \times 0.4 + 600 \times 0.3 = 500$ units
Expected Variable Cost = $10 \times 0.2 + 15 \times 0.5 + 20 \times 0.3 = £15.5$ per unit
Expected Profit = $500 \times (30 - 15.5) - 6,000 = £1,250$ per month

(ii)
Sales	Variable Cost	Total Contribution	Profit	Probability		Expected Profit
400	10	8000	2000	$0.3 \times 0.2 = 0.06$		120
400	15	6000	—	$0.3 \times 0.5 = 0.15$		0
400	20	4000	−2000	$0.3 \times 0.3 = 0.09$		−180
500	10	10000	4000	etc	0.08	320
500	15	7500	1500		0.20	300
500	20	5000	−1000		0.12	−120
600	10	12000	6000		0.06	360
600	15	9000	3000		0.15	450
600	20	6000	—		0.09	0
					1.00	1250

5.6 (a) (i) $\overset{\text{independent}}{\underset{\downarrow}{P(A \text{ and } B)}} = P(A) \times P(B) = \frac{1}{6} \times \frac{1}{8} = \frac{1}{48}$ $\qquad$ Ans $= \frac{1}{48}$

(ii) $P\left(\underset{\text{only}}{A} \text{ or } \underset{\text{only}}{B}\right) = P(A \text{ and not } B) + P(B \text{ and not } A)$

$$= \left(\frac{1}{6} \times \frac{7}{8}\right) + \left(\frac{1}{8} \times \frac{5}{6}\right) = \frac{1}{4}$$

OR

$P(A \text{ or } B \text{ or both}) = P(A) + P(B) - P(AB)$

$$= \frac{1}{6} + \frac{1}{8} - \frac{1}{48}$$

$P\left(\underset{\text{only}}{A} \text{ or } \underset{\text{only}}{B}\right) = \frac{1}{6} + \frac{1}{8} - \frac{1}{48} - \frac{1}{48} = \frac{1}{4}$ $\qquad$ Ans $= \frac{1}{4}$

(iii) $P(\text{not } A \text{ and not } B) = P(\text{not } A) \times P(\text{not } B)$

$$= \frac{5}{6} \times \frac{7}{8} = \frac{35}{48}$$ $\qquad$ Ans $= \frac{35}{48}$

2. **They sum to unity.** = Ans.

(b) $P(C/\text{not } A \text{ and not } B) = \frac{1}{10}$ $\quad \therefore P(\text{not } C/\text{not } A \text{ and not } B) = \frac{9}{10}$

$P(C/A \text{ only or } B \text{ only}) = \frac{2}{10}$ $\quad \therefore P(\text{not } C/A \text{ only or } B \text{ only}) = \frac{8}{10}$

$P(C/\text{both } A \text{ and } B) = \frac{3}{10}$ $\quad \therefore P(\text{not } C/\text{both } A \text{ and } B) = \frac{7}{10}$

(i)   P(no defects)   = P(not A and not B and not C)
                         = P(not A and not B) × P(not C/not A
                           and not B)

$$= \frac{35}{48} \times \frac{9}{10} = \frac{315}{480} \qquad \textbf{Ans} = \frac{315}{480}$$

(ii) $\begin{pmatrix} \text{A or B or C} \\ \text{but not a} \\ \text{combination} \end{pmatrix}$ = P(A and not B and not C) + P(not A and B
                         and not C) + P $\begin{pmatrix} \text{not A and not} \\ \text{B and C} \end{pmatrix}$

$$= \frac{1}{6} \times \frac{7}{8} \times \frac{8}{10} + \frac{5}{6} \times \frac{1}{8} \times \frac{8}{10} + \frac{5}{6} \times \frac{7}{8} \times \frac{1}{10}$$

$$= \frac{131}{480} \qquad\qquad \textbf{Ans} = \frac{131}{480}$$

2.

	£
Out of 480 items 131 will have one defect:	Cost=131×£10 = 1310
·· ·· ·· ·· 315 ·· ·· no defect	No Cost
·· ·· ·· 480–(131+315) will have more than one defect:	Cost=34×30 = 1020
	TOTAL COST = 2330

Ans = £2330

5.9 (i)

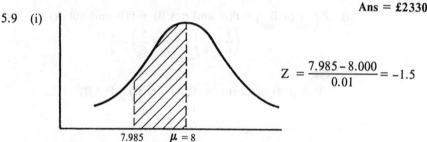

$$Z = \frac{7.985 - 8.000}{0.01} = -1.5$$

7.985 $\mu = 8$

So, this time we need to find the area between the mean and a point 1.5 standard deviations **below** the mean.

As the curve is symmetrical, this is the same as the area between the mean and a point 1.5 standard deviations **above** the mean and so the required probability is again **0.4332**.

(ii)

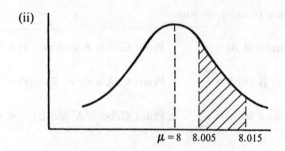

$\mu = 8$ 8.005   8.015

Here, we need to find the area (A_1) between the mean and 8.015 (Z_1) and then substract the area (A_2) between the mean and 8.005 (Z_2).

$$Z_1 = \frac{8.015 - 8.000}{0.01} = 1.5 : A_1 = 0.4332$$

$$Z_2 = \frac{8.005 - 8.000}{0.01} = 0.5 : A_2 = 0.1915$$

The required probability is therefore $0.4332 - 0.1915 = \textbf{0.2417.}$

N.B. The distance between the two points is one standard deviation but that **does not mean** that the required area is that between the mean and a point one standard deviation from the mean, as the diagram shows.

(iii)

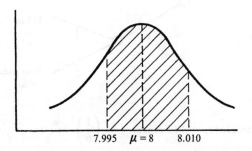

7.995 $\mu = 8$ 8.010

This time we need to add the area between the mean and a point 0.5 standard deviations below the mean to the area between the mean and a point one standard deviation above the mean.

The required probability is therefore $0.1915 + 0.3413 = 0.5238$

5.10 (a)

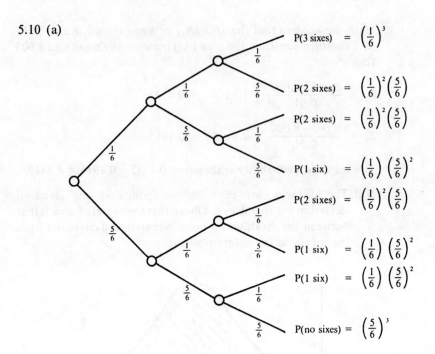

$$P(3 \text{ sixes}) = \left(\frac{1}{6}\right)^3$$

$$P(2 \text{ sixes}) = \left(\frac{1}{6}\right)^2\left(\frac{5}{6}\right)$$

$$P(2 \text{ sixes}) = \left(\frac{1}{6}\right)^2\left(\frac{5}{6}\right)$$

$$P(1 \text{ six}) = \left(\frac{1}{6}\right)\left(\frac{5}{6}\right)^2$$

$$P(2 \text{ sixes}) = \left(\frac{1}{6}\right)^2\left(\frac{5}{6}\right)$$

$$P(1 \text{ six}) = \left(\frac{1}{6}\right)\left(\frac{5}{6}\right)^2$$

$$P(1 \text{ six}) = \left(\frac{1}{6}\right)\left(\frac{5}{6}\right)^2$$

$$P(\text{no sixes}) = \left(\frac{5}{6}\right)^3$$

Therefore,

$$P(3 \text{ sixes}) = \left(\frac{1}{6}\right)^3$$

$$P(2 \text{ sixes}) = \left(\frac{1}{6}\right)^2\left(\frac{5}{6}\right)$$

$$P(1 \text{ six}) = 3\left(\frac{1}{6}\right)\left(\frac{5}{6}\right)^2$$

$$P(\text{no sixes}) = \left(\frac{5}{6}\right)^3$$

The general formula is therefore

$$^3C_r \; p^r \; (1-p)^{3-r}$$

or

$$\left(\frac{3}{r}\right)\left(\frac{1}{6}\right)^r\left(\frac{5}{6}\right)^{3-r}$$

where r = number of successes.

(b) $P(4) = {}^5C_4(0.6)^4(0.4) = 0.2592$
$P(5) = {}^5C_5(0.6)^5 = 0.07776$
$P(\text{at least } 4) = 0.2592 + 0.07776 = 0.33696$

5.11 (a)   Average number of defectives $= \lambda = 100 \times 0.02 = 2$

$$P(x) = \frac{e^{-\lambda} \lambda^x}{x}$$

$P(0) = e^{-2} = 0.135$
$P(r) = e^{-2} .2 = 0.271$
$P(2) = \dfrac{e^{-2} .2^2}{2} = 0.271$
$P(3) = \dfrac{e^{-2} .2^3}{3 \times 2} = 0.180$
$P(\text{passing}) = 0.135 + 0.271 + 0.271 + 0.180$
$\qquad\qquad\quad = 0.857$

(b) $E(x) = \Sigma x_i p_i$
$\qquad\quad = 0 \times 0.135 + 1 \times 0.271 + 2 \times 0.271$
$\qquad\qquad + 3 \times 0.180 \simeq 1.6$

If a batch fails the scheme then all remaining items are inspected and so all the defective items are found.

In a batch of 2000 containing 2% defectives the number of defectives will be $2000 \times 0.02 = 40$.

Prob. (failing) $= 1 - \text{Prob. (passing)} = 1 - 0.857$
$\qquad\qquad\qquad\qquad\qquad\qquad\quad = 0.143$

$$E(x) = \Sigma x_i p_i$$

$\therefore$ Expected number of defectives found $= 1.6 \times 0.855 + 40 \times 0.143$
$\qquad\qquad\qquad\qquad\qquad\qquad\qquad\quad = 7.088$

5.12 (a)   95% of demand will be covered by a range of mean ± 1.96 standard deviations.
$\qquad\qquad = 90 \pm 1.96 \times 10$
$\qquad\qquad = 109.6 \text{ to } 71.4$

Each size must cover $\dfrac{95}{5} = 19\%$ of the normal distribution

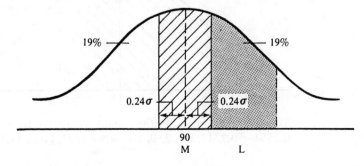

From the normal tables, 9.5% of the curve is contained between the mean and a point 0.24 standard deviations above the mean so the size M must be $90 \pm 0.24 \times 10 = 87.6$ to 92.4.

The size L must take us up to a point containing a further 19% of the area under the curve, i.e. to $0.095 + 0.19 = 0.285$. This area is contained between the mean and a point 0.79 standard deviations above the mean, i.e. 90 to 97.9 so the size L must be 92.4 to 97.9.

Similar reasoning gives the full range as

XL	97.9	—	109.6
L	92.4	—	97.9
M	87.6	—	92.4
S	82.1	—	87.6
XS	71.4	—	82.1

(b) Trying to cater for 99% of demand will increase the range of sizes covered but if equal numbers of each size are produced fewer will be concentrated in the middle of the range where, presumably, most sales will occur.

5.13 Mean $= 3.0 + 2.5 + 6.0 = 11.5$

Standard deviation $= \sqrt{0.2^2 + 0.2^2 + 0.4^2} \simeq 0.5$

(a) (i) The assemblies which exceed 11.8 pounds weigh $\dfrac{0.3}{0.5} = 0.6$ standard deviations, or more, above the mean weight.

From the normal tables the probability of a normally distributed variable being more than 0.6σ above mean is $0.5 - 0.2257 = 0.2743$.

So, 0.27 or 27% of assemblies will exceed 11.8 pounds.

(ii)

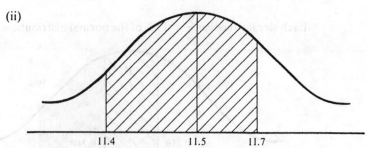

11.4	11.5	11.7

The required area is, in the usual way, shown to be $0.0793 + 0.1554 = 0.2347$. So, 23% are between 11.4 and 11.7 pounds.

(b)

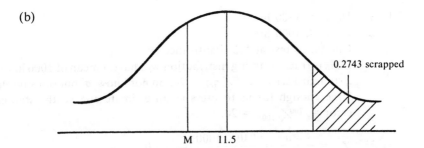

0.2743 scrapped

M   11.5

The satisfactory assemblies represent $1 - 0.2743 = 0.7257$ of the area under the curve. The median will be in the middle with $\frac{1}{2}(0.7257) = 0.36285$ either side. Since the area below the mean $= 0.5$, the area between the mean and the median is $0.5 - 0.36285 = 0.13715$ which, from the normal tables, is 0.35 standard deviations below the mean. The value of the median is, therefore, $11.5 - 0.35 \times 0.5 = 11.325$ pounds.

5.14 (a)   (i) $\bar{x} = 5.68$ hours
            (ii) $s = 2.88$ hours

   (b)   (i) $\bar{x} + s = 8.56$ hours with (from normal tables) a probability of $0.5 + 0.3413 = 84\%$ of the turn-round time being less than this.
         (ii) $\bar{x} + 2s = 11.44$ hours with a probability of $0.5 + 0.4772 = 97.7\%$ chance of the turn-round time being less.

   (c)   see text.

6.1 $\bar{x} = 18,000$
      $s = 1,200$
      $n = 64$ $\qquad \mu = \bar{x} \pm \dfrac{2\sigma}{\sqrt{n}}$ for 95% confidence limits

We do not know σ but n is large enough to use s instead.

$$\therefore \ \mu = 18,000 \pm 2 \times \frac{1200}{\sqrt{64}} = \begin{array}{c} 18,000 \pm 300 \\ \text{or} \\ 18,300 - 17,700 \end{array}$$

6.2 $\bar{x} = 110$
      $s = 12$
      $n = 36$ $\qquad \mu = \bar{x} \pm \dfrac{2\sigma}{\sqrt{n}}$ with 95% confidence limits

$$= 110 \pm 2 \times \frac{12}{\sqrt{36}} = \begin{array}{c} 110 \pm 4 \\ \text{or} \\ 106 \text{ to } 114 \end{array}$$

7.1 1. $H_0: \mu = 1000$ hrs
     2. $H_1: \mu < 1000$ hrs
     3. One-tailed test at 5% significance level.
     4. If H_0 is true, sampling distribution will have a mean of 1000 hrs and a standard error of $\sigma/\sqrt{100}$. We do not know σ but our sample is large enough for us to use s as an estimate and so the standard error = $200/\sqrt{100}$ = 20.

     5. $Z = \dfrac{\bar{x} - \mu}{\sigma_{\bar{x}}} = \dfrac{940 - 1000}{20} = -3.0$

     The critical region on a one-tailed test at the 5% level is $\geqslant 1.64$ standard errors away from the mean, this is exceeded by the sample mean, and so we reject the Null hypothesis. The manufacturer's claim is not justified.

7.2 1. $H_0: \pi = 60\%$
     2. $H_1: \pi < 60\%$
     3. One-tailed test at 5% significance level.
     4. If the Null hypothesis is true, the sampling distribution of the proportion will have a mean of 60% and a standard error of $\sqrt{\dfrac{P(100-P)}{n}} = \sqrt{\dfrac{60 \times 40}{300}} = 2.83\%$.

     Our sample result must be more than 1.64 standard errors below 60% for H_0 to be rejected on a one-tailed test at the 5% significance level.

     5. $Z = \dfrac{P - \pi}{\sigma_{prop}} = \dfrac{53.33 - 60}{2.83} = -2.36$

     This value is well into the critical region and so H_0 is rejected, the manufacturer's claims are exaggerated.

7.3 This example is very similar to 7.2.
     1. $H_0: \pi = 60\%$
     2. $H_1: \pi \neq 60\%$
     3. Two-tailed test at 5% significance level.
     4. Sampling distribution will have a mean of 60% and standard error of $\sqrt{\dfrac{60 \times 40}{500}} = 2.19\%$ if H_0 is true.

     $Z = \dfrac{P - \pi}{\sigma_{prop}} = \dfrac{66\overset{*}{-}60}{2.19} = 2.74$ $* \dfrac{330}{500}$

     The critical region(s) for a two-tailed test at the 5% level is the extreme $2\frac{1}{2}\%$ of each tail and so P must fall $\pm$ 1.96 standard errors away from 60%. The sample proportion does fall in the critical region above the mean and so we reject H_0. Support for the candidate has changed significantly.

7.4 (a) $\bar{x} = 25$ minutes

$\bar{x} \pm s = 22$ to 28

$\bar{x} \pm 2s = 19$ to 31

$\therefore s = 3$ minutes

If $x = 30$, $Z = \dfrac{30 - 25}{3} = 1.67$

$Pr(x \geqslant 30) = Pr(Z \geqslant 1.67) = 0.5 - 0.4525$
$= 0.0475$

No. of journeys taking $\geqslant 30$ mins $= 60 \times 0.0475 = 2.85 \approxeq 3$

(b) (1) $\bar{x} = 20$

$s = 3$

$$Z = \frac{24 - 20}{3} = 1.33$$

$$P(x \geqslant 24) = P(Z \geqslant 1.33) = 0.5 - 0.4082 = 0.0918$$

H_0: $\mu = 20$ mins

H_1: $\mu > 20$ mins

A one-tailed test is appropriate here.

The probability of a journey taking 24 mins or more given a true mean of 20 is .0918 (about 1 in 10 chance). The result is thus not significant at the 5% (0.05) level and there is little evidence that the reduction is not what it was claimed to be.

(2) Standard error, $\sigma_{\bar{x}} = \dfrac{\sigma}{\sqrt{n}} = \dfrac{3}{\sqrt{20}} = 0.671$

$$Z = \frac{21.7 - 20}{0.671} = 2.5$$

$$P(\bar{x} \geqslant 21.7) = P(Z \geqslant 2.5) = 0.5 - 0.4939 = 0.0062$$

On a one-tail test there is therefore evidence, even at the 1% level, that the result is significant and the saving is less than 5 minutes.

7.6

					TOTAL
O	21	13	20	16	70
E	$17\frac{1}{2}$	$17\frac{1}{2}$	$17\frac{1}{2}$	$17\frac{1}{2}$	

χ^2 with $3\,df$ $= \dfrac{12.25 + 20.25 + 6.25 + 2.25}{17.5} = \dfrac{41}{17.5} = 2.34$

which is not significant

7.7 Expected frequencies:

	PERFECT	IMPERFECT	TOTAL
A	40	60	100
B	40	60	100
C	40	60	100
	120	180	300

$$\chi^2 = \frac{7^2 + 1^2 + 8^2}{40} + \frac{7^2 + 1^2 + 8^2}{60} = 4.75$$

$$df = (3-1)(2-1) = 2\,df.$$

$$\chi^2_{0.05} \text{ with } 2\,df = 5.99$$

So, the result is not statistically significant and there is no evidence of an association between machine type and proneness to imperfection.

8.1 (a) See graph opposite.

(b) $$b = \frac{\Sigma XY - n\bar{X}\bar{Y}}{X^2 - n\bar{X}^2} = \frac{24,686 - 12 \times 17.25 \times 103.33}{4,565 - 12 \times 17.25 \times 17.25} = 3.315$$

$$X = \frac{207}{12} = 17.25$$

$$Y = \frac{1240}{12} = 103.33$$

$$a = \bar{Y} - b\bar{X} = 103.33 - 3.315 \times 17.25$$
$$= 46.15$$

Regression equation is $Y = a + bX$

$$Y = 46.15 + 3.315X$$

(see graph for diagram)

(c) There is a strong positive correlation of, perhaps, $+0.9$ (check for yourself).

(d) If $X = 20$

$$Y = 46.15 + 3.315 \times 20 = £112.45.$$

The high correlation suggests the prediction will be fairly accurate and this is supported by the fact that we are interpolating.

Of course, any particular observation may (will) be outside the regression line as is shown by the diagram.

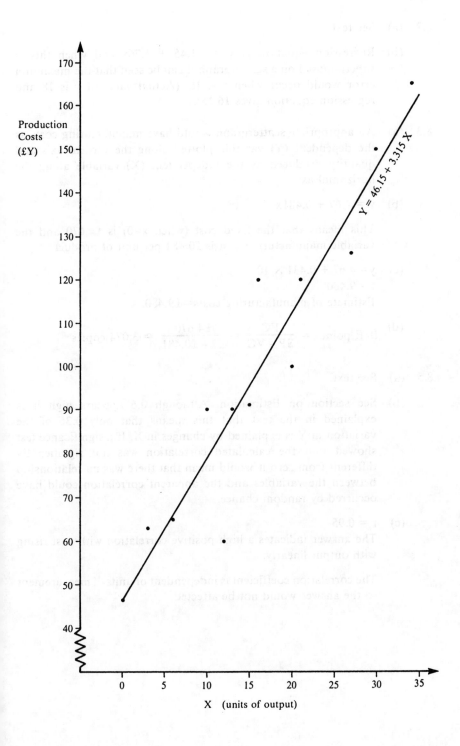

Production
Costs
(£Y)

$Y = 46.15 + 3.315\ X$

X   (units of output)

8.2 (a) See text.

    (b) Regression equation is $y = -1.45 + 1.76x$ and when this is superimposed on a scattergraph it can be seen that the maximum error would occur when $x = 10$. (Actual value of y is 18 and regression equation gives 16.15).

8.3 (a) An appropriate scattergraph would have manufacturing costs as the dependent (Y) variable plotted along the vertical axis and quantity produced as the independent (X) variable along the horizontal axis.

    (b) $y = 4.67 + 0.481x$

    This means that the fixed cost (when x=0) is £4,670 and the variable manufacturing cost is £0.481 per unit of product.

    (c) $y = 4.67 + 0.481 \times 10$
        $= 9.480$
    Estimate of manufacturing costs $= £9,480$.

    (d) $\text{B/E point} = \dfrac{\text{FC}}{\text{SP} - \text{VC}} = \dfrac{£4,670}{£2 - £0.481} \simeq 3,074 \text{ copies}$

8.5 (a) See text.

    (b) See section on Estimation. Although 0.6 appears high it is explained in the text that this means that only 0.36 of the variation in Y is explained by changes in X. If a significance test showed that the calculated correlation was not significantly different from zero it would mean that there was no relationship between the variables and the apparent correlation could have occurred by random chance.

    (c) $r = 0.95$
    The answer indicates a high positive correlation with cost rising with output linearly.

    The correlation coefficient is independent of units of measurement so the answer would not be affected.

8.6 (1)

	Rankings		
SALES	PRICE	d	d^2
1	2	−1	1
10	9	1	1
9	8	1	1
3.5	1	2.5	6.25
3.5	4	−0.5	0.25
6	5	1	1
5	7	−1	4
7	10	−3	9
2	3	−1	1
8	6	2	4
			28.5

$$r_s = 1 - \frac{6 \times 28.5}{10(10^2 - 1)} = 0.827$$

SALES	QUALITY	d^2
1	3	4
10	7	9
9	4	25
3.5	8	20.25
3.5	2	2.25
6	5	1
5	10	25
7	9	4
2	1	1
8	6	4
		95.5

$$r_s = 1 - \frac{6 \times 95.5}{10(10^2 - 1)} = 0.421$$

Therefore price is the more important factor with quite a high correlation.

(2)

Rankings		
SERVICE	SIZE	d^2
3	8	25
7	4	9
4	10	36
8	2	36
2	1	1
5	3	4
10	9	1
9	6	9
1	4	9
6	7	1
		131

$r_s = 0.21$ indicating little relationship

(3) Traffic density would, no doubt, prove to be the overwhelmingly important factor and the effects of the other factors would be disguised if the study included stations with dissimilar traffic densities.

8.7 (1)

$r =$		72	128	200	288
$t=3.5+r/50$	$=$	4.94	6.06	7.5	9.26
$t=2+\sqrt{r/8}$	$=$	5	6	7	8

(2) A graph of the observed data with the two relationships superimposed shows that $t=2+\sqrt{r/8}$ is closer to the observed data points.

(3) If we wish to fit $t=a+b\sqrt{r}$ using least squares then $t=y$ and $\sqrt{r}=x$ in the more familiar $y=a+bx$ equation.

	x	x^2	y	xy
or	$\sqrt{r}$	r	t	$t\sqrt{r}$
	7.1	50	4.0	28.4
	9.5	90	5.8	55.1
	12.2	150	6.8	83.0
	14.8	220	7.6	112.5
	16.7	280	7.6	126.9
	18.7	350	8.6	160.8
	79	1,140	40.4	566.7

N.B. $\sqrt{r}$ is found as the square root of the observed values of the batch size, r.

$$b = \frac{566.7 - 6 \times \dfrac{79}{6} \times \dfrac{40.4}{6}}{1{,}140 - 6 \left(\dfrac{79}{6}\right)^2} = 0.35$$

$$a = \frac{40.4}{6} - 0.35 \times \frac{79}{6} = 2.125$$

Equation is $\quad t = 2.125 + 0.35\sqrt{r}$

9.1

	1 Qtr	2 Sales	3 MAT	4 MQA	5 Re-centred trend estimate	6 Seasonal factor Col.2/Col.5
73	1	100				
	2	125	454	113.5	114.0	1.114
	3	127	458	114.5	114.9	0.888
	4	102	461	115.25	115.6	0.900
74	1	104	464	116.0	116.6	1.098
	2	128	469	117.25	118.0	1.102
	3	130	475	118.75	119.1	0.898
	4	107	478	119.5	119.9	0.917
75	1	110	481	120.25	120.3	1.089
	2	131	481	120.25	120.1	1.107
	3	133	480	120.0	120.1	0.891
	4	107	481	120.25		
76	1	109				
	2	132				
	3					
	4					

(a) Col.(4) or Col.(5).

(b)

QTR	Average Seasonal Factors
1	$\frac{1}{2}(0.900+0.917) = 0.909$
2	$\frac{1}{2}(1.098+1.089) = 1.093$
3	$\frac{1}{3}(1.114+1.102+1.107) = 1.108$
4	$\frac{1}{3}(0.888+0.898+0.891) = 0.892$

Year	Qtr.	Actual Sales	Deseasonalised Sales (Actual Sales/ Avg. Seasonal Factor)
73	1	100	109.9
	2	125	114.7
	3	127	114.4
	4	102	114.6
74	1	104	114.3
	2	128	117.4
	3	130	117.1
	4	107	120.2
75	1	110	120.9
	2	131	120.2
	3	133	119.8
	4	107	120.2
76	1	109	119.8
	2	132	121.1

(c)

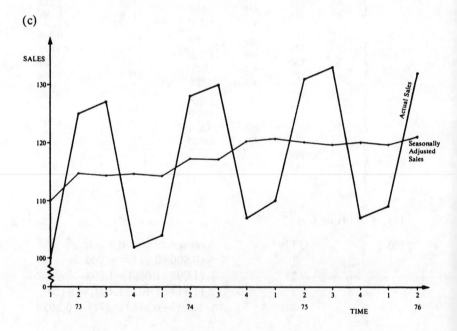

(d) The seasonally adjusted sales figures show a generally rising trend with an upsurge in 1974 followed by a fairly stable trend since then.

The actual sales figures exhibit a regular seasonal variation with a drop in sales in the 4th qtr. following a peak in the 3rd qtr.

9.2

1	2	3	4	5	6
Year	Period	2-Month Total	MAT	2-Month Moving Average (Col.4/6)	Re-centred Trend
1973	1				
	2				
	3	10.3			
	4	12.8			
	5	20.3	91.6	15.2	
	6	32.4	92.2	15.4	15.3
1974	1	6.8	93.8	15.6	15.5
	2	9.0	96.6	16.1	15.9
	3	10.9	99.6	16.6	16.3
	4	14.4	99.8	16.6	16.6
	5	23.1	100.3	16.7	16.7
	6	35.4	101.0	16.8	16.8
1975	1	7.0	101.9	17.0	16.9
	2	9.5	103.3	17.2	17.1
	3	11.6	105.3	17.5	17.4
	4	15.3	105.6	17.6	17.6
	5	24.5	106.0	17.7	17.7
	6	37.4			
1976	1	7.3			
	2	9.9			

(1)   Col.(5) or Col.(6).

(2)

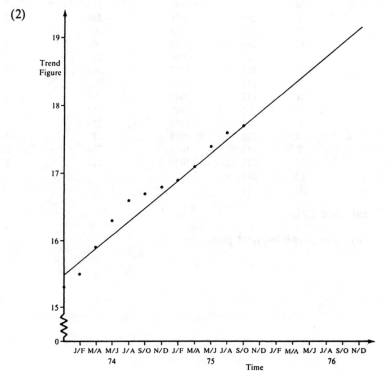

From the graph, trend values for

$$1976 \left\{ \begin{array}{ll} \text{May/June} & 18.5 \\ \text{July/Aug} & 18.75 \\ \text{Sept/Oct} & 18.95 \\ \text{Nov/Dec} & 19.2 \end{array} \right.$$

(3)

$$\text{SEASONAL FACTOR} = \frac{\text{ACTUAL SALES}}{\text{TREND}}$$

$$\text{July/Aug is Period (4)} = \frac{1}{2} \left(\frac{14.4}{16.6} + \frac{15.3}{17.6} \right) = 0.868$$

Seasonally adjusted
trend figure for $= 18.75 \times 0.868 = 16.3$ (thousand)
July/Aug 1976

9.3

1 Week	2 Day	3 Output	4 5-Day Moving Total	5 5-Day Moving Avg.	6 Deviation (Col.3–Col.5)
1	M	187			
	T	203			
	W	208	1022	204	4
	Th	207	1042	208	−1
	F	217	1047	209	8
2	M	207	1049	210	−3
	T	208	1048	210	−2
	W	210	1043	209	1
	Th	206	1038	208	−2
	F	212	1040	208	4
3	M	202	1042	208	−6
	T	210	1041	208	2
	W	212	1043	209	3
	Th	205	1049	210	−5
	F	214	1054	211	3
4	M	208	1059	212	−4
	T	215	1071	214	1
	W	217	1070	214	3
	Th	217			
	F	213			

(a) See Col.5.

(b) See graph on next page.

(b)

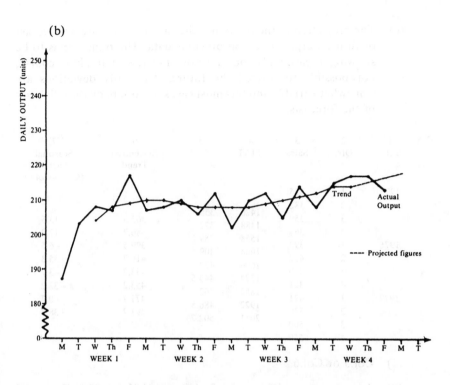

(c)   DAILY DEVIATIONS FROM TREND

	M	T	W	Th	F	
Wk 1			4	−1	8	
2	−3	−2	1	−2	4	
3	−6	2	3	−5	3	
4	−4	1	3			
Total	−13	1	11	−8	15	Total
Avg.	−4.33	0.33	2.75	−2.67	5	1.08

Since the total of the deviations must sum to zero we subtract 1.08/5 from each of the daily deviations.

| Adjusted avg. | −4.5 | 0 | 2.5 | −3 | 5 | 0 |

(d) The average incremental increase over the last five trend figures is 1 unit. The trend figures for Monday and Tuesday are therefore 217 and 218.

Adjusting for the daily deviations:
Forecast Output for Monday = 217 − 4.5 = 212.5
Forecast Output for Tuesday = 218 + 0 = 218

(e) The projection of the trend into the future merely gives a forecast of future output based on previous data. The trend seems to be showing a reasonably constant rate of increase but it is, of course, not possible to foretell the future. The daily deviations are somewhat variable and this must cast some doubt on the reliability of the forecasts.

9.5

1 Year	2 Qtr.	3 Sales	4 MAT	5 MQA	6 Re-centred Trend	7 Seasonal Factor (Col.3–Col.6)
1975	1	325				
	2	382				
	3	350	1420	355	363.5	– 13.5
	4	363	1488	372	380.7	– 17.7
1976	1	393	1558	389.5	399.5	– 6.5
	2	452	1638	409.5	416.7	+35.3
	3	430	1696	424	433.7	– 3.7
	4	421	1774	443.5	453.2	– 32.2
1977	1	471	1852	463	471.7	– 0.7
	2	530	1922	480.5	491.7	+38.3
	3	500	2011	502.75		
	4	510				

(1) Col.5 or Col.6.

(2) Average seasonal factor for 2nd Qtr. = (+35.3 + 38.3)/2 = +36.8
Average seasonal factor for 4th Qtr. = (–17.7 – 32.2)/2 = –25.0

If the trend was constant then the difference $s_2 - s_4$ would be 36.8 + 25.0 ≏ 62 so that sales in the 4th Qtr. would be about 62 lower than sales in the 2nd Qtr. due to seasonal effects. A value of 70 for $s_2 - s_4$ would therefore be reasonable evidence that the sales are falling.

9.6 (a)

Average hours	frequency
38.5 – 40.4	16
40.5 – 42.4	5
42.5 – 44.4	12
44.5 – 46.4	7
	40

(b) $\bar{x} = 42$

(c) $s = 2.3$

(d) see text.

(e)

Week	Hours worked	Smoothed hours
t	A_t	$S_t = S_{t-1} + 0.1\,(A_t - S_{t-1})$
0	—	40
1	44.2	40.4 [40+0.1(44.2−40)]
2	45.4	40.9
3	46.2	41.5
4	46.0	41.9
5	45.7	42.3

(f) The smoothing process is designed to calculate the trend in the data whilst placing most emphasis on the most recent data.

9.7

1 Year	2 Month	3 Production	4 Rounded values	5 5 month moving total	6 5 month moving average	7 Rounding error	8 5 month moving total of rounding error	9 5 month moving average of rounding error
1974	April	37.7	38			−0.3		
	May	32.3	32			0.3		
	June	39.3	39	189	37.8	0.3	0.3	0.06
	July	42.0	42	192	38.4	0	0.8	0.16
	Aug	38.0	38	196	39.2	0	0.5	0.10
	Sept	41.2	41	186	37.2	0.2	−0.3	−0.06
	Oct	36.0	36	179	35.8	0	0	0
	Nov	28.5	29	174	34.8	−0.5	−0.1	−0.02
	Dec	35.3	35	171	34.2	0.3	0.1	0.02
1975	Jan	32.9	33	172	34.4	−0.1	0	0
	Feb	38.4	38	178	35.6	0.4	0.8	0.16
	Mar	36.9	37	177	35.4	−0.1	0.6	0.12
	April	35.3	35	176	35.2	0.3	0.6	0.12
	May	34.1	34	178	35.6	0.1	−0.3	−0.06
	June	31.9	32			−0.1		
	July	39.5	40			−0.5		

(a) Col.4

(b) Col.6

(c) Graph not reproduced

(d) Col.9 (strictly, one might add 0.05 to Col.9 since the original values are rounded to one decimal place).

10.1 (a) (i) Total Cost $= 10,000 + 7.5x$

(ii) Let demand be $x = a + bp$ where $p =$ price

Then
$$400 = a + b.40 \quad \textcircled{1}$$
$$800 = a + b.20 \quad \textcircled{2}$$
$$400 = -20b \quad \textcircled{1} - \textcircled{2}$$
$$b = -20$$
$$a = 1200$$

demand curve is $x = 1200 - 20p$ or $p = 60 - \dfrac{x}{20}$

Total Revenue $= x.p = (1200 - 20p)p$ or $TR = 60x - \dfrac{x^2}{60}$

(iii) Profit $= TR - TC = 60x - \dfrac{x^2}{20} - 10,000 - 7.5x$

$$= 52.5x - \dfrac{x^2}{20} - 10,000$$

(b)

Output	0	200	400	600	800	1000	1200
TC	10,000	11,500	13,000	14,500	16,000	17,500	19,000
TR	0	10,000	16,000	18,000	16,000	10,000	0
Profit	-10,000	-1,500	3,000	3,500	0	-7,500	-19,000

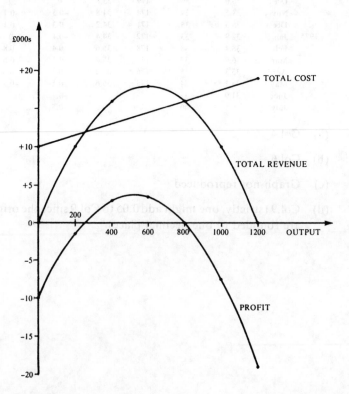

(c)   From the graph, a maximum profit of about £3,800 is achieved at an output of 525 units/week.

Selling price, $p = 60 - \dfrac{1}{20}x$

$$= 60 - \frac{1}{20} \times 525 = £33.75$$

N.B. We can check this by differentiation (see later)

$$\pi = \text{Profit} = 52.5x - \frac{x^2}{20} - 10{,}000$$

$$\frac{d\pi}{dx} = 52.5 - \frac{x}{10} = 0 \text{ at max or min.}$$

$$\underline{\underline{x = 525}}$$

10.2 (a)   The problem here is to decide for what range of values of x the graph should be plotted.

A little contemplation should reveal that the equation represents a parabola with a minimum of –4 at x=2 and when x=0, y=4.

Therefore, we should calculate y for a range of values of x from, say, –2 to +6.

x	-2	-1	0	1	2	3	4	5	6
y	28	14	4	-2	-4	-2	4	14	28

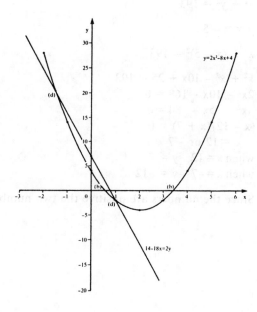

(b)

$$\text{Roots given by} \quad \frac{-b \pm \sqrt{b^2 - 4ac}}{2a}$$

$$x = \frac{8 \pm \sqrt{64 - 32}}{4} = 2 \pm \sqrt{2}$$

$$= 0.586 \text{ and } 3.414$$

(c) The equation $14 - 18x = 2y$ is a straight line so we need only two points

$$\text{e.g.} \quad x = 0, \quad y = 7$$
$$x = 1 \quad y = -2$$

(see graph)

(d)

$$\text{Two equations are} \quad y = 2x^2 - 8x + 4$$
$$\text{and} \quad y = 7 - 9x$$
$$\text{Therefore,} \quad 7 - 9x = 2x^2 - 8x + 4$$
$$0 = 2x^2 + x - 3$$
$$= (x - 1)(2x + 3)$$
$$\text{Therefore,} \quad x = 1 \text{ or } \tfrac{-3}{2}$$
$$\text{when} \quad y = -2 \text{ and } \tfrac{41}{2}$$

(e) See graph.

10.3 (a) $x = 10$, $y = 5$, $z = 7$.

(b) $x - y = 5$
$x^2 + y^2 = 193$

$y = x - 5$

$x^2 + (x - 5)^2 = 193$

$x^2 + x^2 - 10x + 25 = 193$
$2x^2 - 10x - 168 = 0$
$x^2 - 5x - 84 = 0$
$(x - 12)(x + 7) = 0$
$x = 12 \text{ or } - 7$
when $x = 12$ $y = 7$
when $x = -7$ $y = -12$

Since the numbers are positive the two numbers are 7 and 12.

(c)   Let x = length and y = breadth

$$\text{Then,} \quad 2x + 2y = 114$$
$$\text{and} \quad xy = 800$$

$$x = 57 - y$$
$$(57 - y)y = 800$$
$$y^2 - 57y + 800 = 0$$
$$(y - 25)(y - 32) = 0 \qquad \text{(or take roots)}$$
$$\therefore \quad y = 25 \text{ or } 32$$

If y = 25 then x = 32 and vice versa. So, dimensions are 25 metres and 32 metres.

10.4 (a)   Let $a = \dfrac{1}{x}, \; b = \dfrac{1}{y}, \; c = \dfrac{1}{z}$

Then $a + b + c = 5$ ①
$$4a + 2b + 3c = 9 \quad ②$$
$$3a - 3b - 3c = -3 \quad ③$$

$$2a = 4 \qquad ① + ③ \, /2$$

$$a = 2$$

$$7a - b = 6 \qquad ② + ③$$
$$14 - b = 6$$
$$b = 8$$

$$2 + 8 + c = 5 \qquad ①$$
$$c = -5$$

$$x = \frac{1}{2}, \; y = \frac{1}{8}, \; z = -\frac{1}{5}$$

(b) $2x - 2y - 3xy = 8$

$$\frac{x}{y} = \frac{3}{-4} \qquad \text{i.e.} \quad x = \frac{-3y}{4}$$

$$\frac{y}{z} = \frac{-4}{4} \qquad \text{i.e.} \quad z = -y$$

$$2\left(\frac{-3y}{4}\right) - 2y - 3\left(\frac{-3y}{4}\right)y = 8$$

gives $6y^2 - 7y - 16 = 0$ which is of the form $ax^2 + bx + c = 0$

$$\text{Roots are} \quad y = \frac{7 \pm \sqrt{49 - 4 \times 6 \times (-16)}}{12}$$

$$= 2.317 \text{ or } -1.151$$

$$\text{Two solutions} \quad \begin{array}{ccc} x & -1.738 & 0.863 \\ y & 2.317 & -1.151 \\ z & -2.317 & 1.151 \end{array}$$

(c)
$$\frac{\left(a + \dfrac{1}{b}\right)^x \cdot \left(a - \dfrac{1}{b}\right)^y}{\left(b + \dfrac{1}{a}\right)^x \cdot \left(b - \dfrac{1}{a}\right)^y} = \frac{\dfrac{(ab+1)^x}{b^x} \cdot \dfrac{(ab-1)^y}{b^y}}{\dfrac{(ab+1)^x}{a^x} \cdot \dfrac{(ab-1)^y}{a^y}}$$

$$= \frac{a^x \cdot a^y}{b^x \cdot b^y} = \frac{a^{x+y}}{b^{x+y}} = \left(\frac{a}{b}\right)^{x+y}$$

10.7 (i) When $Q = 20$ $C = 1300$
        When $Q = 30$ $C = 1700$

Variable cost is therefore $\dfrac{1700 - 1300}{30 - 20} = £40/\text{unit}$

When $Q = 20$, Total Variable Cost $= 20 \times 40 = 800$
But, $Q = 20$, Total Cost is 1300 so Fixed Cost $= 1300 - 800 = 500$
$C = 500 + 40Q$.

(ii) $P = 100 - Q$
(iii) $R = 100Q - Q^2$
(iv) $Q = 10$ tonnes
      $P = £90$
      $R = £900$.

10.8 (a) GP $= a, ar, ar^2, - - - - - ar^{n-1}$

$$\begin{aligned} a &= 4 \\ ar &= -6 \end{aligned}$$

Therefore, $r = \dfrac{-6}{4} = -1.5$

$$\begin{aligned} \text{10th Term} &= ar^{10-1} = ar^9 \\ &= 4 \times (-1.5)^9 = 153.77 \end{aligned}$$

$$S_n = \frac{a(1 - r^n)}{1 - r}$$

$$S_{10} = \frac{a(1 - r^{10})}{1 - r} = \frac{4(1 - (-1.5)^9)}{1 - (-1.5)} = 63.11$$

(b)
$$\frac{1}{x} - \frac{1}{x+3} = \frac{1}{x+2} - \frac{1}{x+5}$$

$$\frac{x+3-x}{x(x+3)} = \frac{x+5-x-2}{(x+2)(x+5)}$$

$$\frac{3}{x(x+3)} = \frac{3}{(x+2)(x+5)}$$

$$x(x+3) = (x+2)(x+5)$$
$$x^2 + 3x = x^2 + 7x + 10$$
$$4x + 10 = 0$$
$$x = -2.5$$

(c)
$$\frac{x}{y} = \frac{4}{-3} \qquad \therefore \qquad y = \frac{-3x}{4}$$

$$\frac{x}{z} = \frac{4}{8} \qquad \therefore \qquad z = 2x$$

$$x - 4y - z = 48$$

$$x - 4\left(\frac{-3x}{4}\right) - 2x = 48$$
$$2x = 48$$
$$x = 24, \ y = -18, \ z = 48$$

10.9 (a) (i) Sales Revenue = $15x$

Total cost = $800 + 5x + 0.009x^2$

Profit = $15x - [800 + 5x + 0.009x^2]$

If weekly profit is exactly 200

Then, $200 = 15x - [800 + 5x + 0.009x^2]$

$$0 = 15x - 1000 - 5x - 0.009x^2$$
$$0.009x^2 - 10x + 1000 = 0$$
$$9x^2 - 10,000x + 1,000,000 = 0$$
$$(9x - 1000)(x - 1000) = 0$$
$$x = \frac{1000}{9} \quad \text{or} \quad 1,000$$

Therefore, range of production 112 to 1,000 gives a profit of at least £200.

(ii) Graph not reproduced.

(b) If rate of depreciation = r% per annum

$$32{,}000 \left(1 - \frac{r}{100}\right)^6 = 23{,}500$$

$$\left(1 - \frac{r}{100}\right)^6 = \left(\frac{23500}{32000}\right)$$

$$1 - \frac{r}{100} = \sqrt[6]{\frac{23500}{32000}} = 0.9498 = 0.95$$

$$\frac{r}{100} = 0.05$$

$$r = 5\% \text{ p.a.}$$

11.1 (a) 2
    (b) 2x
    (c) $3x^2 + 2$
    (d) $-\dfrac{2}{x^3}$
    (e) 24x + 5
    (f) $9x^2 + 3$
    (g) $2 - \dfrac{5}{x^2}$
    (h) $-\left[\dfrac{15}{x^4} + \dfrac{8}{x^3} + \dfrac{2}{x^2}\right]$
    (i) $\dfrac{ds}{dt} = u + at$ [this is the equation for velocity i.e. v = u + at]

11.2 (a) 0
    (b) 2
    (c) 6x
    (d) $\dfrac{6}{x^4}$
    (e) 24
    (f) 18x
    (g) $\dfrac{10}{x^3}$
    (h) $\dfrac{60}{x^5} + \dfrac{24}{x^4} + \dfrac{4}{x^3}$
    (i) $\dfrac{d^2s}{dt^2} = a$ $\left[\dfrac{d^2s}{dt^2}\text{ is the acceleration}\right]$

11.3 (i) $\dfrac{x^2}{2} + C$
    (ii) $x^4 + C$

(iii) $\frac{2}{21} (7x+1)^{\frac{3}{2}} + C$

(iv) $\frac{5}{3} x^3 + \frac{3}{2} x^2 + 10x + C$

(v) $\frac{x^3}{24} - \frac{3}{2} x^2 + 2x + C$

(vi) $-\frac{1}{x} + \frac{2}{3} x^3 + 7x + C$

(vii) $10x + 6x^2 - \frac{x^3}{3} + C$

(viii) $3x^2 + 20x + C$

(ix) $-\frac{5}{6} x^{-2} - \frac{7}{3} \log x - \frac{8}{9} x^{-3} + C$

(x) $\int \frac{x}{\sqrt{1-x}} dx = \int \left[\frac{1}{\sqrt{1-x}} - \frac{1-x}{\sqrt{1-x}} \right] dx = \int \left[(1-x)^{-\frac{1}{2}} - (1-x)^{\frac{1}{2}} \right] dx$

$$= \frac{2}{3} (1-x)^{\frac{3}{2}} - 2(1-x)^{\frac{1}{2}} + C$$

11.4 Total Cost = Fixed Cost + Variable Cost.

Marginal cost is the increase in variable cost for an increase of one unit of output i.e. $\frac{dc}{dq}$ where c is the variable cost.

$$\text{Variable Cost} = \int \frac{dc}{dq} \cdot dq = \int 50 + (q-2)^2 \ dq$$

$$= 50q + \frac{(q-2)^3}{3} + C$$

When output is zero, variable cost will be zero so C = 0.

Therefore, Total Cost $= 10{,}000 + 50q + \frac{(q-2)^3}{3}$

11.5 (i) $\quad R = 14 + 81x - \frac{x^3}{12}$

$$\frac{dR}{dx} = 81 - \frac{x^2}{4} = 0 \text{ at max or min}$$

$$\frac{x^2}{4} = 81$$

$$x^2 = 324$$

$$x = \pm 18 \text{ at max or min.}$$

Reject the negative value since we cannot have negative output.

Therefore, revenue is maximised when output is 18 units.

(ii) Max. revenue $= 14 + 81 \times 18 - \dfrac{18^3}{12} = £986$

(iii) Price $= \dfrac{\text{Revenue}}{\text{Output}} = \dfrac{986}{18} = £54.78$ per unit.

11.6 (a) Profit, $\pi = R - C$

$$= (100x - x^2) - \left(100 + 23x + \frac{1}{2}x^2\right)$$

$$= -100 + 77x - \frac{3}{2}x^2$$

$$\frac{d\pi}{dx} = 77 - 3x = 0 \text{ at max or min.}$$

$$3x = 77$$

$$x = 25.7 \text{ tonnes at max or min.}$$

$$\frac{d^2\pi}{dx^2} = -3 \text{ therefore } x = 25.7 \text{ is at max.}$$

(b) At Break even, $R = C$

$$100x - x^2 = 100 + 23x + \frac{x^2}{2}$$

$$100 - 77x + \frac{3}{2}x^2 = 0$$

$$200 - 154x + 3x^2 = 0$$

$$(3x - 4)(x - 50) = 0 \quad \text{(factorising)}$$

Therefore, break-even at $x = 1.3$ tonnes and 50 tonnes.

(c) $R = 100x - x^2$

$$\frac{dR}{dx} = 100 - 2x = 0 \quad \text{at max or min}$$

$$x = 50 \text{ tonnes at max.}$$

(d)

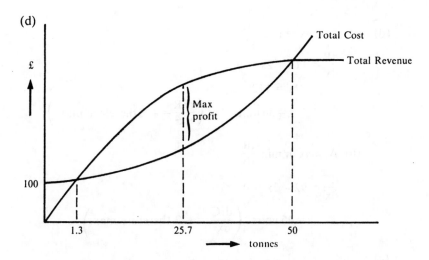

(e) It is rational to produce 1.3 and 50 tonnes since profits are earned. The profit maximising level of output is 25.7 tonnes and, assuming that the functions whole good for $x < 100$, this would be the recommended level of output.

11.8 (a) $\dfrac{dC}{dx} = (92 - 2x)$ £000's

$C = \int (92 - 2x)dx$

$= 92x - x^2 + k$ where k is a constant

When $x = 0$, $C =$ Fixed Cost $= 800$

$\therefore$ $k = 800$

$C = 800 + 92x - x^2$

(b) $\dfrac{dR}{dx} = 112 - 2x$

$R = \int (112 - 2x)dx$

$R = 112x - x^2 + C$ where C is a constant

When $x = 0$, $R = 0$, $\therefore C = 0$

$R = 112x - x^2$

(c) At Break-even $R = C$

$112x - x^2 = 800 + 92x - x^2$

$\therefore$ $20x = 800$

$x = 40$ units

(d) (i) At max or min $\dfrac{dR}{dx} = 0$

$$\dfrac{dR}{dx} = 112 - 2x = 0$$

$$2x = 112$$

$$x = 56 \text{ units} \qquad \left(\dfrac{d^2R}{dx^2} = -2 \text{ therefore max.} \right)$$

(ii) At max or min $\dfrac{dC}{dx} = 0$

$$\dfrac{dC}{dx} = 92 - 2x = 0$$

$$x = 46 \text{ units} \qquad \left(\dfrac{d^2C}{dx^2} = -2 \text{ therefore max.} \right)$$

(e)

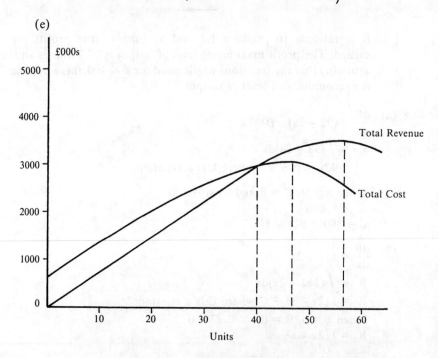

As can be seen, the rate of increase of revenue is greater than the rate of increase of cost up to 40 units after which revenue exceeds cost and profits are made.

After 46 units cost starts to fall while revenue is still rising and profits increase. After 56 units revenue starts to decrease also, but at a slower rate than cost and so profits increase up to and beyond 60 units.

11.9 (i) $\begin{pmatrix} 2 & -1 \\ -1 & 3 \end{pmatrix}$ $\begin{pmatrix} P \\ q \end{pmatrix}$ $=$ $\begin{pmatrix} 15 \\ 5 \end{pmatrix}$

(ii) $\begin{pmatrix} P \\ q \end{pmatrix}$ $=$ $\begin{pmatrix} 2 & -1 \\ -1 & 3 \end{pmatrix}^{-1}$ $\begin{pmatrix} 15 \\ 5 \end{pmatrix}$

Therefore we need to find the inverse of $\begin{pmatrix} 2 & -1 \\ -1 & 3 \end{pmatrix}$

Writing in the form of a partitioned matrix and applying suitable transformations

$$\left(\begin{array}{cc|cc} 2 & 1 & 1 & 0 \\ -1 & 3 & 0 & 1 \end{array} \right)$$

Add ½ row 1 to row 2

$$\left(\begin{array}{cc|cc} 2 & -1 & 1 & 0 \\ 0 & 2\tfrac{1}{2} & \tfrac{1}{2} & 1 \end{array} \right)$$

Multiply row 1 by 2½

$$\left(\begin{array}{cc|cc} 5 & -2\tfrac{1}{2} & 2\tfrac{1}{2} & 0 \\ 0 & 2\tfrac{1}{2} & \tfrac{1}{2} & 1 \end{array} \right)$$

Add row 2 to row 1

$$\left(\begin{array}{cc|cc} 5 & 0 & 3 & 1 \\ 0 & 2\tfrac{1}{2} & \tfrac{1}{2} & 1 \end{array} \right)$$

Divide row 1 by 5 and row 2 by 2½

$$\left(\begin{array}{cc|cc} 1 & 0 & \tfrac{3}{5} & \tfrac{1}{5} \\ 0 & 1 & \tfrac{1}{5} & \tfrac{2}{5} \end{array} \right)$$

Inverse is thus $\begin{pmatrix} \tfrac{3}{5} & \tfrac{1}{5} \\ \tfrac{1}{5} & \tfrac{2}{5} \end{pmatrix}$

and $\begin{pmatrix} p \\ q \end{pmatrix}$ $=$ $\begin{pmatrix} \tfrac{3}{5} & \tfrac{1}{5} \\ \tfrac{1}{5} & \tfrac{2}{5} \end{pmatrix}$ $\begin{pmatrix} 15 \\ 5 \end{pmatrix}$ $=$ $\begin{pmatrix} 10 \\ 5 \end{pmatrix}$

p = £10 and q = 5 tonnes which satisfy both equations.

(b) $q = 2p^3 - 21p^2 + 36p + 9$

$\dfrac{dq}{dp} = 6p^2 - 42p + 36 = 0$ at max or min.

$6p^2 - 42p + 36 = 0$

∴ $p^2 - 7p + 6 = 0$

∴ $(p - 6)(p - 1) = 0$

$p = 6$ or 1 at max or min.

$$\frac{d^2q}{dp^2} = 12p - 42$$

$$= 30 \text{ when } p = 6 \text{ or } -30 \text{ when } p = 1$$

$$\frac{d^2q}{dp^2} \text{ is } < 0 \text{ at max}$$

$\therefore$ Max. demand when $p = 1$ and $q = 2 \times 1^3 - 21 \times 1^2 + 36 \times 1 + 9$

$= 26$

(c) $q = 90p^{-3}$

$$\frac{dq}{dp} = - \frac{270}{p^4}$$

Elasticity of demand $= \left(\dfrac{dq}{dp} \right) \dfrac{p}{q}$

$$= \frac{-270}{p^4} \cdot \frac{p}{90p^{-3}} = \frac{-270}{p^4} \times p \times \frac{p^3}{90}$$

$= -3$ which is constant

11.10 Average Net Revenue per unit $= \dfrac{R}{Q} = 100 - 0.01Q$

$R = 100Q - 0.01Q^2$

Variable Cost per unit $= \dfrac{V}{Q} = 10 + 0.015Q + 2 + 0.001Q$

$V = 12Q + 0.016Q^2$

TOTAL COST $= 60,000 + 12Q + 0.016Q^2$

Profit $= \pi = 100Q - 0.01Q^2 - (60,000 + 12Q + 0.016Q^2)$

$\pi = 88Q - 0.026Q^2 - 60,000$

(a) $\dfrac{d\pi}{dQ} = 88 - 0.052Q = 0$ at max or min.

$$Q = \frac{88}{0.052} = 1692 \text{ units}$$

(b) $\pi = 88Q - 0.026Q^2 - 60,000 = £14,462$ when $Q = 1692$

(c) Manufacturing Division profit $= \pi_m = 73Q - [40,000 + 10Q + 0.015Q^2]$

$= 63Q - 40,000 - 0.015Q^2$

$\dfrac{d\pi_m}{dQ} = 63 - 0.03Q = 0$ at max or min.

$Q = 2100$

(d) $\pi_m = 63Q - 40,000 - 0.015Q^2$
$\pi_D = 100Q - 0.01Q^2 - 73Q - (20,000 + 2Q + 0.001Q^2)$
$= 25Q - 20,000 - 0.011Q^2$
$\pi_{Total} = 88Q - 60,000 - 0.026Q^2$

If $Q = 2100$ units
$\pi_m = £26,150$
$\pi_D = £16,010$

Company Profit $= \overline{10,140}$

12.1 See answer to Question 3.10

12.2 (a) 6% p.a. is equivalent to $\frac{1}{2}$% per month.
£100 invested would grow to $100(1 + 0.005)^{12} = 106.17$
Therefore, effective annual rate = 6.17%

Similarly, $6\frac{1}{4}$% p.a. is equivalent to $\frac{6\frac{1}{4}}{4} = 1.5625$ per qtr.

£100 would grow to $100(1 + 0.015625)^4 = 106.398$
Therefore, effective annual rate = 6.40%

(b) (i) If $r =$ annual compound rate of change
$107(1+r)^{10} = 208$

$$r = \sqrt[10]{\frac{208}{107}} - 1 = 0.06873 = 6.9\% \text{ p.a.}$$

(ii) Purchasing power of £1 in 1964 $= \frac{100}{107} = £0.9346$

Purchasing power of £1 in 1974 $\frac{100}{208} = £0.4808$

If $r =$ annual compound rate of change
$0.9346(1 + r)^{10} = 0.4808$
$r = -0.0643 =$ a reduction of 6.43% p.a.

12.3 (a) (i) $A_n = P(1+r)^n$
$280,000 = P(1+0.03)^{12}$
$P = £196,386$

(ii) If r is the effective annual rate
$(1+r)^3 = (1+0.03)^{12}$
$(1+r) = (1.03)^4$
$r = (1.03)^4 - 1 = 0.1256 = 12.56\%$ p.a.

(b) £4000 at the end of each quarter will grow to

$$A_n = a \left[\frac{(1+r)^n - 1}{r} \right] = 4000 \left[\frac{1.03^{12} - 1}{0.03} \right] = £56,768$$

There is a shortfall of $280,000 - 56,768 = £223,232$

If P is the amount we need to set aside now

$$P = 223,232 \times (1.03)^{-12} = £156,570$$

12.4 (a)

$$F = \left(A + \frac{p}{r} \right) R^t - \frac{p}{r}$$

$$F + \frac{p}{r} = AR^t + \frac{pR^t}{r}$$

$$\frac{p}{r} \left(1 - R^t \right) = AR^t - F$$

$$p = r \frac{(AR^t - F)}{(1 - R^t)}$$

(b) (i) PV of annuity $= a \left[\frac{1 - (1+r)^{-n}}{r} \right]$

$$= 2500 \left[\frac{1 - (1.09)^{-15}}{0.09} \right]$$

$$= £20,152$$

(ii) If we assume the annuity is paid in two equal instalments of £1250 and that the rate of interest is 4.5% per half year

$$PV = 1250 \left[\frac{1 - (1.045)^{-30}}{0.045} \right] = £20,361$$

12.6 (a)

$$A_n = a \left[\frac{(1+r)^n - 1}{r} \right] = 1000 \left[\frac{(1.075)^7 - 1}{0.075} \right] - 1000 = £7,787$$

(b) PV of annuity of £5000 p.a. over the next 10 years.

$$= a \left[\frac{1 - (1+r)^{-n}}{r} \right] = 5,000 \left[\frac{1 - (1.1)^{-10}}{0.1} \right] = £30,723$$

Since the income generated by the machine is only worth £30,723 it should not be bought at a cost of £35,000.

(c)

$$\text{Amount} = 1000 (1.07)^{18} + 1000 (1.07)^{17} + 500 \left[\frac{(1.07)^{17} - 1}{0.07} \right] - 500$$

$$= £21,459$$

12.7 A worked answer is not provided here but you can check the accuracy of your calculations against the answers below.

(a) (i) £3,621.22
    (ii) APR = 7.12%

(b) (i) Annual payment = £10,402.80
    (ii) See 12.5.3 for example of amortisation schedule.

(c) (i) Deposit = £10,431.21
    (ii) Your schedule should show that the amount in the fund and the debt outstanding at the end of the period are both equal to £66,088 with some slight discrepancy due to rounding error.

13.1 (a) (i) B 2⅔ years
             C 3 years
             A 5 years

     (ii) A 8.9% $\left[\dfrac{180{,}000 - 100{,}000}{100{,}000} \times 100 \times \dfrac{1}{9} \right]$
           C 8.3%
           B 8%

     (iii) C £16,970
           A £15,180
           B £11,800

(b) Project B ranks highest for payback because it has the highest early receipts. Project A is top on the BRR because it has more receipts over a long period after payback. On the NPV criterion, project C is top because, although receipts are less than for project A overall, more receipts occur during the early part of the project.

(c) See text for a full discussion. The main points are as follows:
    Payback: In a sense, payback does take account of the time value of money because there is an implicit assumption that the sooner the money comes in the better. This also, in a way, recognises that forecasts are more suspect the further ahead they are made. Of course, no account is taken of receipts after the payback period.

    Book rate of return: The advantage of BRR over payback is that it takes account of all receipts (but not their timing).

    Net Present Value: Takes account of all receipts and the time value of money.

13.2 (a) $PV = 4000 + 4000 (1+0.2)^{-1} + 4000 (1+0.2)^{-2} = £10,111.11$

(b)   If £10,000 is the PV of the instalments

$$10,010 = 4000 + 4000 (1+r)^{-1} + 4000 (1+r)^{-2}$$

$$\frac{6,000}{4,000} = (1+r)^{-1} + (1+r)^{-2}$$

$$\frac{3}{2} = \frac{1}{1+r} + \frac{1}{(1+r)^2} = \frac{r+2}{(1+r)^2}$$

$$3(1+r)^2 = 2r + 4$$

$$3r^2 + 4r - 1 = 0$$

Taking roots, $r = \dfrac{-4 \pm \sqrt{16 - 4 \times 3 \times -1}}{6}$

$$= \frac{-4 \pm 5.29}{6}$$

$$= 0.215 \quad \text{(ignoring negative root)}$$

$$\therefore r = 21.5\%$$

13.3 (a) $r = 1 - \sqrt[n]{\dfrac{s}{C}}$ (see section 12.5.1 for development from first principles)

$$= 1 - \sqrt[20]{\frac{4,000}{40,000}} = 1 - \sqrt[20]{0.1} = 1 - 0.8912$$

$$= 10.87\%$$

(b)

Year	Net Cash Flow	Discount Factors $(1+r)^{-n}$ at 15%	P.V.
0	−60,000	—	−60,000
1	−10,000	0.8696	−8,696
2	15,000	0.7561	11,342
3	20,000	0.6575	13,150
4	20,000	0.5718	11,435
5	20,000	0.4972	9,944
6	20,000	0.4323	8,647
		NPV =	−14,178

The negative NPV indicates that with a target rate of return of 15% the investment is not worthwhile.

13.4 (a) $a = \dfrac{Pr}{1 - (1+r)^{-n}}$ (see section 12.5.3)

$$= \frac{12,000 \times 0.15}{1 - (1+0.15)^{-5}} = £3579.79$$

SCHEDULE:-

	Year	Balance Outstanding (£)	Interest (£)	Instalment
Start of	1983	12,000	1800	
	1984	10,220.21	1533.03	3579.79
	1985	8173.45	1226.02	3579.79
	1986	5819.68	872.95	3579.79
	1987	3112.84	466.93	3579.79
	1988	3579.77		3579.79

(b) Value of debt at start of $1988 = 12,000(1 + 0.15)^5 = £24136.29$

$$\text{Payment into sinking fund} = a = \frac{rA_n}{(1+r)^n - 1} \qquad \begin{array}{l}\text{(see section}\\ \text{12.5.2)}\end{array}$$

$$= \frac{0.10 \times 24136.29}{(1+0.1)^5 - 1} = £3953.46$$

SCHEDULE:

Year	Deposit	Amount in fund	Interest
1984	3,953.46	3,953.46	395.35
1985	3,953.46	8,302.27	830.23
1986	3,953.46	13,085.96	1308.60
1987	3,953.46	18,348.02	1834.80
1988	3,953.46	24,136.28	

(c)

Year	Cash Flow	Disc. Factors at 10%	PV	Disc. Factors at 15%	PV
1983	-12,000	—	-12,000	—	-12,000
1984	-6,600	0.9091	6,000.06	0.8696	5,739.36
1985	6,000	0.8264	4,958.40	0.7561	4,536.60
1986	4,500	0.7513	3,380.85	0.6575	2,958.75
1987	-1,000	0.6830	-683.00	0.5718	-571.80
1988	-2,600	0.6209	-1,614.34	0.4972	-1,292.72
		NPV =	+41.97		-629.81

(d)

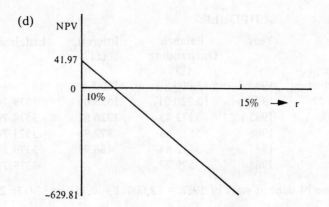

$$IRR = 10\% + \left(\frac{41.97}{41.97 + 629.81} \right) 5\% = 10.3\%$$

The payments into the sinking fund are greater than those required to repay the loan under equal instalments. This, of course, is because the return on deposits in the fund earn only 10% while the interest on the loan is 15%.

The internal rate of return is only just above the rate on the sinking fund and well below the rate on the loan suggesting that the project is not worthwhile.

13.6 (a) Value at end of year   = $C(1 - r)^n$ (see section 12.5.1)
     Value at end of 5th year = $50{,}000 (1 - 0.075)^5$
                              = £33,859

(b) $r = 1 - \sqrt[n]{\dfrac{S}{C}}$ (see section 12.5.1)

    $= 1 - \sqrt[8]{\dfrac{40{,}000}{70{,}000}} = 6.8\%$

(c) PV of annuity $= a \left[\dfrac{1-(1+r)^{-n}}{r} \right]$

PV of six years total rental $= 30{,}000 + 30{,}000 \left[\dfrac{1 - (1+0.065)^{-5}}{0.065} \right]$

                                   $= 30{,}000 + 124{,}670$
                                   $= £154{,}670$

(d)

	CASH FLOW			Disc. factors at 11%	PRESENT VALUE		
Year	Purchase	H.P.	Lease		Purchase	H.P.	Lease
0	−29,000	−10,000	−9,000	—	−29,000	−10,000	−9,000
1	—	−5,500	−7,875	.9009	—	−4,955	−7,095
2	—	−5,500	−6,891	0.8116	—	−4,464	−5,593
3	—	−5,500	−6,029	0.7312	—	−4,022	−4,408
4	—	−5,500	−5,276	0.6587	—	−3,623	−3,475
5	+5,000	+5,000	—	0.5935	+2,968	+2,968	—
				NPV	−26,032	−24,096	−29,571

Therefore, HP is the best method of acquisition.

13.9 (a)

Month	Balance at start of month	Interest for month	Repayment at end of month
1	500.00	—	100.00
2	400.00	10.00	100.00
3	310.00	7.75	100.00
4	217.75	5.44	100.00
5	123.19	3.08	100.00
6	26.27	0.66	26.93

(b)
$$a = \frac{Pr}{1-(1+r)^{-n}} = \frac{3000 \times 0.2}{1-(1.2)^{-5}} = £1003.14$$

Year	Balance	Interest	Repayment
1	3,000	600.00	1003.14
2	2,596.86	519.37	1003.14
3	2,113.09	422.62	1003.14
4	1,532.57	306.51	1003.14
5	835.94	167.19	1003.14

(c)

Year End	Gross Earnings	Expenses	Net Earnings	Sale/ Purchase	Net Cash Flow	Disc. Factor at 20%	PV
1985				−12,000	−12,000	—	−12,000
1986	9,000.00	4,500.00	4,500.00		4,500.00	0.8333	3,749.85
1987	9,675.00	4,770.00	4,905.00		4,905.00	0.6944	3,406.03
1988	10,400.63	5,056.20	5,344.43		5,344.43	0.5787	3,092.82
1989	11,180.67	5,359.57	5,821.10		5,821.10	0.4823	2,807.52
1990	12,019.22	5,681.15	6,338.07	+1,500	7,838.07	0.4019	3,150.12
						NPV =	4,206.34

14.1 (a) $A + B = \begin{pmatrix} 5 & 2 \\ 5 & 5 \end{pmatrix}$

(b) $B + C = \begin{pmatrix} 2 & 3 \\ 3 & -3 \end{pmatrix}$

(c) $AB = \begin{pmatrix} 8 & 5 \\ 13 & 9 \end{pmatrix}$

(d) $AC = \begin{pmatrix} -1 & -2 \\ -1 & -6 \end{pmatrix}$

(e) $A^{-1} = \begin{pmatrix} 2 & -1 \\ -3 & 2 \end{pmatrix}$

(f) $AB = \begin{pmatrix} 8 & 5 \\ 13 & 9 \end{pmatrix}$

$(AB)C = \begin{pmatrix} 8 & 5 \\ 13 & 9 \end{pmatrix} \begin{pmatrix} -1 & 2 \\ 1 & -6 \end{pmatrix} = \begin{pmatrix} -3 & -14 \\ -4 & -28 \end{pmatrix}$

$BC = \begin{pmatrix} -2 & 0 \\ 1 & -14 \end{pmatrix}$

$A(BC) = \begin{pmatrix} 2 & 1 \\ 3 & 2 \end{pmatrix} \begin{pmatrix} -2 & 0 \\ 1 & -14 \end{pmatrix} = \begin{pmatrix} -3 & -14 \\ -4 & -28 \end{pmatrix}$

Therefore, $(AB)C = A(BC)$

(g) $BC = \begin{pmatrix} -2 & 0 \\ 1 & -14 \end{pmatrix}$ as above.

$CB = \begin{pmatrix} -1 & 2 \\ 1 & -6 \end{pmatrix} \begin{pmatrix} 3 & 1 \\ 2 & 3 \end{pmatrix} = \begin{pmatrix} 1 & 5 \\ -9 & -17 \end{pmatrix}$

Therefore, $BC \neq CB$.

14.2 E

14.3 D

14.4 $\begin{pmatrix} 2 & 1 \\ 3 & 2 \end{pmatrix} \begin{pmatrix} x \\ y \end{pmatrix} = \begin{pmatrix} 7 \\ 12 \end{pmatrix}$

$\begin{pmatrix} 2 & -1 \\ -3 & 2 \end{pmatrix} \begin{pmatrix} 2 & 1 \\ 3 & 2 \end{pmatrix} \begin{pmatrix} x \\ y \end{pmatrix} = \begin{pmatrix} 2 & -1 \\ -3 & 2 \end{pmatrix} \begin{pmatrix} 7 \\ 12 \end{pmatrix}$ pre-multiplying by the inverse

$\begin{pmatrix} x \\ y \end{pmatrix} = \begin{pmatrix} 2 \\ 3 \end{pmatrix}$ Therefore, $x = 2$ and $y = 3$

14.5 $\begin{pmatrix} 1 & 2 & 1 \\ 3 & 2 & 1 \\ 2 & 3 & 2 \end{pmatrix} \begin{pmatrix} x \\ y \\ z \end{pmatrix} = \begin{pmatrix} 0 \\ 2 \\ 2 \end{pmatrix}$

First we need to find the inverse so we write in the form of a partition matrix.

$$\left(\begin{array}{ccc|ccc} 1 & 2 & 1 & 1 & 0 & 0 \\ 3 & 2 & 1 & 0 & 1 & 0 \\ 2 & 3 & 2 & 0 & 0 & 1 \end{array}\right)$$

which after a number of row transformations yields

$$\left(\begin{array}{ccc|ccc} 1 & 0 & 0 & -\frac{1}{2} & +\frac{1}{2} & 0 \\ 0 & 1 & 0 & 2 & 0 & -1 \\ 0 & 0 & 1 & -\frac{5}{2} & -\frac{1}{2} & 2 \end{array}\right)$$

Pre-multiplying both sides of the equation by the inverse

$$\left(\begin{array}{ccc} -\frac{1}{2} & +\frac{1}{2} & 0 \\ 2 & 0 & -1 \\ -\frac{5}{2} & -\frac{1}{2} & 2 \end{array}\right)\left(\begin{array}{ccc} 1 & 2 & 1 \\ 3 & 2 & 1 \\ 2 & 3 & 2 \end{array}\right)\left(\begin{array}{c} x \\ y \\ z \end{array}\right) = \left(\begin{array}{ccc} -\frac{1}{2} & +\frac{1}{2} & 0 \\ 2 & 0 & -1 \\ -\frac{5}{2} & -\frac{1}{2} & 2 \end{array}\right)\left(\begin{array}{c} 0 \\ 2 \\ 2 \end{array}\right)$$

$$\left(\begin{array}{c} x \\ y \\ z \end{array}\right) = \left(\begin{array}{c} 1 \\ -2 \\ 3 \end{array}\right)$$

$x = 1$, $y = -2$, $z = 3$.

14.6 Since row 1 is twice row 2 it is not possible, by row transformations, to produce the identity matrix.

$$\text{Suppose } B = \text{ inverse of } A = \left[\begin{array}{cc} w & x \\ y & z \end{array}\right]$$

$$\text{Then} \quad \left(\begin{array}{cc} 4 & 2 \\ 2 & 1 \end{array}\right) B = \left(\begin{array}{cc} 1 & 0 \\ 0 & 1 \end{array}\right)$$

$$\left(\begin{array}{cc} 4 & 2 \\ 2 & 1 \end{array}\right)\left(\begin{array}{cc} w & x \\ y & z \end{array}\right) = \left(\begin{array}{cc} 1 & 0 \\ 0 & 1 \end{array}\right)$$

$$\begin{array}{llll} 4w + 2y = 1 & \text{or} & 2w + y = \frac{1}{2} & (1) \\ 4x + 2z = 0 & \text{or} & 2x + z = 0 & (2) \\ 2w + y = 0 & & & (3) \\ 2x + z = 1 & & & (4) \end{array}$$

It can be seen that equations (1) and (3) are inconsistent, as are (2) and (4), and so there is no solution.

14.7 $$\left(\begin{array}{cc} 20 & 25 \\ 30 & 20 \end{array}\right)\left(\begin{array}{c} A \\ B \end{array}\right) = \left(\begin{array}{cc} 115 & 120 \\ 120 & 110 \end{array}\right)\left(\begin{array}{c} x \\ y \end{array}\right)$$

We may find the inverse of $\left(\begin{array}{cc} 20 & 25 \\ 30 & 20 \end{array}\right)$ by using the determinant,

$|d| = 20 \times 20 - 30 \times 25 = -350.$

$$\text{Inverse} = -\frac{1}{350} \begin{pmatrix} 20 & -25 \\ -30 & 20 \end{pmatrix} = \begin{pmatrix} -\frac{2}{35} & \frac{1}{14} \\ \frac{3}{35} & -\frac{2}{35} \end{pmatrix}$$

Pre-multiplying both sides of the equation by the inverse gives us:—

$$\begin{pmatrix} A \\ B \end{pmatrix} = \begin{pmatrix} -\frac{2}{35} & \frac{1}{14} \\ \frac{3}{35} & -\frac{2}{35} \end{pmatrix} \begin{pmatrix} 115 & 120 \\ 120 & 110 \end{pmatrix} \begin{pmatrix} x \\ y \end{pmatrix}$$

$$\begin{pmatrix} A \\ B \end{pmatrix} = \begin{pmatrix} 2 & 1 \\ 3 & 4 \end{pmatrix} \begin{pmatrix} x \\ y \end{pmatrix}$$

Therefore, 1 unit of A requires 2 Kg. of X and 1 Kg. of Y
1 unit of B requires 3 Kg. of X and 4 Kg. of Y.

14.8 (a) (i)

	BM1	BM2	BM3	
S =	0.7	0.2	0.1	BM1
	0.25	0.65	0.1	BM2
	0.05	0.15	0.8	BM3

The first row, for example, shows that 70% remain loyal to BM1, 20% switch to BM2, and 10% switch to BM3.

(ii) $S^2 = \begin{bmatrix} 0.7 & 0.2 & 0.1 \\ 0.25 & 0.65 & 0.1 \\ 0.05 & 0.15 & 0.8 \end{bmatrix} \begin{bmatrix} 0.7 & 0.2 & 0.1 \\ 0.25 & 0.65 & 0.1 \\ 0.05 & 0.15 & 0.8 \end{bmatrix}$

$$= \begin{bmatrix} 0.5450 & 0.2850 & 0.1700 \\ 0.3425 & 0.4875 & 0.1700 \\ 0.1125 & 0.2275 & 0.6600 \end{bmatrix}$$

(iii) If you consider how you arrive at S^2 you will realise that it simply shows what would happen if the same pattern of retentions and transfers was repeated over the next month.

So, for example, the first row shows that 54.5% of the original purchasers of BM1 remain loyal, 28.5% switch to BM2 and 17% to BM3.

The first column shows that of the purchasers of BM1, 54.5% were original purchasers of BM1, 34.25 have switched from BM2 and 11.25 came from BM3 etc.

(b)(i) Total Revenue = price × sales units = £(43,750–112.5x)x = £(43,750x–112.5x²)

(ii) Marginal Revenue = $\dfrac{\text{d(Total Revenue)}}{\text{dx}}$ = £(43,750–225x)

(iii) If MR = MC then $43,750 - 225x = 200x - x^2$
$$x^2 - 425x + 43750 = 0$$
$$(x-175)(x-250) = 0$$

Therefore, x = 175 or 250 items.

(iv) If x = 250 then Marginal Cost = (200–x)x is negative which is nonsense.

Profits are therefore maximised at an output of 175 items at which MR = MC.

14.9   See answer to 11.9

14.10 (a)   This part of the question has nothing to do with matrices so we will provide an answer:—

(i) The "break-even" position occurs when the Net Present Value is neither positive nor negative and equals zero.
i.e. $192 - 28r + r^2 = 0$
or $(16-r)(12-r) = 0$
$r = 16$ or 12

(ii) If we examine the values of $P = (16-r)(12-r)$ we see that P is positive for values of r less than 12 or greater than 16; P is negative for values of r between 12 and 16. In present value terms, the project is profitable for all values of r other than those between 12 and 16.

15.1 (a)   Objective function $Z = 0.5x + y$

(b)   Equations:
Blending $3x + y \leqslant 900$
Baking $5x + 4y \leqslant 1800$
Packaging $x + 3y \leqslant 900$
$x, y \geqslant 0$

(c)   **GRAPH OF EQUATIONS/INEQUALITIES**

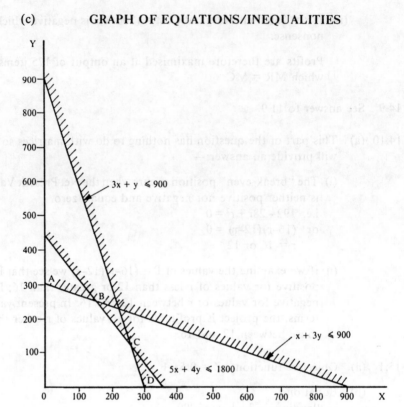

From the graph, the possible solutions are denoted as A,B,C,D.

A	(0, 300)	=	£600
B	(164, 245)	=	£654
C	(257, 129)	=	£515
D	(300, 0)	=	£300
E	(0, 0)	=	£0

(d)   Production point B gives the maximum contribution of £654 with an output of 164 boxes of x and 245 boxes of y.

(e)   The solution makes no allowance for breakdowns. It also does not take account of marketing strategy or materials handling costs. These could be particularly relevant considering that the next best solution is A, a single product solution.

In some LP examples the assumption of linear constraints can be challenged.

15.2 (a) If the manufacturer produces x tonnes of X and y tonnes of Y, the maximum contribution Z is represented by

$$Z = 4x + 3y$$

(b) The raw material constraint is
$$4x + y \leqslant 90$$
The machine constraint is
$$2x + y \leqslant 50$$
The labour constraint is
$$x + y \leqslant 40$$
with $x, y \geqslant 0$

(c)

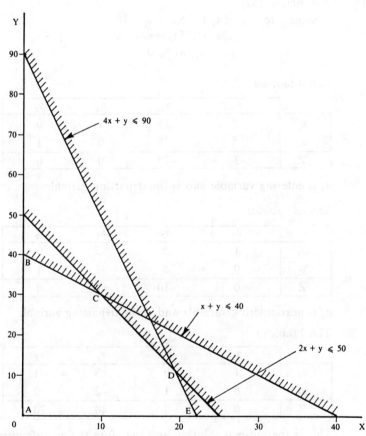

(d) From the graph, the possible solutions are denoted as A, B, C, D, E.

$$
\begin{aligned}
\text{A } (0, 0) &= £0 \\
\text{B } (0, 40) &= £120 \\
\text{C } (10, 30) &= £130 \\
\text{D } (20, 10) &= £110 \\
\text{E } (^{45}\!/_2, 0) &= £90
\end{aligned}
$$

Production point C is seen to be best, giving the highest contribution of £130 for the production of 10 tonnes of X and 30 tonnes of Y.

15.4 $Z = 30a_1 + 25a_2$

subject to

$$.5a_1 + .25a_2 + s_1 = 10$$
$$.5a_1 + .75a_2 + s_2 = 15$$
$$a_1, a_2 \geqslant 0.$$

Initial tableau

	a_1	a_2	s_1	s_2	
s_1	.5	.25	1	0	10
s_2	.5	.75	0	1	15
Z	−30	−25	0	0	0

a_1 is entering variable and s_1 the departing variable.

Second tableau

	a_1	a_2	s_1	s_2	
a_1	1	.5	2	0	20
s_2	0	.5	−1	1	5
Z	0	−10	60	0	600

a_2 is next entering variable and s_2 the departing variable.

Third tableau

	a_1	a_2	s_1	s_2	
a_1	1	0	3	−1	15
a_2	0	1	−2	2	10
Z	0	0	40	20	700

This is the optimal solution and therefore the manufacturer should make 15 tonnes of alloy A_1 and 10 tonnes of alloy A_2 which will give him a daily profit of £700.

16.1 (a)

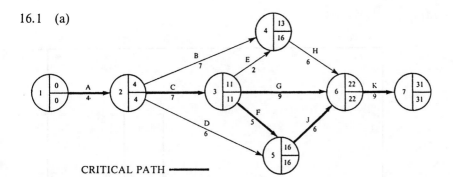

CRITICAL PATH ————

(b) The critical path is A – C – F – J – K with a minimum duration of
31 days.
N.B. Activity D is not critical, there is a float of 6 days before the
start of J is affected.

(c)

Activity	Event Numbers		Duration (Days)	EET		LET		Total Float (days)	Free Float (days)
	i	j		i	j	i	j		
A	1	2	4	0	4	0	4	0	0
B	2	4	7	4	13	4	16	5	2
C	2	3	7	4	11	4	11	0	0
D	2	5	6	4	16	4	16	6	6
E	3	4	2	11	13	11	16	3	0
F	3	5	5	11	16	11	16	0	0
G	3	6	9	11	22	11	22	2	2
H	4	6	6	13	22	16	22	3	3
J	5	6	6	16	22	16	22	0	0
K	6	7	9	22	31	22	31	0	0

(d)

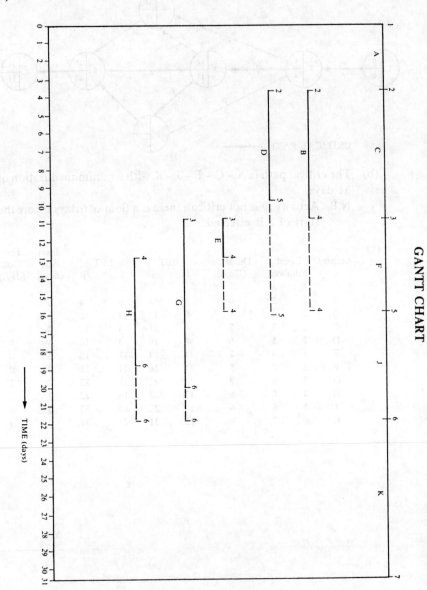

GANTT CHART

16.2 (a)

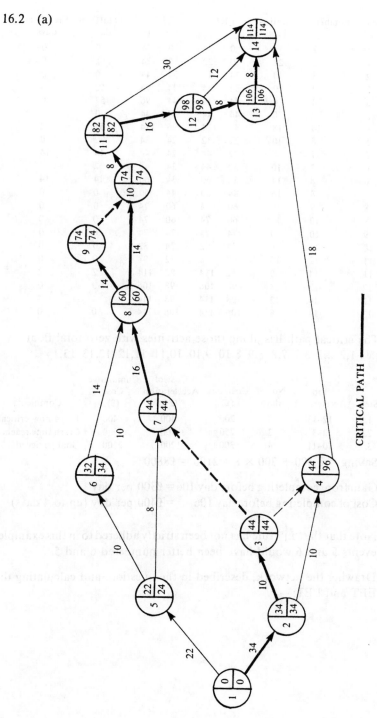

CRITICAL PATH ▬▬▬▬▬

Event numbers		Duration	EET		LET		Total float	Free float
i	j	days	i	j	i	j	days	days
1	2	34	0	34	0	34	0	0
1	5	22	0	22	0	24	2	0
2	3	10	34	44	34	44	0	0
2	4	10	34	44	34	96	52	0
3	4	0	44	44	44	96	52	0
3	7	0	44	44	44	44	0	0
4	14	18	44	114	96	114	52	52
5	6	10	22	32	24	34	2	0
5	7	8	22	44	24	44	14	14
6	7	10	32	44	34	44	2	2
6	8	14	32	60	34	60	14	14
7	8	16	44	60	44	60	0	0
8	9	14	60	74	60	74	0	0
8	10	14	60	74	60	74	0	0
9	10	0	74	74	74	74	0	0
10	11	8	74	82	74	82	0	0
11	12	16	82	98	82	98	0	0
11	14	30	82	114	82	114	2	2
12	13	8	98	106	98	106	0	0
12	14	12	98	114	98	114	4	4
13	14	8	106	114	106	114	0	0

The critical path lies along those activities with zero total float
i.e. 1,2 2,3 3,7 7,8 8,9 8,10 9,10 10,11 11,12 12,13 13,14

(b)

Step	Job Accelerated	No. of days	Cost/day (£)	Cost of Acceleration (£)	Cumulative Cost (£)	Comments
1.	12–13	2	200	400	400	11–14 now critical
2.	2–3	2	250	500	900	Crash time reached
3.	10–11	4	300	1200	2100	Goal achieved

Saving = 8,500 + 300 × 8 − 2100 = £8800

(c) Gain from completing before day 106 = £300 per day
Cost of completing before day 106   = £400 per day (up to 4 days)

16.3 Note that the "i,j" rule has not been strictly adhered to in this example, events 5 and 6 would have been better numbered 6 and 5.

Drawing the network, described in the question, and calculating the EET and LET:—

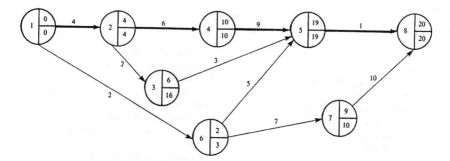

(a) The critical path is (1–2–4–5–8) where EET = LET and it can be easily seen that the total float is zero on each of the activities making up the critical path.

(b) Expected cost is given by 5+3+4+9+2+12+20+7+14+4=80
Expected cost = £80,000.

(c) Expected time = 20 months which is the expected duration of the critical path.

(d) It is assumed that the variance of the duration of the whole project is the sum of the variances along the critical path.
i.e. 1+2+5+1=9
Therefore, standard deviation of expected time $= \sqrt{9} = 3$ months.

(e) We assume that the total duration is distributed normally with a mean of 20 months and a standard deviation of 3 months.

The probability of the project taking more than 24 months is the same as the probability of a normally distributed variable taking a value more than $\frac{24-20}{3} = 1.33$ standard deviations above the mean i.e. 0.5 – 0.4082 = 0.0918.

The probability of completing the project in 24 months or less is therefore 1.000 – 0.0918 = 0.9082.

If we wish to be a little more rigorous, we might observe that the total float along the path (1–6–7–8) is only one month. The expected duration along this path is 19 months with a standard deviation of 5 months. The probability of this path taking longer than 24 months is similarly shown to be 0.8413.

The probability that neither of the two paths will take longer than 24 months is therefore 0.9082 × 0.8413 = 0.7641.

INDEX

S/AM

1532